Calculations in Advanced Physical Chemistry

Third Edition

P. J. F. Griffiths
M.SC., C.CHEM., F.R.S.C.

and

J. D. R. Thomas
D.SC., C.CHEM., F.R.S.C.

University of Wales Institute of
Science and Technology, Cardiff

Edward Arnold

First Published 1962
by Edward Arnold (Publishers) Ltd.,
41 Bedford Square,
London WC1B 3DQ

Reprinted 1963, 1965, 1967, 1969
Second Edition 1971
Reprinted with corrections 1975
Reprinted 1978
Third Edition 1983

British Library Cataloguing in Publication Data

Griffiths, P. J. F.
Calculations in advanced physical chemistry.
—3rd ed.
1. Chemistry, Physical and theoretical—
Problems, exercises, etc.
I. Title II. Thomas, J. D. R.
541.3'0151 QD455.3.M3

ISBN 0-7131-3483-6

Printed and bound in Great Britain at The Pitman Press, Bath

Preface to Third Edition

This book has already helped several generations of students to acquire an enhanced perception of physical chemistry through problem solving during their university or equivalent courses. Since pocket calculators have become generally available, previously tedious arithmetical chores can now be completed in a very short time so that present day students can obtain very quickly a wider experience of problem solving than was previously possible. Problem solving ability may be measured by examining authorities by means of numerical multiple choice questions. Such questions are in wide use by universities throughout the world, and particularly so in North America. These questions can be answered more efficiently if the student has acquired the kind of understanding that may be obtained through dedicated practice via the wide variety of additional problems following each chapter of worked examples in this book.

Correspondence received shows that this book is used in many parts of the world (the second edition has also been translated into Hungarian), so that the authors have taken the opportunity in this third edition to include questions from a greater range of universities and examining bodies. The following are thanked for their goodwill in sending questions, for their kind permission to use the questions, and in some instances for allowing them to be adapted to a more conventional form, especially when they were of the multiple choice variety:

University of Toronto, Canada
Professor M. Thompson, University of Toronto,
Professor Henry Freiser and Professor W. R. Salzman, University of Arizona, Tucson, USA;
Professor G. G. Guilbault, University of New Orleans, USA;
Professor Gary D. Christian and Professor E. R. Davidson, University of Washington, Seattle, USA;
Professor J. M. Bobbitt, University of Connecticut, Storrs, USA;
Examinations Committee, Division of Chemical Education, American Chemical Society (ACS), USA;

University of Oxford, England, for questions for Final Examination papers set by the Honour School of Natural Science, Oxford: General Physical Chemistry II, reprinted by permission of Oxford University Press.

The authors also reiterate their thanks to the examining authorities named in the preface to the first edition. Among these authorities was the Royal Institute of Chemistry (R.I.C.), now unified with the Chemical Society into the Royal Society of Chemistry (R.S.C.). Hence the questions of R.I.C. origin are now attributed to R.S.C.

In addition to the larger number and wider range of questions now included, nomenclature has been modernized, and Chapter 10 (Spectra) has been substantially extended to cover statistical thermodynamics.

Finally the authors acknowledge a debt of gratitude to all those who have provided such a useful feedback through their comments on the earlier editions of this work.

UWIST

PJFG
JDRT

1983

Preface to second edition (1975 impression)

This impression is based on the International System of Units (Systéme International d'Unités-SI) in that the various examples are generally worked out in terms of basic and derived SI units as set out in Sections I.3.3 to I.3.7 of '*Symbols, Signs, and Abbreviations Recommended for British Scientific Publications*' (The Symbols Committee of the Royal Society, 1969). However, some units outside the International System, such as the standard atmosphere (atm), ångström (Å), barn (b), curie (Ci), minute (min), hour (h), electron volt (eV) and unified atomic mass (u) have been retained in certain instances in accordance with the 1969 considerations of the International Committee of Weights and Measures (CIPM) as summarized in Tables 8 to 10 of '*The International System of Units*' (National Physical Laboratory: HMSO, London, 1973). Observations such as pressure (in mmHg) and temperature (in °C) given in questions have been converted to SI Units during the working-out stage.

The authors thank the examining authorities named in the preface to the first edition for permitting such amendments to be made, where necessary, to the numerical data of their questions.

UWIST PJFG
1974 JDRT

Preface to first edition

In producing this book, the authors' aim has been to provide an illustration, by means of typical worked examples, of the calculations encountered in the study of advanced physical chemistry. Each set of worked examples in a particular branch of the subject is followed by a series of problems (with answers) to be solved by the reader.

Detailed theoretical discussion of equations used has been avoided where it was considered that an adequate treatment was to be found in current text-books of physical chemistry. In this way a wide selection of material could be made, without producing an unnecessarily bulky volume.

The authors have solved problems selected mainly from papers set in university degree examinations and in the examinations of the Royal Institute of Chemistry and the Pharmaceutical Society. In a number of instances the problems are based on data taken from original papers, to which full reference is made.

The authors wish to thank the Royal Institute of Chemistry, the Pharmaceutical Society and the authorities of the following universities for permission to use questions set in their examinations:

Birmingham, Bristol, Durham, Glasgow, Leeds, Liverpool, London, Nottingham, Queen's University of Belfast, Sheffield, Southampton and Wales.

PJFG
JDRT

April 1962

Contents

Constants and Conversion Factors

EXCEPT where otherwise stated, the following values for constants and conversion factors have been used throughout this book:

1 atmosphere	760 mmHg
	1.013×10^5 N m^{-2}
Molar gas constant (R)	8.31 J K^{-1}
Boltzmann constant (k)	1.381×10^{-23} J K^{-1}
Molar volume of gas at s.t.p.	22.4 dm^3
Avogadro constant (L)	6.02×10^{23} mol^{-1}
0°C	273 K
Faraday (F)	96 500 coulombs (C)
$\frac{2.303\ RT}{F}$	0.0591 V
Acceleration of gravity (g)	9.81 m s^{-2}
Planck constant (h)	6.624×10^{-34} J s
Velocity of light (c)	3.00×10^8 m s^{-1}
π	3.142
1 Ångström (Å)	10^{-10} m (100 pm)
1 Debye (D)	3.336×10^{-30} C m
ln x	2.303 log x
1 Joule (J)	1 N m
1 Newton (N)	kg m s^{-2}

1

First Law of Thermodynamics

Example 1.1 Hess' law of constant heat summation

From the following data, calculate the heat of formation of anhydrous aluminium chloride:

$$\begin{aligned}
&(i)\ 2Al(s)+6HCl(aq) &&= Al_2Cl_6(aq)+3H_2(g); && \Delta H = -1007\ \text{kJ}\\
&(ii)\ H_2(g)+Cl_2(g) &&= 2HCl(g); && \Delta H = -184.8\ \text{kJ}\\
&(iii)\ HCl(g)+aq &&= HCl(aq); && \Delta H = -72.73\ \text{kJ}\\
&(iv)\ Al_2Cl_6(s)+aq &&= Al_2Cl_6(aq); && \Delta H = -645.5\ \text{kJ}
\end{aligned}$$

This is a straightforward example involving the application of Hess' law of constant heat summation. However, the symbol 'aq' often presents difficulty to students. This symbol merely indicates that sufficient water is present to produce a solution which has a negligible or zero heat of dilution and is NOT to be treated as a molecular proportion, that is, '1 aq' is treated as equal to '2 aq' or any other number of 'aq' as illustrated by the multiplication of equation (iii) by 6 to give equation (vi) below.

Multiply (ii) by 3.

$$\text{(v)}\ 3H_2(g)+3Cl_2(g) = 6HCl(g); \quad \Delta H = -554.4\ \text{kJ}$$

Multiply (iii) by 6.

$$\text{(vi)}\ 6HCl(g)+aq = 6HCl(aq); \quad \Delta H = -436.38\ \text{kJ}$$

Add (i), (v) and (vi).

$$\text{(vii)}\ 2Al(s)+3Cl_2(g)+aq = Al_2Cl_6(aq); \quad \Delta H = -1997.78\ \text{kJ}$$

Subtract (iv) from (vii).

$$\text{(viii)}\ 2Al(s)+3Cl_2(g) = Al_2Cl_6(s); \quad \Delta H = -1352.28\ \text{kJ}$$

By equation (viii), the heat of formation ($-\Delta H$) of aluminium chloride is 1352 kJ.

Example 1.2 The Kirchhoff equation

The heat of formation of one mole HI (gas) from hydrogen and iodine vapour at 25°C is 33.6 kJ (endothermic). Find the heat of *formation at 10°C given that the heat capacities (J K^{-1} mol^{-1}) of hydrogen, iodine vapour and HI vapour are given by the equations:*

Hydrogen:	$C_p = 27.3+0.0071\,T$;
Iodine vapour:	$C_p = 27.3+0.0160\,T$;
Hydrogen iodide gas:	$C_p = 27.3+0.0067\,T$;

where T is the thermodynamic (absolute) temperature.

(*B.Pharm., London*)

From the given data, it may be written:

$$\tfrac{1}{2}H_2(g) + \tfrac{1}{2}I_2(g) = HI(g); \quad \Delta H_{298} = 33.6 \text{ kJ}$$

The general expression for the change in heat capacity (ΔC_p) accompanying the reaction, in the temperature range for which the heat capacity data are applicable, is given by:

$$\begin{aligned}\Delta C_p &= C_{p(HI)} - \tfrac{1}{2}[C_{p(H_2)}+C_{p(I_2)}] \text{ J K}^{-1}\\ &= 27.3+0.0067T - \tfrac{1}{2}[27.3+0.0071T+27.3+0.0160T] \text{ J K}^{-1}\\ &= -0.00485T \text{ J K}^{-1}\end{aligned}$$

The Kirchhoff equation relates ΔH_{283} to ΔH_{298}.

$$\Delta H_{298} = \Delta H_{283} + \int_{283}^{298} \Delta C_p \mathrm{d}T$$

(the temperatures, including integration limits, being shown in K)

Therefore $$33\,600 = \Delta H_{283} - 0.00485 \int_{283}^{298} T\mathrm{d}T \text{ J}$$

and $$\begin{aligned}\Delta H_{283} &= 33\,600 + \frac{0.00485}{2}\Big[T^2\Big]_{283}^{298} \text{ J}\\ &= 33\,600 + \frac{0.00485}{2}[298^2 - 283^2] \text{ J}\\ &= 33\,621 \text{ J}\end{aligned}$$

The heat of formation ($-\Delta H$) of 1 mole of HI (gas) at 10°C is -33.62 kJ.

Example 1.3 Hess' law of constant heat summation and the Kirchhoff equation

(a) Calculate the heat of formation (x) of gaseous hydrogen chloride at 25°C using the following data:

$$NH_3(aq)+HCl(aq) = NH_4Cl(aq); \ \Delta H = -50.4 \text{ kJ (at 25°C)}$$

Substance	*NH_3(gas)*	*HCl(gas)*	*NH_4Cl(solid)*
Heat of formation (ΔH) at 25°C/kJ mol^{-1}	*−46.2*	*(x)*	*−315*
Heat of solution (ΔH) at 25°C/kJ mol^{-1}	*−35.7*	*−73.5*	*+16.4*

***(b)* Use the result of *(a)* and the following heat capacity equations to calculate the heat of formation of gaseous hydrogen chloride at 727°C.**

H_2 (gas): $C_p = 27.8 + 3.4 \times 10^{-3}T\ (J\ K^{-1}\ mol^{-1})$
Cl_2 (gas): $C_p = 34.8 + 2.4 \times 10^{-3}T\ (J\ K^{-1}\ mol^{-1})$
HCl (gas): $C_p = 28.1 + 3.5 \times 10^{-3}T\ (J\ K^{-1}\ mol^{-1})$ *(R.S.C.)*

(*a*) From the information given, it may be written:

(i) $NH_3(aq) + HCl(aq) = NH_4Cl(aq);\quad \Delta H_{298} = -50.4$ kJ
(ii) $NH_3(g) + aq = NH_3(aq);\quad \Delta H_{298} = -35.7$ kJ
(iii) $HCl(g) + aq = HCl(aq);\quad \Delta H_{298} = -73.5$ kJ
(iv) $NH_4Cl(s) + aq = NH_4Cl(aq);\quad \Delta H_{298} = +16.4$ kJ
(v) $\frac{1}{2}N_2(g) + 1\frac{1}{2}H_2(g) = NH_3(g);\quad \Delta H_{298} = -46.2$ kJ
(vi) $\frac{1}{2}N_2(g) + 2H_2(g) + \frac{1}{2}Cl_2(g) = NH_4Cl(s);\quad \Delta H_{298} = -315$ kJ

By the application of Hess' law of constant heat summation, the heat of formation of gaseous hydrogen chloride may be found as follows:

Add equations (i), (ii) and (iii).

(vii) $NH_3(g) + HCl(g) + aq = NH_4Cl(aq);\quad \Delta H_{298} = -159.6$ kJ

Subtract (v) from (vi).

(viii) $\frac{1}{2}H_2(g) + \frac{1}{2}Cl_2(g) + NH_3(g) = NH_4Cl(s);\quad \Delta H_{298} = -268.8$ kJ

Add (viii) and (iv).

(ix) $\frac{1}{2}H_2(g) + \frac{1}{2}Cl_2(g) + NH_3(g) + aq = NH_4Cl(aq);\quad \Delta H_{298} = -252.4$ kJ

Subtract (vii) from (ix).

(x) $\frac{1}{2}H_2(g) + \frac{1}{2}Cl_2(g) = HCl(g);\quad \Delta H_{298} = -92.8$ kJ

By equation (x) the heat of formation of gaseous hydrogen chloride at 25°C is 92.8 kJ mol^{-1} evolved, that is, ΔH is negative.

(*b*) For the reaction

$\frac{1}{2}H_2(g) + \frac{1}{2}Cl_2(g) = HCl(g)$; at 298 K and 1000 K, we have, according to Kirchhoff's law

$$\Delta H_{298} + \int_{298}^{1000} C_{p\,(HCl)} dT = \Delta H_{1000} + \int_{298}^{1000} [\tfrac{1}{2}C_{p\,(H_2)} + \tfrac{1}{2}C_{p\,(Cl_2)}] dT \text{ J}$$

or

$$\Delta H_{1000} = \Delta H_{298} + \int_{298}^{1000} \Delta C_p dT \text{ J}$$

where

$$\begin{aligned}\Delta C_p &= C_{p\,(HCl)} - \tfrac{1}{2}[C_{p\,(H_2)} + C_{p\,(Cl_2)}] \text{ J K}^{-1} \\ &= 28.1 + 3.5\times10^{-3}T - \tfrac{1}{2}[27.8 + 3.4\times10^{-3}T \\ &\qquad + 34.8 + 2.4\times10^{-3}T] \text{ J K}^{-1} \\ &= -3.2 + 0.6\times10^{-3}T \text{ J K}^{-1}\end{aligned}$$

$$\begin{aligned}\Delta H_{1000} &= -92\,800 + \int_{298}^{1000} (-3.2 + 0.6\times10^{-3}T) dT \text{ J} \\ &= -92\,800 + \left[-3.2T + \frac{0.6\times10^{-3}T^2}{2}\right]_{298}^{1000} \text{ J} \\ &= -94\,773 \text{ J}\end{aligned}$$

The heat of formation of gaseous hydrogen chloride at 727°C is 94.8 kJ mol^{-1} evolved.

Example 1.4 Hess' law of constant heat summation

The heats of formation of carbon monoxide and steam are 111 and 244 kJ respectively. Calculate (a) the heat of the reaction: $H_2O + C = CO + H_2$, and (b) the proportion by volume, of air and steam which, if passed into a mass of coke at about 1000°C, will maintain a constant temperature. A 20% allowance for dissipation (by radiation, etc.) of heat produced in the reaction with oxygen is to be assumed. (*University of Durham*)

From the information given, we can formulate

(i) $C + \frac{1}{2}O_2 = CO$; $\Delta H = -111$ kJ

and (ii) $H_2 + \frac{1}{2}O_2 = H_2O$; $\Delta H = -244$ kJ (*a*) The heat of the reaction: $H_2O+C = CO+H_2$ can now be determined by subtracting (ii) from (i) (by Hess' law of constant heat summation) to give

(iii) $H_2O+C = CO+H_2$; $\Delta H = +133$ kJ

(*b*) A mass of coke is to be maintained at 1000°C by allowing air and steam to pass into it, that is, by allowing the exothermic reaction (i) to occur along with the endothermic reaction (iii). 20% of the heat produced by (i) is assumed to be dissipated.

Therefore, effectively, the decrease in heat content ($-\Delta H$) per mole of carbon monoxide produced by (i) is 88.8 kJ, that is, $\Delta H = -88.8$ kJ.

To maintain constant temperature, the heat required for the endothermic reaction (iii) must balance that produced in the exothermic reaction (i).

Hence the proportion, by volume, of steam and oxygen required is

One part of steam to $\frac{1}{2}\times\frac{133}{88.8}$ parts of oxygen.

And the proportions, by volume, of steam and air required are

One part of steam to $5\times\frac{1}{2}\times\frac{133}{88.8}$ parts of air.

$= 3.74$ parts of air.

Summary (*a*) The heat ($-\Delta H$) of the reaction $H_2O+C = CO+H_2O$ is -133 kJ.

(*b*) The proportion, by volume, of air and steam which, if passed into a mass of coke to maintain a constant temperature of about 1000°C, assuming a 20% allowance for dissipation, is

One part of steam to 3.74 parts of air.

Example 1.5 Calculation of bond energy and resonance energy

What do you understand by the terms 'bond energy' and 'resonance energy'?

The heat of formation of methane from solid carbon and gaseous molecular hydrogen is 74.8 kJ. The heat required to convert 1 mol of hydrogen into atoms is 436 kJ and that required to convert 1 mol of solid carbon into atoms may be assumed to be 717 kJ. Calculate the heat of formation of methane from gaseous atoms.

The heats of formation of ethane, ethene and benzene from gaseous atoms are 2839, 2275, and 5509 kJ respectively. Calculate the resonance energy of benzene compared with one Kekulé structure.
(*B. Pharm., Nottingham*)

'Bond energy' is the average amount of energy, per mole, required to break a bond and separate the resulting atoms from each other. Thus, one quarter of the energy required to dissociate 1 mole of methane into atomic carbon and hydrogen is taken as the bond energy of the C—H linkage. Equation (v) below shows that the energy required to dissociate 1 mole of methane into gaseous atoms, that is, to break four C—H bonds, is 1664 kJ. Hence, the C—H bond energy,

$$E_{C-H} = \frac{1664}{4} = 416 \text{ kJ}$$

Because of resonance, the benzene molecule, for example, has a lower energy and greater stability than any of its resonating structures. Hence, its heat of formation from its gaseous atoms will be greater than that of a resonating structure, such as a Kekulé structure. The extra energy given out is the 'resonance energy'.

Calculation of the heat of formation of methane from gaseous atoms

From the information given, it may be written:

(i) $C(s) + 2H_2(g) = CH_4(g)$; $\Delta H = -74.8$ kJ
(ii) $H_2(g) = 2H(\text{atoms, g})$; $\Delta H = 436$ kJ
(iii) $C(s) = C(\text{atoms, g})$; $\Delta H = 717$ kJ

By the application of Hess' law of constant heat summation, the heat of formation of methane from gaseous atoms may be found as follows:

Multiply (ii) by 2 and add to (iii).
(iv) $C(s) + 2H_2(g) = 4H(\text{atoms, g}) + C(\text{atoms, g})$; $\Delta H = 1589$ kJ
Subtract (iv) from (i).
(v) $4H(\text{atoms, g}) + C(\text{atoms, g}) = CH_4(g)$; $\Delta H = -1664$ kJ

By equation (v), the heat of formation of methane from gaseous atoms is 1664 kJ mol^{-1} (evolved).

Calculation of resonance energy of benzene

To evaluate the resonance energy of benzene from the given data, it is first necessary to evaluate the energies of the C—H, C=C, and C—C bonds, and then to calculate the heat of formation of a Kekulé structure, which is subtracted from the given heat of formation of benzene to yield the resonance energy.

The C—H bond energy, as shown above, is 416 kJ

Ethane contains 6 C—H bonds and 1 C—C bond. Hence, the energy absorbed in the dissociation of ethane into gaseous atoms, that is, 2839 kJ, will be equal to the sum of these bond energies:

$$6E_{\text{C-H}} + E_{\text{C-C}} = 2839 \text{ kJ}$$

Therefore

$$E_{\text{C-C}} = 2839 - 6\times 416 \text{ kJ}$$
$$= 343 \text{ kJ}$$

Therefore, the C—C bond energy is 343 kJ.

Ethene contains 4 C—H bonds and 1 C=C bond. Hence, the energy absorbed in the dissociation of ethene to gaseous atoms, that is, 2275 kJ, will be equal to the sum of these bond energies:

$$4E_{\text{C-H}} + E_{\text{C=C}} = 2275 \text{ kJ}$$

Therefore

$$E_{\text{C=C}} = 2275 - 4\times 416 \text{ kJ}$$
$$= 611 \text{ kJ}$$

Therefore the C=C bond energy is 611 kJ.

The heat of formation of a Kekulé structure from gaseous atoms will be equal to the heat liberated on the formation of 3 C=C, 6 C—H, and 3 C—C bonds.
That is, the heat of formation of a Kekulé structure is given by

$$3E_{\text{C=C}} + 6E_{\text{C-H}} + 3E_{\text{C-C}} = 1833 + 2496 + 1029 \text{ kJ}$$
$$= 5358 \text{ kJ}$$

The observed heat of formation of benzene from its elements is 5509 kJ and hence the resonance energy is equal to

$$5509 - 5358 = 151 \text{ kJ}$$

The resonance energy of benzene, compared with one Kekulé structure, is 151 kJ mol^{-1}.

Example 1.6 The Born-Haber cycle

From the data given below draw an energy cycle and from it calculate the lattice energy of lithium chloride.

Enthalpy of atomization of lithium, (Li(s) → Li(g)),

$$\Delta H = +159 \text{ kJ mol}^{-1}$$

Dissociation energy of chlorine, ($\frac{1}{2}Cl_2(g) \rightarrow Cl(g)$),

$$\Delta H = +121 \text{ kJ mol}^{-1} \text{ of Cl (g)}$$

Ionization energy of lithium, ($Li(g) \rightarrow Li^+(g) + e^-$),

$$\Delta H = +520 \text{ kJ mol}^{-1}$$

Electron affinity of chlorine, ($Cl(g) + e^- \rightarrow Cl^-(g)$),

$$\Delta H = -370 \text{ kJ mol}^{-1}$$

Enthalpy of formation of lithium chloride, ($Li(s) + \frac{1}{2}Cl_2(g) \rightarrow LiCl(s)$),

$$\Delta H = -402 \text{ kJ mol}^{-1}$$

(*G.C.E. 'A' Level (Nuffield), London*)

The Born-Haber cycle is an energy cycle which presents a breakdown pattern of compounds possessing an *ideal* electrovalency. It collates in a simple quantitative manner several fundamental enthalpic energy quantities (that is, of the ΔH type), as illustrated by the data of this question:

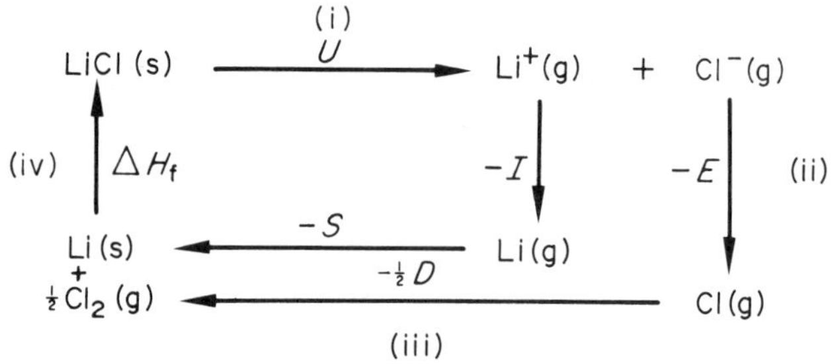

In the cycle, the first step (i) is the complete break-up of the lithium chloride crystal, LiCl(s), into gaseous Li^+ and Cl^- ions. This is accompanied by an increase in the enthalpy (heat content), $\Delta H_{(i)}$ which is the *lattice energy, U.*

The second operation (ii) is the simultaneous discharging of the metal Li^+ ions and of the Cl^- ions. This stage is accompanied by an enthalpy change, $\Delta H_{(ii)}$, corresponding to $-(E - I)$, where E is the electron affinity of the Cl atom and I is the ionization energy of the Li atom.

In the third step (iii), the gaseous lithium is condensed to the solid state and the chlorine atoms are combined to give Cl_2 molecules, the processes being accompanied by a change in enthalpy, $\Delta H_{(iii)}$, corresponding to the sum of $-S$, that is, minus the *enthalpy of atomization* of lithium, and of $-\frac{1}{2}D$, that is, minus one half of the *dissociation enthalpy* (or *energy*) of molecular chlorine.

The final step (iv) corresponds to the interaction of the solid lithium with gaseous Cl_2 molecules, that is, in the forms they normally exist at 298 K, to reform the crystalline lithium chloride. The attendant enthalpy change, $\Delta H_{(iv)}$, is the *enthalpy of formation*, ΔH_f, of the lithium chloride. All the other quantities referred to in the cycle are also for 298 K.

By Hess' law of constant heat summation

$$\Delta H_{(i)} + \Delta H_{(ii)} + \Delta H_{(iii)} + \Delta H_{(iv)} = 0$$

that is,

$$U - E - I - S - \tfrac{1}{2}D + \Delta H_f = 0 \qquad (1)$$

The value of any quantity in equation (1) may be calculated, provided the other five are known. Information on five of the six quantities is given in the question, hence the value of the sixth, namely the lattice energy of lithium chloride (U), may be calculated by substituting the appropriate data in equation (1):

$$U = -370 + 520 + 159 + 121 + 402 \text{ kJ mol}^{-1} = \underline{+832 \text{ kJ mol}^{-1}}$$

Example 1.7 Reversible isothermal expansion

2 dm³ of hydrogen, initially at s.t.p., are expanded isothermally and reversibly to a volume of 4 dm³. Calculate the work done.

Since 22.4 dm³ is the volume occupied by 1 mole at s.t.p., 2 dm³ is the volume occupied by $1 \times \frac{2}{22.4}$ mole at s.t.p. The work done (W) in the isothermal, reversible expansion of 1 mole of an ideal gas is given by:

$$W = RT \ln \frac{V_2}{V_1} \text{ J}$$

where V_1 and V_2 are the initial and final gas volumes.

Assuming ideal behaviour by the hydrogen, the work done in the expansion of 2 dm³ of the gas to a volume of 4 dm³ will, therefore, be given by

$$W = \frac{2}{22.4} RT \ln \frac{V_2}{V_1} = \frac{2 \times 8.31 \times 273}{22.4} \ln \frac{4}{2} = \underline{140.5 \text{ J}}$$

Example 1.8 Reversible adiabatic expansion of an ideal gas

Two moles of an ideal gas ($C_v = 12.5$ J K⁻¹ mol⁻¹) at 300 K are compressed adiabatically to one quarter of the original volume; what is the temperature of the gas after compression? (*B.Pharm., London*)

For a definite quantity of gas, the relationship between absolute temperature (T) and volume (V) in an adiabatic process is:

$$\frac{T_1}{T_2} = \left(\frac{V_2}{V_1}\right)^{(\gamma-1)}$$

where T_1, T_2 and V_1, V_2 are the initial and final temperatures and volumes respectively.

$$= \left(\frac{V_2}{V_1}\right)^{\frac{C_p - C_v}{C_v}}$$

But $$C_p - C_v = R = 8.31 \text{ J K}^{-1}\text{ mol}^{-1}$$

and $$C_v = 12.5 \text{ J K}^{-1}\text{ mol}^{-1}$$

Therefore $$\frac{C_p - C_v}{C_v} = \frac{8.31}{12{\cdot}5} = 0.665$$

Letting $$T_1 = 300 \text{ K}, \quad \frac{V_2}{V_1} = \frac{1}{4}$$

Then $$\frac{300}{T_2} = \left(\frac{1}{4}\right)^{0.665}$$

and $$T_2 = 754 \text{ K}$$

The temperature of the gas after compression is 754 K.

Example 1.9 Reversible adiabatic expansion of an ideal gas

To what pressure must a given volume of nitrogen, originally at 100°C and 1 atm pressure, be adiabatically compressed in order to raise its temperature to 400°C?

For a definite quantity of gas, the relationship between absolute temperature (T) and pressure (P) in an adiabatic process is:

$$\frac{T_2}{T_1} = \left(\frac{P_2}{P_1}\right)^{\frac{\gamma-1}{\gamma}}$$

where T_1, T_2 and P_1, P_2 are the initial and final temperatures and pressures respectively.

Since nitrogen is a diatomic gas γ or $\left(\frac{C_p}{C_v}\right) = 1.4.$

Substituting the relevant values in the above equation, we have:

$$\frac{673}{373} = \left(\frac{P_2}{1}\right)^{\frac{1.4-1}{1.4}}$$

and $P_2 = 7.891$ atm.

A pressure of 7.89 atm is required to raise the temperature to 400°C.

Example 1.10 Adiabatic reactions

From the data listed below, calculate the adiabatic flame temperature of the gas mixture Q when this mixture is burned with 100% excess air, both air and gas being at an initial temperature of 25°C.

(*a*) $CO(g) + \frac{1}{2}O_2(g) = CO_2(g);\ \Delta H^{\ominus}_{25\,°C} = -283.0\ kJ$

(*b*)

Gas	Composition
Q	CO 20%; N_2 80%
Air	O_2 21%; N_2 79%

(*c*)

Substance	C_p/J K^{-1} mol^{-1}
CO(g)	$26.6+0.76\times10^{-2}T$
$CO_2(g)$	$26.4+4.26\times10^{-2}T$
$N_2(g)$	$27.1+0.58\times10^{-2}T$
$O_2(g)$	$25.6+1.32\times10^{-2}T$

where T is the absolute temperature.

If a reaction proceeds adiabatically and all the products of the reaction remain together in a single mass or stream, these products will attain a definite final temperature called the adiabatic-reaction temperature. For a strongly exothermic reaction this final temperature will be very high.

Consider the process $a\text{A}+b\text{B}\rightarrow m\text{M}+n\text{N}$ which is assumed to proceed adiabatically.

The initial state is $(a\text{A}+b\text{B})$ at some temperature T_1 and the final state is $(m\text{M}+n\text{N})$ at some temperature T_2.

The passage from the initial state to the final state may be imagined as proceeding in two stages:

(i) $(a\text{A}+b\text{B}) \xrightarrow{\Delta H_{T1}} (m\text{M}+n\text{N})$ at T_1

(ii) $(m\text{M}+n\text{N})$ at $T_1 \xrightarrow[\text{of heat released in (i)}]{\text{By absorption}} (m\text{M}+n\text{N})$ at T_2

that is the thermal energy available from the exothermic reaction (i) is employed in heating the products from T_1 to the final temperature T_2. The corresponding increase in enthalpy of the products is given by

$$\int_{T_1}^{T_2} C_p \mathrm{d}T,$$

where C_p is the heat capacity of the products.

The enthalpy change in a process depends on the initial and final states only and is independent of the route between these states. The total enthalpy change is zero for the process considered since heat neither enters nor leaves the system. Thus

$$0 = \Delta H_{T_1} + \int_{T_1}^{T_2} C_p \mathrm{d}T$$

and

$$\Delta H_{T_1} = -\int_{T_1}^{T_2} C_p \mathrm{d}T \qquad \text{(i)}$$

To use equation (i) to evaluate T_2 it is necessary to know the heat of the reaction (ΔH_{T_1}) and the heat capacity (C_p) of the products. There are two important points which must be remembered:

(*a*) If the reaction is incomplete, only the heat of reaction corresponding to the actual extent of reaction is used.
(*b*) The products include all substances actually present in the final state. Any unreacted substances and inert substances which are present must be included as products, since they are also heated to the final temperature (T_2).

Implicit in the above procedure are the assumptions that the exact composition of the products is known and that the normal values of their heat capacities are relevant. If the reaction is strongly exothermic, the high final temperature achieved may result in chemical dissociation and the formation of free atoms and radicals. The heats of dissociation should then be included in the calculation.

The temperature achieved when a fuel is burned in air or oxygen without gain or loss of heat is called the theoretical adiabatic flame temperature, and the method given above may be employed to calculate this temperature. The theoretical maximum adiabatic flame temperature is reached when the fuel is burned in the stoichiometrically required amount of pure oxygen.

Note If mean molar heat capacities are available for the products, a final temperature may be assumed and the mean molar heat capacities for the assumed temperature range are used to get an approximate value of T_2 from the equation

$$\Delta H_{T_1} = -\bar{C}_p(T_2 - T_1)$$

in which $\bar{C}_p$ is the mean heat capacity of the products.

The calculation is then repeated with $\bar{C}_p$ values for the new temperature range $T_2 - T_1$ to get a further value of T_2. Only a few approximations are necessary to reach a constant value for T_2.

Compositions of gaseous mixtures are so often quoted on the basis of % by volume at s.t.p., that if percentage figures are quoted, with no specification to the contrary, they are taken to be % by volume at s.t.p. In these conditions the behaviour of the gases is so nearly ideal that it may be assumed to be so. By Avogadro's law, which states that equal volumes of gases in the same conditions of temperature and pressure contain equal numbers of molecules, the % by volume at s.t.p. is thus also the mole % for gaseous mixtures.

For the gas mixture Q it is convenient to work on the basis of 1 mole of carbon monoxide and calculate the number of moles of the other reactants relative to this as follows:

Reactants

From the stoichiometry of the equation given in the problem, the number of moles of oxygen required per mole of carbon monoxide is 0.50. Since 100% excess air is supplied the number of moles of oxygen supplied must, therefore, be 1.00.

The air contains 21% of oxygen so that the number of moles of nitrogen associated with the mole of oxygen is $\frac{1}{21}\times 79 = 3.76$.

The number of moles of nitrogen in Q itself associated with the mole of carbon monoxide $= \frac{1}{20}\times 80 = 4.00$, so that the total number of moles of nitrogen $= 3.76+4.00 = 7.76$.

Products

Moles of carbon dioxide formed	$= 1.00$
Moles of oxygen remaining	$= 0.50$
Moles of nitrogen	$= 7.76$

Thus, working on the basis of 1 mole of carbon monoxide

$$\int_{T_1}^{T_2} C_p\mathrm{d}T = \int_{T_1}^{T_2}[1.00C_p(CO_2)+7.76C_p(N_2)+0.5C_p(O_2)]\mathrm{d}T$$

$$= \int_{T_1}^{T_2}[26.4+7.76\times 27.1+0.5\times 25.6]\mathrm{d}T + \int_{T_1}^{T_2}[4.26+7.76\times 0.58+0.5\times 1.32]\times 10^{-2}T\mathrm{d}T$$

$$= \int_{T_1}^{T_2} 249.5\mathrm{d}T + \int_{T_1}^{T_2} 9.42\times 10^{-2}T\mathrm{d}T$$

In the present problem $T_1 = 298$ K so that the integration yields

$$\int_{T_1}^{T_2} C_p \mathrm{d}T = [249.5T]_{298}^{T_2} + \left[\frac{9.42\times10^{-2}T^2}{2}\right]_{298}^{T_2}$$

$$= 249.5T_2 - 74\,350 + 4.71\times10^{-2}T_2^2 - 4182$$

From equation (i)

$$\Delta H_{298} = -\int_{298}^{T_2} C_p \mathrm{d}T$$

and $$-283\,000 = -0.0471T_2^2 - 249.5T_2 + 78\,532$$

whence $$0.0471T_2^2 + 249.5T_2 - 361\,532 = 0$$

This equation is of the form $ax^2+bx+c = 0$ for which the possible values of x are given by

$$x = \frac{-b \pm \sqrt{b^2-4ac}}{2a}$$

For the given equation

$$T_2 = \frac{-249.5 \pm \sqrt{249.5^2 + 4\times0.0471\times361\,532}}{2\times0.0471}$$

$$= \frac{-249.5 \pm 361.1}{0.0942} = \frac{111.6}{0.0942} \text{ or } \frac{-610.6}{0.0942}$$

The negative value for T_2 is inadmissible so that

$$T_2 = 111.6/0.0942 = \underline{1184 \text{ K}}$$

The adiabatic flame temperature of the mixture Q = 1184 K.

Additional Examples

1 Calculate the heat of the reaction

$$C_2H_4(g) + H_2(g) = C_2H_6(g)$$

at 298 K from the following data:

(i) $C_2H_4(g) + 3O_2(g) = 2CO_2(g) + 2H_2O(g)$; $\Delta H_{298} = -1395$ kJ
(ii) $C_2H_6(g) + \frac{7}{2}O_2(g) = 2CO_2(g) + 3H_2O(g)$; $\Delta H_{298} = -1550$ kJ
(iii) $H_2(g) + \frac{1}{2}O_2(g) = H_2O(g)$; $\Delta H_{298} = -243$ kJ

2 Given that the average heat capacity change for the reaction

$$C_2H_4(g) + H_2(g) = C_2H_6(g)$$

is 10.9 J K^{-1} within the range 298 K to 1000 K, use the result from the above example to calculate the heat of the reaction at 1000 K.

3 Given the heats of formation ($\Delta H_f^\ominus$) of ethanoic acid, carbon dioxide and water as -504, -399 and -252 kJ mol^{-1}, respectively, calculate the heat of combustion ($\Delta H^\ominus$) of ethanoic acid.

(Adapted from ACS Cooperative Examination: Physical Chemistry (Thermodynamics).)

4 At 18°C the heat of reaction ($-\Delta H$) at constant pressure for the reaction $C + CO_2 = 2CO$ is -176.4 kJ. Calculate the heat of reaction at 60°C, given that the mean atomic and molecular heats (C_p) of solid C and gaseous CO_2 and CO are 10.00, 38.15 and 29.26 J K^{-1} mol^{-1}, respectively, for the given temperature range.

5 State the thermochemical laws associated with the names of Hess and Kirchhoff and show their thermodynamic basis. Calculate the heat of formation of benzoic acid, given that its heat of combustion is 3243 kJ mol^{-1} and that the heats of formation of carbon dioxide and of water are 397 and 287 kJ mol^{-1} respectively. (R.S.C.)

6 For the reaction $CO(g) + \frac{1}{2}O_2(g) \rightarrow CO_2(g)$, ΔH is -286.0 kJ at 0°C. The true molar heats (J K^{-1}) at constant volume (C_v) are as follows:

$21.45 + 0.01405T$ for CO_2
$19.66 + 0.00113T$ for both CO and O_2

Calculate the heat formation of CO_2 from CO and O_2 at constant pressure and 2500°C. (R.S.C.)

7 Derive the Kirchhoff equation.

The enthalpy of formation of ammonia gas at 298 K is -46.1 kJ mol^{-1}. The mean molar heat capacities, in J K^{-1} mol^{-1}, of gaseous H_2, N_2 and NH_3 in the temperature range 250–450 K are given by the equations:

$$C_p(H_2) = 29.6 + 0.00231T$$
$$C_p(N_2) = 27.9 + 0.00418T$$
$$C_p(NH_3) = 29.9 + 0.00261T.$$

Calculate ΔH and ΔU for the formation of ammonia at 398 K.

(R.S.C.)

8 The average bond energies associated with the C—H bond, the C—C bond and the C=C bond are respectively 415, 348 and 613 kJ mol^{-1}. Use these values to calculate the theoretical enthalpy of formation of the molecule:

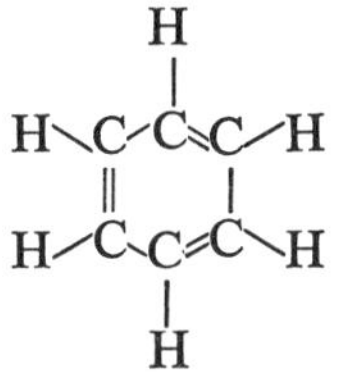

In practice, the enthalpy of formation of benzene from atoms is 5520 kJ mol^{-1}. How do you account for the difference in these quantities?

(G.C.E. 'A' Level (Nuffield), London)

9 Explain the terms (*a*) heat of dissociation, (*b*) bond dissociation energy, (*c*) mean bond energy. What are the special relationships between these quantities in a diatomic molecule?

For $N_2(g)+3H_2(g) = 2NH_3(g)$; $\Delta H^\ominus = -92.0$ kJ

and for $N_2(g)+2H_2(g) = N_2H_4(g)$; $\Delta H^\ominus = +42.0$ kJ.

Given that the heat of dissociation of hydrogen is 436 kJ mol^{-1} and that of nitrogen is 712 kJ mol^{-1}, calculate the mean bond energies of (*a*) the N—H and (*b*) the N—N single bonds. (R.S.C.)

10 The heat of combustion of graphite is 396 and of carbon monoxide 284 kJ mol^{-1}. Dissociation of O_2 and CO into gaseous atoms takes place with the absorption of 492 and 970 kJ mol^{-1} respectively. Calculate the heat of sublimation of carbon. (B.Sc., Bristol)

11 From the following data, calculate the value of the energy of the C—S bond in carbon disulphide. The molar heats of combustion (ΔH) of CS_2(l) C(s) and S(s) are −1113 kJ, −395 kJ and −298 kJ respectively. The molar heats of atomization (ΔH) of C(s) and S(s) are 714 kJ, and 287 kJ respectively. The molar vaporization of CS_2 is 27 kJ.

12 From the following data, calculate the value of the energies of the bonds C—H, C—C, C═C, C—Cl.

(i) $CH_2{=}CH_2(g)+Cl_2(g) = CH_2Cl\text{-}CH_2Cl(g)$; $\Delta H = -184$ kJ
(ii) C(atoms, g)+4H(atoms, g) $= CH_4(g)$; $\Delta H = -1664$ kJ
(iii) 2C(atoms, g)+6H(atoms, g) $= C_2H_6(g)$; $\Delta H = -2839$ kJ
(iv) 2C(atoms, g)+4H(atoms, g) $= C_2H_4(g)$; $\Delta H = -2275$ kJ
(v) 2Cl(atoms, g) $= Cl_2(g)$; $\Delta H = -240$ kJ.

13 It has been shown by pyrolytic methods that the C—H bond in methyl benzene, $C_6H_5CH_2$—H, has a dissociation energy of 326 kJ. Calculate the heat of formation, ΔH_f, of the phenyl methyl radical and hence the strength of the central C—C bond in 1,2-diphenyl ethane $C_6H_5.CH_2$—$CH_2.C_6H_5$.

ΔH_f (methyl benzene vapour) = 50.4 kJ mol^{-1}
ΔH_f (1,2-diphenyl ethane vapour) = 116.8 kJ mol^{-1}
D (H—H) = 437 kJ mol^{-1}

(B.Sc., Wales)

14 Explain the basis of Hess' law of constant heat summation and use this to estimate the electron affinity of chlorine from the following data:

	ΔH/kJ mol^{-1}
$Na(g) \rightarrow Na^+(g)+e$	502
$\frac{1}{2}Cl_2(g) \rightarrow Cl(g)$	121
$Na(s) \rightarrow Na(g)$	109
$Na(s)+\frac{1}{2}Cl_2(g) \rightarrow NaCl(s)$	−413
$Na^+(g)+Cl^-(g) \rightarrow NaCl(s)$	−777

(B.Sc., Bristol)

15 A metal M can react with gaseous chlorine to form compounds of stoichiometry MCl or MCl_2. From the data given below calculate the heat of formation for each case, and hence deduce which chloride will be formed preferentially by reaction of the elements in their standard states.

(First ionization potential of M	=	496 kJ
Second ionization potential of M	=	4570 kJ
Electron affinity of chlorine	=	−342 kJ
Heat of dissociation of chlorine	=	244 kJ mol^{-1}
Heat of sublimation of M	=	109 kJ mol^{-1}

Assume that the lattice energy of MCl = +773 kJ mol^{-1} and that the lattice energy of MCl_2 = +4450 kJ mol^{-1})

(B.Sc. (Special), London)

16

	LiCl	NaCl	KCl
Enthalpy of atomization of the metal. $M(s) \rightarrow M(g)$ /kJ mol^{-1}	+160	+109	+84
Dissociation energy of chlorine. $\frac{1}{2}Cl_2(g) \rightarrow Cl(g)$ /kJ mol^{-1}	+121	+121	+121
Electron affinity of chlorine. $Cl(g)+e^- \rightarrow Cl^-(g)$ /kJ mol^{-1}	−370	−370	−370
Enthalpy of formation of metal chloride. $M(s)+\frac{1}{2}Cl_2(g) \rightarrow MCl(s)$ /kJ mol^{-1}	−397	−402	−435
Lattice energy of metal chloride. $MCl(s) \rightarrow M^+(g)+Cl^-(g)$ /kJ mol^{-1}	+840	+770	+705

(*a*) Draw an energy cycle (Born–Haber cycle) for the general case MCl.

(*b*) Use this cycle to calculate the ionization energies of the metals lithium, sodium and potassium ($M(g) \rightarrow M^+(g)+e^-$).

(G.C.E. 'A' Level (Nuffield), London)

17 10 dm^3 of an ideal gas at 273 K and 100 atm pressure are allowed to expand isothermally and reversibly to a pressure of 10 atm. Calculate the work done and internal energy change in this process.

(B, Sc. and B.Met., Sheffield)

18 10 dm^3 of oxygen, initially at 2 atm pressure, are expanded adiabatically and reversibly to 30 dm^3. Calculate the work done (C_p/C_v for oxygen = 1.4).

19 14 g of oxygen at 0°C and 10 atm are subjected to a reversible adiabatic expansion to a pressure of one atm. Calculate the work done (C_p/C_v for oxygen = 1.4).

20 Use the data given below to calculate the adiabatic flame temperature for methane burnt with the stoichiometric amount of pure oxygen, the gases being mixed at 25°C.

(*a*) $CH_4(g)+2O_2(g) = CO_2(g)+2H_2O(g)$; $\Delta H^{\ominus}_{298} = -820$ kJ.

(*b*)

Substance	C_p/J K^{-1} mol^{-1}
CO_2	$26.4+4.26 \times 10^{-2}T$
H_2O	$32.4+0.21 \times 10^{-2}T$

where T is the absolute temperature.

21 A gas mixture, containing sulphur dioxide, oxygen and nitrogen, enters a catalytic converter at 427°C. In the converter, 75% of the sulphur dioxide is oxidized to sulphur trioxide by the oxygen present in the mixture. Assuming that heat losses from the converter are negligible, use the data given to calculate the temperature of the gases leaving the converter.

(*a*) $SO_2(g)+\frac{1}{2}O_2(g) = SO_3(g)$

(*b*) $SO_2(g)$; $\Delta H^{\ominus}_{f(298\,K)} = -298$ kJ; $SO_3(g)$; $\Delta H^{\ominus}_{f(298\,K)} = -397$ kJ

(*c*)

Gas	O_2	N_2	SO_2	SO_3
$\bar{C}_p$/J K^{-1} mol^{-1}	32.0	31.5	47.8	68.5

(*d*) Gas composition: SO_2: 4.0 moles; O_2: 4.5 moles; N_2: 41.4 moles

2

Second and Third Laws of Thermodynamics

Example 2.1 Thermodynamic efficiency

The boiling point of water at a pressure of 50 atm is 265°C and at 1 atm 100°C. Compare the theoretical efficiencies of a steam engine operating between the boiling point of water at (a) 1 atm, (b) 50 atm, assuming the temperature of the refrigerator to be 40°C in each case.

For the hypothetical Carnot engine

$$\text{Efficiency} = \frac{W}{q_2} = \frac{T_2 - T_1}{T_2},$$

that is, the efficiency of a reversible heat engine is given by the fraction of the heat absorbed (q_2) which it can convert into work (W) and depends only on the temperatures of the boiler (T_2) and refrigerator (T_1), and does NOT depend on the medium by which the heat is transported.

(*a*) At 1 atm pressure, the boiling point of water is 100°C, that is, 373 K, and this represents the upper temperature T_2; the lower temperature T_1 is 40°C, that is, 313 K.
Therefore

$$\text{Efficiency} = \frac{T_2 - T_1}{T_2} = \frac{373 - 313}{373} = 0.161$$

(*b*) Similarly, at 50 atm pressure, T_2 is 265°C, that is, 538 K, and T_1 is 313 K.
Hence

$$\text{Efficiency} = \frac{T_2 - T_1}{T_2} = \frac{538 - 313}{538} = 0.418$$

The increased efficiency of (*b*) over (*a*) is very marked.

Example 2.2 Carnot cycle

In Example 2.1 above, what is the amount of heat that must be withdrawn from the hot reservoir to produce 1000 J of work in each case?

(*a*) Using $\frac{W}{q_2} = \text{Efficiency}$

and substituting 1000 J for W and the calculated value of 0.161 for efficiency, we have

$$q_2 = \frac{1000}{0.161} = \underline{6212 \text{ J}}$$

(*b*) Similarly $q_2 = \frac{1000}{0.418} = \underline{2392 \text{ J}}$

Note It is clear from the above results that, for a given temperature of the refrigerator, the efficiency is increased by using a high temperature source. Similarly, the efficiency is also increased by lowering the temperature of the refrigerator for a given temperature of the hot reservoir. Since it is not convenient for the refrigerator to be below atmospheric temperature, the upper temperature limit is extended in boilers used for power production, by the use of high pressure steam or of mercury.

Example 2.3 Entropy change

Calculate (a) the heat absorbed, and (b) the entropy change when 0.5 mole of perfect gas is allowed to expand at 300 K from a volume of 1 dm³ to a volume of 10 dm³ against a constant pressure of 1 atm.

(R.S.C.)

(*a*) The internal energy of a perfect gas is a function of temperature only; hence, if the temperature is held constant, as in this case, the internal energy cannot change. Therefore, by the first law of thermodynamics, the heat absorbed (q) is equal to the work done (W):

$$q = W$$

As the gas expands against a *constant pressure* of 1 atm (1.013×10^5 N m^{-2})

$$W = P(V_2 - V_1)$$

Since 1 dm^3 = 10^{-3} m^3

$$q = W = 1.013 \times 10^5(10 \times 10^{-3} - 1 \times 10^{-3}) \text{ N m}$$
$$= 911.7 \text{ N m}$$
$$= 912 \text{ J.}$$

(*b*) To find the entropy change corresponding to isothermal expansion against a constant pressure it is necessary to imagine the same process conducted reversibly.

The heat absorbed (q_r) in the reversible isothermal expansion of one mole of perfect gas is given by

$$q_r = RT \ln \frac{V_2}{V_1}$$

The entropy change (ΔS) is given by

$$\Delta S = \frac{q_r}{T} = R \ln \frac{V_2}{V_1}$$

For 0.5 mole

$$\begin{aligned}\Delta S &= 0.5 \times 8.31 \times 2.303 \times \log 10 \text{ J K}^{-1} \\ &= 9.570 \text{ J K}^{-1}\end{aligned}$$

(*a*) The heat absorbed is 912 J,

(*b*) The entropy change is 9.57 J K^{-1}.

Example 2.4 Entropy change in non-isothermal processes

The molar heat capacity at 1 atm pressure of solid magnesium in the temperature range 0°–600°C is given by:

$$C_p = 26.0 + 5.46 \times 10^{-3}T - 28.6 \times 10^4 T^{-2} \text{ J K}^{-1} \text{ mol}^{-1}$$

Calculate the entropy change when 1 mole of metal is heated from 27°C to 227°C at 1 atm pressure.

For temperature change at constant pressure, the entropy change is given by

$$S_B - S_A = \int_{T_A}^{T_B} \frac{C_p}{T} \mathrm{d}T$$

where T is the absolute temperature, and S_A and S_B, the entropy in the initial and final states.

From the given data

$$\frac{C_p}{T} = \frac{26.0}{T} + 5.46 \times 10^{-3} - 28.6 \times 10^4 T^{-3} \text{ J K}^{-2} \text{ mol}^{-1}$$

Therefore

$$S_B - S_A = \int_{300}^{500} \frac{26.0}{T}\,dT + \int_{300}^{500} 5.46\times10^{-3}dT - \int_{300}^{500} 28.6\times10^{4}\frac{dT}{T^3}\ \text{J K}^{-1}$$

$$= 26.0\Big[\ln T\Big]_{300}^{500} + 5.46\times10^{-3}\Big[T\Big]_{300}^{500} - \frac{28.6\times10^{4}}{-2}\left[\frac{1}{T^2}\right]_{300}^{500}\ \text{J K}^{-1}$$

$$= 26.0 \ln\frac{500}{300} + 5.46\times10^{-3}\times200 + 14.3\times10^{4}\left[\frac{1}{500^2} - \frac{1}{300^2}\right]\ \text{J K}^{-1}$$

$$= 13.28 + 1.092 - 1.016\ \text{J K}^{-1}$$

$$= 13.4\ \text{J K}^{-1}$$

The entropy change when 1 mol of magnesium metal is heated from 27°C to 227°C at 1 atm pressure is 13.4 J K^{-1}.

Example 2.5 Entropy change in non-isothermal processes

From K. K. Kelley (Bull. U.S. Bur. Mines (1949), No. 476) the following data for sulphur have been obtained.

$S_{(rh)}$ $\quad C_p = 15.0 + 26.2\times10^{-3}T$ *J* K^{-1} *mol*$^{-1}$ *for 298–368.6K*

$S_{(mono)}$ $\quad C_p = 14.9 + 29.2\times10^{-3}T$ *J* K^{-1} *mol*$^{-1}$ *for 368.6K to m.p.*

$S_{(l)}$ $\quad C_p = 22.7 + 21.0\times10^{-3}T$ *J* K^{-1} *mol*$^{-1}$ *for m.p. to b.p.*

Transition point (rhombic to monoclinic sulphur) = 95.6°C
Melting point (monoclinic sulphur) = 119°C
Latent heat of transition (L_t) *= 0.361 kJ mol*$^{-1}$
Latent heat of fusion (L_f) *= 1.26 kJ mol*$^{-1}$
(0°C = 273K)

From the data, evaluate the entropy change when sulphur is heated from 27°C to 137°C.

Heating sulphur from 27°C to 137°C involves two isothermal and three non-isothermal stages. The entropy change corresponding to each stage is evaluated separately, the total entropy change being obtained by taking the sum for the various stages.

Entropy change when rhombic sulphur is heated from 27°C to 95.6°C is given by

$$\int_{T_1}^{T_2} \frac{C_p}{T}\,dT = \int_{300}^{368.6} \frac{15.0 + 26.2\times10^{-3}T}{T}\,dT\ \text{J K}^{-1}\,\text{mol}^{-1}$$

$$= 15.0 \ln\frac{368.6}{300} + 26.2\times10^{-3}(368.6 - 300)\ \text{J K}^{-1}\,\text{mol}^{-1}$$

$$= 3.088 + 1.797\ \text{J K}^{-1}\,\text{mol}^{-1}$$

$$= 4.885\ \text{J K}^{-1}\,\text{mol}^{-1}$$

Entropy change for the transition of rhombic sulphur to monoclinic sulphur at 95.6°C is given by

$$\frac{L_t}{T} = \frac{361}{368.6} = 0.980 \text{ J K}^{-1}\text{ mol}^{-1}$$

Entropy change when monoclinic sulphur is heated from 95.6°C to 119°C is given by

$$\int_{T_1}^{T_2} \frac{C_p}{T}\, dT = \int_{368.6}^{392} \frac{14.9 + 29.2 \times 10^{-3}T}{T}\, dT \text{ J K}^{-1}\text{ mol}^{-1}$$

$$= 14.9 \ln \frac{392}{368.6} + 29.2 \times 10^{-3}(392 - 368.6) \text{ J K}^{-1}\text{ mol}^{-1}$$

$$= 0.920 + 0.683 \text{ J K}^{-1}\text{ mol}^{-1}$$

$$= 1.603 \text{ J K}^{-1}\text{ mol}^{-1}$$

Entropy change when monoclinic sulphur melts at 199°C is given by

$$\frac{L_f}{T} = \frac{1260}{392} = 3.215 \text{ J K}^{-1}\text{ mol}^{-1}$$

Entropy change when liquid sulphur is heated from 119°C to 137°C is given by

$$\int_{T_1}^{T_2} \frac{C_p}{T}\, dT = \int_{392}^{410} \frac{22.7 + 21.0 \times 10^{-3}T}{T}\, dT \text{ J K}^{-1}\text{ mol}^{-1}$$

$$= 22.7 \ln \frac{410}{392} + 21.0 \times 10^{-3}(410 - 392) \text{ J K}^{-1}\text{ mol}^{-1}$$

$$= 1.020 + 0.378 \text{ J K}^{-1}\text{ mol}^{-1}$$

$$= 1.398 \text{ J K}^{-1}\text{ mol}^{-1}$$

Therefore, the total entropy change when sulphur is heated from 27°C to 137°C is the sum of the various entropy changes evaluated above:

$$\Delta S = 4.885 + 0.980 + 1.603 + 3.215 + 1.398 \text{ J K}^{-1}\text{ mol}^{-1}$$

$$\underline{= 12.08 \text{ J K}^{-1}\text{ mol}^{-1}}$$

Example 2.6 Entropy change

Calculate the entropy change per mole when cadmium vapour at 767°C and 1 atm pressure is heated to 1027°C and compressed so that its final pressure is 6 atm. Assume that the vapour behaves as an ideal monatomic gas. ($C_v = 12.5 \text{ J K}^{-1}\text{ mol}^{-1}$)

The entropy change ΔS is given by

$$\Delta S = \int_{T_1}^{T_2} \frac{C_p}{T}\,dT + R\ln\frac{p_1}{p_2}$$

But for an ideal gas $\qquad C_p = C_v + R$

In this case C_p is therefore 20.81 J K^{-1} mol^{-1}.

By substitution of the data in the above equation we have

$$\Delta S = \int_{1040}^{1300} \frac{20.81}{T}\,dT + 8.31\times 2.303\log\frac{1}{6}\ \text{J K}^{-1}\,\text{mol}^{-1}$$

$$= 20.81\times 2.303\times\log\frac{1300}{1040} - 8.31\times 2.303\times\log\frac{6}{1}\ \text{J K}^{-1}\,\text{mol}^{-1}$$

$$= 4.644 - 14.89\ \text{J K}^{-1}\,\text{mol}^{-1}$$

$$= -10.25\ \text{J K}^{-1}\,\text{mol}^{-1}$$

The entropy change when cadmium vapour at 767°C and 1 atm pressure is heated to 1027°C and compressed to 6 atm is $\underline{-10.25\ \text{J K}^{-1}\,\text{mol}^{-1}}$.

Example 2.7 Entropy of mixing

Assuming ideal behaviour, what would be the entropy change per mole of air, consisting of 21 mole per cent of oxygen and 79 mole per cent of nitrogen, at 1 atm pressure, if it could be separated into its pure component gases, each at 1 atm at the same temperature?

The change in entropy, ΔS_m, corresponding to the mixing of ideal gases at constant temperature and pressure is given by

$$\Delta S_m = -R\Sigma N_i \ln N_i$$

where N_i is the mole fraction of the given gas in the mixture and R is the gas constant.

This problem is concerned with the reverse situation, namely, that of separation. Hence, the entropy change

$$\Delta S = R\frac{21}{100}\ln\frac{21}{100} + R\frac{79}{100}\ln\frac{79}{100}$$

$$= 8.31\times 2.303(0.21\log 0.21 + 0.79\log 0.79)\ \text{J K}^{-1}\,\text{mol}^{-1}\ \text{air}$$

$$= 8.31\times 2.303(0.21\times\bar{1}.3222 + 0.79\times\bar{1}.8976)\ \text{J K}^{-1}\,\text{mol}^{-1}\ \text{air}$$

$$= 8.31\times 2.303[0.21\times(-0.6778) + 0.79\times(-0.1024)]\ \text{J K}^{-1}\,\text{mol}^{-1}\text{air}$$

$$= -8.31\times 2.303\times 0.2232\ \text{J K}^{-1}\,\text{mol}^{-1}\ \text{air}$$

$$= -4.272\ \text{J K}^{-1}\,\text{mol}^{-1}\ \text{air.}$$

The entropy change corresponding to the separation of 1 mol of air into its constituent gases, each at 1 atm pressure and at the same temperature is -4.27 J K^{-1}.

Example 2.8 Entropy change in chemical reactions

Calculate the entropy change for the reaction

$$2C(graphite)+2H_2(g) = C_2H_4(g),$$

given the following standard entropies at 25°C, in units of J K^{-1} mol^{-1}:

C(graphite)	*5.7*
$H_2(g)$	*131.2*
$C_2H_4(g)$	*221.0*

Values of standard entropies at 25°C and 1 atm pressure for most elements and many compounds are tabulated in the chemical literature. The entropy changes involved in chemical reactions are therefore readily calculated.

Using the molar entropies given

$$\Delta S^{\ominus}_{298\mathrm{K}} = S^{\ominus}_{\mathrm{C_2H_4}} - (2S^{\ominus}_{\mathrm{C}} + 2S^{\ominus}_{\mathrm{H_2}})$$
$$= 221.0 - (11.4 + 262.4) \text{ J K}^{-1}$$
$$= -52.8 \text{ J K}^{-1}$$

The entropy change for the reaction

$2\mathrm{C(graphite)} + 2\mathrm{H_2(g)} = \mathrm{C_2H_4(g)}$ is -52.8 J K^{-1}

Example 2.9 Gibbs free energy change

Given the following standard entropies and heats of combustion to gaseous carbon dioxide and liquid water for 25°C:

	$S^{\ominus}$/J K^{-1} mol^{-1}	$\Delta H^{\ominus}$/kJ mol^{-1}
C(graphite)	*5.9*	*−396*
$H_2(g)$	*131.0*	*−287*
$C_2H_4(g)$	*220.0*	*−1400*
$C_2H_6(g)$	*231.0*	*−1567*

calculate the enthalpy change and Gibbs free energy change for the reactions

(*a*) $2C(graphite)+2H_2(g) = C_2H_4(g)$

(*b*) $2C(graphite)+3H_2(g) = C_2H_6(g)$

State whether the reactions are thermodynamically possible.

Calculation of enthalpy change

From the information given

(i) $C(\text{graphite}) + O_2(g) = CO_2(g)$; $\Delta H^{\ominus}_{298} = -396$ kJ

(ii) $H_2(g) + \frac{1}{2}O_2(g) = H_2O(l)$; $\Delta H^{\ominus}_{298} = -287$ kJ

(iii) $C_2H_4(g) + 3O_2(g) = 2CO_2(g) + 2H_2O(l)$; $\Delta H^{\ominus}_{298} = -1400$ kJ

(iv) $C_2H_6(g) + 3\frac{1}{2}O_2(g) = 2CO_2(g) + 3H_2O(l)$; $\Delta H^{\ominus}_{298} = -1567$ kJ

By the application of Hess' law of constant heat summation we can calculate the enthalpy change ($\Delta H^{\ominus}$) for each of reactions (*a*) and (*b*):

(*a*) Add (i) and (ii) and multiply by 2.

(v) $2C(\text{graphite}) + 3O_2(g) + 2H_2(g) = 2CO_2(g) + 2H_2O(l)$;
$$\Delta H^{\ominus}_{298} = -1366 \text{ kJ}$$

Subtract (iii) from (v).

$$2C(\text{graphite}) + 2H_2(g) = C_2H_4(g); \quad \Delta H^{\ominus}_{298} = +34 \text{ kJ}$$

The enthalpy change for reaction (*a*) is +34 kJ

(*b*) Multiply (i) by 2, (ii) by 3 and add.

(vi) $2C(\text{graphite}) + 3\frac{1}{2}O_2(g) + 3H_2(g) = 2CO_2(g) + 3H_2O(l)$;
$$\Delta H^{\ominus}_{298} = -1653 \text{ kJ}$$

Subtract (iv) from (vi).

$$2C(\text{graphite}) + 3H_2(g) = C_2H_6(g); \quad \Delta H^{\ominus}_{298} = -86 \text{ kJ}$$

The enthalpy change for reaction (*b*) is −86 kJ.

Calculation of Gibbs free energy change

It is first of all necessary to calculate the entropy change for reactions (*a*) and (*b*).

Using the standard entropies given, the entropy change for reaction (*a*) is

$$= S^{\ominus}_{C_2H_4} - (2S^{\ominus}_{C} + 2S^{\ominus}_{H_2})$$
$$= 220.0 - (11.8 + 262.0) = -53.8 \text{ J K}^{-1}$$

Similarly, the entropy change for reaction (*b*) is

$$= S^{\ominus}_{C_2H_6} - (2S^{\ominus}_{C} + 3S^{\ominus}_{H_2})$$
$$= 231.0 - (11.8 + 393.0) = -173.8 \text{ J K}^{-1}$$

Using the relationship

$$\Delta G^{\ominus} = \Delta H^{\ominus} - T\Delta S^{\ominus}$$

we can now calculate the Gibbs free energy change ($\Delta G^\ominus$) in each case:

Reaction (*a*) $\quad \Delta G^\ominus = 34\,000 + 298 \times 53.8$ J
$= \underline{+50\,030 \text{ J}}$

Reaction (*b*) $\quad \Delta G^\ominus = -86\,000 + 298 \times 173.8$ J
$= \underline{-34\,220 \text{ J}}$

Summary

	Reaction (*a*)	*Reaction* (*b*)
Enthalpy change ($\Delta H^\ominus$)	+34 kJ	−86 kJ
Gibbs free energy change ($\Delta G^\ominus$)	+50 kJ	−34 kJ

Reaction (*a*) has a positive sign for ΔG. This signifies that the reaction in the given direction is NOT spontaneous. ΔG is negative for reaction (*b*) and this reaction tends to proceed spontaneously, that is, it is thermodynamically possible and the process can occur provided the conditions are suitable.

Example 2.10 Free energy change

Calculate the Gibbs free energy change (ΔG) at 25°C for the reaction

$$C_2H_5OH(l) + O_2(g) = CH_3COOH(l) + H_2O(l)$$

from the following data, also at 25°C.

(*i*) $H_2(g) + \frac{1}{2}O_2(g) = H_2O(l)$; $\quad \Delta G = -238$ kJ

(*ii*) $2C(graphite) + 3H_2(g) + \frac{1}{2}O_2(g) = C_2H_5OH(l)$; $\quad \Delta G = -176$ kJ

(*iii*) $2C(graphite) + 2H_2(g) + O_2(g) = CH_3COOH(l)$; $\Delta G = -394$ kJ

The free energy changes of reactions are expressed in equations similar to the thermochemical ones already dealt with in Chapter 1, and can be similarly added and subtracted in the following way.

Subtract (ii) from (iii).

(iv) $C_2H_5OH(l) + \frac{1}{2}O_2(g) = CH_3COOH(l) + H_2(g)$; $\quad \Delta G = -218$ kJ

Add (iv) to (i).

(v) $C_2H_5OH(l) + O_2(g) = CH_3COOH(l) + H_2O(l)$; $\Delta G = -456$ kJ

The required value for the Gibbs free energy change (ΔG) at 25°C is $\underline{-456 \text{ kJ}}$.

Example 2.11 Equilibrium constants and van't Hoff isotherm

Given that the values of the standard free energies of formation of NO_2 and N_2O_4 at 25°C are 51.5 and 98.5 kJ mol^{-1} respectively, calculate K_p, K_c and K_x at one atmosphere and 25°C for the reaction:

$$N_2O_4 = 2NO_2 \qquad \text{(B.Sc., Durham)}$$

From the data given it may be written

(i) $\frac{1}{2}N_2(g)+O_2(g) = NO_2(g); \quad \Delta G^{\ominus} = 51.5 \text{ kJ}$

(ii) $N_2(g)+2O_2(g) = N_2O_4(g); \quad \Delta G^{\ominus} = 98.5 \text{ kJ}$

Multiply equation (i) by 2 and subtract equation (ii).

(iii) $N_2O_4(g) \qquad = 2NO_2(g); \quad \Delta G^{\ominus} = 4.5 \text{ kJ}$

By the van't Hoff isotherm, for a gaseous reaction.

$$\Delta G^{\ominus} = -RT \ln K_p$$

Therefore
$$4500 = -8.31 \times 298 \ln K_p$$
$$= -8.31 \times 298 \times 2.303 \log K_p$$

Hence
$$\log K_p = -0.7891$$

and
$$\underline{K_p = 0.1625 \text{ atm}}$$

For the reaction under consideration
$$K_p = \frac{p^2_{NO_2}}{p_{N_2O_4}}$$

But the partial pressure (p) of any gas in N m^{-2}, for which ideal behaviour may be assumed, is given by $p = cRT$, where c is the concentration in mol m^{-3} and R has the value 8.31 N m K^{-1}
Therefore

$$K_p = \frac{c^2_{NO_2}\,(RT)^2}{c_{N_2O_4}\,(RT)} = \frac{c^2_{NO_2}}{c_{N_2O_4}}\,RT = K_c \,.\, RT$$

Hence $K_c = K_p/RT$

$$= \frac{0.1625 \times 1.013 \times 10^5}{8.31 \times 298} = \underline{6.645 \text{ mol m}^{-3}}$$

$$= 6.65 \times 10^{-3} \text{ mol dm}^{-3}$$

By Dalton's Law, the partial pressure (p) is also related to the total pressure (P) by the relationship $p = xP$, where x is the mole fraction, that is, the ratio of the number of molecules of the particular gas to the total number of molecules of all gases in the system.

K_p may be written, therefore, in terms of mole fractions, as

$$K_p = \frac{x^2_{NO_2}\ P^2}{x_{N_2O_4}\ P} = K_x \,.\, P$$

Hence
$$K_x = \frac{K_p}{P}$$

Since, in this case, $P = 1$ atm, $K_x = K_p = 0.1625$.

Note Units are quoted for the equilibrium constants in this and succeeding problems. Each pressure in the expression for K_p is in fact a ratio of the pressure of the gas to a standard pressure of 1 atm and hence has no units. This arises from the derivation of the equation $\Delta G^\ominus = -RT \ln K_p$ for a reaction involving ideal gases, in which the chemical potential of each gas is expressed in the form $\mu = \mu^\ominus + RT \ln p$, (where p is the partial pressure of the gas when its chemical potential is μ and $\mu^\ominus$ is the chemical potential when the gas is in the reference state at a pressure of 1 atm and temperature, T). Strictly speaking, the equation is $\mu = \mu^\ominus + RT \ln p/1$, and it is the dimensionless quantity (p atm/1 atm) which appears in the expression for K_p.

Example 2.12 Van't Hoff isotherm and heterogeneous equilibrium

If for the reaction $NiO + H_2 \rightleftharpoons Ni + H_2O$, $\Delta G^\ominus = -37.8$ kJ at 500°C, what ratio of pressures of hydrogen and water vapour will be in equilibrium with nickel oxide at 500°C?

(B.Sc.(Eng.) in Metallurgy, London)

By the van't Hoff isotherm

$$\Delta G^\ominus = -RT \ln K_p$$

By substitution of the relevant data in the isotherm we can obtain a value for K_p, the equilibrium constant expressed in terms of partial pressures.

$$-37\,800 = -8.31 \times 773 \times 2.303 \times \log K_p$$

Therefore $\log K_p = 2.555$

and $K_p = 3.589 \times 10^2$

For the reaction $NiO + H_2 \rightleftharpoons Ni + H_2O$

$$K_p = \frac{a_{Ni} \times p_{H_2O}}{a_{NiO} \times p_{H_2}}$$

The activities of the non-gaseous phases are taken as unity at all temperatures up to fairly high pressures.

Therefore $$K_p = \frac{p_{H_2O}}{p_{H_2}}$$

Thus K_p gives directly the ratio of pressures of water vapour and hydrogen in equilibrium with nickel oxide and nickel. At 500°C, this is equal to 3.59×10^2.

Example 2.13 Free energy change and fugacity

Reference tables give:

$3C_2H_2(gas) = C_6H_6(gas)$; $\Delta H^\ominus_{298} = -550$ kJ, and the molar entropy values, also at 298K, $S^\ominus_{(C_2H_2,\ gas)} = 202$ JK^{-1}, and $S^\ominus_{(C_6H_6,\ gas)} = 271$ JK^{-1}.

From the data determine an equilibrium constant at 298 K for this benzene synthesis, indicating the units in which it is expressed.

(R.S.C.)

Using the molar entropy values given, the entropy change for the synthesis is

$$\Delta S^\ominus = S^\ominus_{(C_6H_6,\ gas)} - 3 \times S^\ominus_{(C_2H_2,\ gas)}$$
$$= 271 - 3 \times 202 = -335 \text{ J K}^{-1}.$$

The standard free energy change ($\Delta G^\ominus$) for the synthesis can now be determined by substituting the relevant data in the relationship:

$$\Delta G^\ominus = \Delta H^\ominus - T\Delta S^\ominus$$
$$= -550\,000 + 298 \times 335 = -450\,180 \text{ J}.$$

For ideal gases the equilibrium constant (K_p) in terms of partial pressures should be independent of total pressure, but for real gases considerable deviations from ideal behaviour are apparent at high pressures. Therefore, knowing the standard free energy change ($\Delta G^{\ominus}$) for a gas reaction, the equilibrium concentrations in a reaction mixture are calculated by obtaining the equilibrium constant in terms of fugacities (K_f) from the relationship $\Delta G^{\ominus} = -RT \ln K_f$, and then by calculating the partial pressures from

$$K_p = \frac{K_f}{K_\gamma},$$

K_γ being expressed in terms of activity coefficients.
Substitution of the data in the relationship

$$\Delta G^{\ominus} = -RT \ln K_f$$

permits the evaluation of the equilibrium constant (K_f):

$$450\,180 = 8.31 \times 298 \ln K_f$$

Hence
$$\log K_f = 78.94$$
$$K_f = 8.71 \times 10^{78} \text{ atm}^{-2}$$

The equilibrium constant for the benzene synthesis is given by $K_f = 8.71 \times 10^{78} \text{ atm}^{-2}$.

Example 2.14 Equilibrium constants and van't Hoff isochore

At constant pressure of atmospheric, N_2O_4 is 50% dissociated at 60°C, and 79% at 100°C.

Calculate the equilibrium constant at these temperatures for the reaction $N_2O_4 \rightleftharpoons 2NO_2$ and determine the heat of dissociation.

(*B.Sc.* (*Subsid. Subject*), *Bristol*)

Calculation of equilibrium constant at 60°C

The total pressure is constant at one atm and N_2O_4 is 50% dissociated. The partial pressure of each constituent is given by the product of the mole fraction and the total pressure. The mole fractions are as shown:

$$N_2O_4 \rightleftharpoons 2NO_2$$
$$\frac{1-\alpha}{1+\alpha} \qquad \frac{2\alpha}{1+\alpha}$$

where α is the degree of dissociation of N_2O_4.

By the law of mass action

$$K_p = \frac{(p_{NO_2})^2}{(p_{N_2O_4})}$$

where $p_{N_2O_4}$ and p_{NO_2} are the equilibrium partial pressures of N_2O_4 and NO_2 respectively.

Since the total pressure is unity, the mole fractions at equilibrium correspond to the equilibrium partial pressures.

Therefore $$K_{p333} = \frac{(2\times 0.5)^2}{(1+0.5)(1-0.5)} = \underline{1.33 \text{ atm}}$$

Calculation of the equilibrium constant at 100°C

At this temperature, at a total pressure of one atmosphere, the N_2O_4 is 79% dissociated.
By a similar argument to that used above

$$K_{p373} = \frac{(2\times 0.79)^2}{(1+0.79)(1-0.79)} = \underline{6.64 \text{ atm}}$$

Calculation of the heat of dissociation

The heat of dissociation ($-\Delta H$) can now be determined by making use of the integrated form of the van't Hoff isochore, the assumption being made that ΔH is independent of temperature over the range under consideration:

$$\ln\frac{K_{p,T_2}}{K_{p,T_1}} = -\frac{\Delta H}{R}\left(\frac{T_1-T_2}{T_1T_2}\right)$$

$$\ln\frac{6.64}{1.33} = -\frac{\Delta H}{8.31}\left(\frac{333-373}{333\times 373}\right)$$

Therefore

$$\Delta H = \frac{2.303\times 8.31\times 333\times 373}{40}\log\frac{6.64}{1.33} \text{ J}$$

$$= \underline{41\ 500 \text{ J.}}$$

Summary The value of the equilibrium constant for the reaction $N_2O_4 \rightleftharpoons 2NO_2$ is 1.33 at 60°C, and 6.64 at 100°C. The heat of dissociation is 41.5 kJ absorbed per mole of N_2O_4 dissociated.

Example 2.15 Equilibrium constants and van't Hoff isochore

A mixture of nitrogen and hydrogen in the molar ratio 1:3 was passed over an efficient catalyst, and the exit gases analysed for ammonia with the following results:

T/°C	*Total pressure = 10 atm* *Percentage* NH_3	*Total pressure = 50 atm* *Percentage* NH_3
350	*7.35*	*25.11*
450	*2.04*	*9.17*

Calculate K_p *for each of these experimental measurements, and the molar enthalpy change for the reaction at each pressure.*

(*B.Sc., B.Met., Sheffield*)

The reaction under consideration is:

$$\tfrac{1}{2}N_2 + \tfrac{3}{2}H_2 \rightleftharpoons NH_3$$

Calculations of K_p

By the law of mass action we have for the equilibrium

$$K_p = \frac{p_{NH_3}}{(p_{N_2})^{1/2}(p_{H_2})^{3/2}}$$

where the various 'p' values refer to the appropriate partial pressures at equilibrium.

At 350°C the respective partial pressures, corresponding to a total pressure of 10 atm (by Dalton's law of partial pressures) are:

$$NH_3 = 0.735 \text{ atm}, \quad H_2 = 6.949 \text{ atm}, \quad N_2 = 2.316 \text{ atm}$$

Therefore $$K_p = \frac{0.735}{(2.316)^{1/2}(6{\cdot}949)^{3/2}} = 2.64 \times 10^{-2} \text{ atm}^{-1}$$

At 350°C and 50 atm pressure, the respective partial pressures are:

$$NH_3 = 12.555 \text{ atm}, H_2 = 28.084 \text{ atm}, \quad N_2 = 9.361 \text{ atm}$$

Therefore $$K_p = \frac{(12.56)}{(9.36)^{1/2}(28.08)^{3/2}} = 2.76 \times 10^{-2} \text{ atm}^{-1}$$

At 450°C and 10 atm pressure, the respective partial pressures are:

$$NH_3 = 0.204 \text{ atm}, \quad H_2 = 7.347 \text{ atm}, \quad N_2 = 2.449 \text{ atm}$$

$$\text{Therefore } K_p = \frac{0.204}{(2.449)^{1/2}(7.347)^{3/2}} = 6.55 \times 10^{-3} \text{ atm}^{-1}$$

At 450°C and 50 atm pressure, the respective partial pressures are:

$$NH_3 = 4.585 \text{ atm}, \quad H_2 = 34.061 \text{ atm},$$
$$N_2 = 11.354 \text{ atm}$$

$$\text{Therefore } K_p = \frac{4.585}{(11.35)^{1/2}(34.06)^{3/2}} = 6.84 \times 10^{-3} \text{ atm}^{-1}$$

Calculation of molar enthalpy change

The molar enthalpy change (ΔH) is calculated by substitution of the relevant data in the integrated form of the van't Hoff isochore, the assumption being made that ΔH is independent of temperature over a small range:

$$\ln \frac{K_{p,T_2}}{K_{p,T_1}} = -\frac{\Delta H}{R}\left(\frac{T_1 - T_2}{T_1 T_2}\right)$$

At 10 atm pressure:

$$\bar{3}.8162 - \bar{2}.4216 = \frac{\Delta H}{2.303 \times 8.31}\left(\frac{100}{723 \times 623}\right)$$

$$-0.6054 = \frac{\Delta H}{19.14}\left(\frac{100}{723 \times 623}\right)$$

Therefore $\Delta H = -52\,190 \text{ J mol}^{-1}$

At 50 atm pressure:

$$\bar{3}.8351 - \bar{2}.4409 = \frac{\Delta H}{2.303 \times 8.31}\left(\frac{100}{723 \times 623}\right)$$

$$-0.6058 = \text{R.H.S.}$$

Therefore $\Delta H = -52\,230 \text{ J mol}^{-1}$

Summary

	10 atm pressure		50 atm total pressure	
	350°C	450°C	350°C	450°C
K_p	2.64×10^{-2}	6.55×10^{-3}	2.76×10^{-2}	6.84×10^{-3}
ΔH	$-52\,190 \text{ J mol}^{-1}$		$-52\,230 \text{ J mol}^{-1}$	

Example 2.16 Van't Hoff isotherm and isochore

At high temperatures carbon dioxide dissociates according to the equation $2CO_2 = 2CO + O_2$.

At 1 atm pressure the percentage decomposition is 2.0×10^{-5} *at 1000K, and at 1400K is* 1.27×10^{-2}. *Assuming that the enthalpy change* (ΔH) *of the reaction is independent of temperature, calculate the standard free energy change and the standard entropy change at 1000K.* *(R.S.C.)*

The partial pressures, in atmospheres, of the constituents are as shown in the equation:

	$2CO_2 =$	$2CO$	$+ \quad O_2$
At 1000K:	1	2.0×10^{-7}	1.0×10^{-7}
At 1400K:	1	1.27×10^{-4}	0.635×10^{-4}

(**Note** Due to the very small percentage decomposition, the partial pressure of carbon dioxide is approximated to unity.)

Therefore
$$K_{p1000} = \frac{4.0 \times 10^{-14} \times 1.0 \times 10^{-7}}{1}$$
$$= 4.0 \times 10^{-21} \text{ atm}$$

and
$$K_{p1400} = \frac{(1.27 \times 10^{-4})^2 \times (0.635 \times 10^{-4})}{1}$$
$$= 1.024 \times 10^{-12} \text{ atm}$$

The standard free energy change can now be determined by means of the van't Hoff isotherm.

$$\begin{aligned}-\Delta G^\ominus &= RT \ln K_{p1000} \\ &= 8.31 \times 1000 \times 2.303 \times \log 4.0 \times 10^{-21} \text{ J} \\ &= -8.31 \times 1000 \times 2.303 \times 20.398 \text{ J} \\ &= -390\,400 \text{ J}\end{aligned}$$

To calculate the standard entropy change, $\Delta H^\ominus$ is first of all determined by means of the integrated form of the van't Hoff isochore (assuming that ΔH is constant over the temperature range under consideration):

$$\ln \frac{K_{p,T_2}}{K_{p,T_1}} = -\frac{\Delta H^\ominus}{R}\left(\frac{T_1 - T_2}{T_1 T_2}\right)$$

$$-11.99 + 20.398 = \frac{\Delta H^\ominus}{2.303 \times 8.31}\left(\frac{400}{1400 \times 1000}\right)$$

Hence
$$\Delta H^\ominus = 563\,200 \text{ J}$$

The standard entropy change at 1000K, is obtained by substitution of the data in the following relationship:

$$\Delta G^{\ominus}{}_{1000} = \Delta H^{\ominus} - T\Delta S^{\ominus}{}_{1000}$$

That is
$$\Delta S^{\ominus}{}_{1000} = \frac{-390\,400 + 563\,200}{1000}\ \mathrm{J\,K^{-1}}$$

$$= 172.8\ \mathrm{J\,K^{-1}}.$$

Standard free energy change at 1000K = 390 kJ

Standard entropy change at 1000K = 173 J K^{-1}

Example 2.17 Calculation of absolute entropy

Given that $S_{298} = 38.77\,J\,K^{-1}\,mol^{-1}$ for grey tin, calculate ΔG at 298 K for the transformation $Sn_{(grey)} \rightarrow Sn_{(white)}$; $\Delta H = 2234\,J$, from the following atomic heat capacities:

T/K	*0*	*20*	*30*	*40*	*60*	*80*	*197.2*
$C_{p(white)}/J\,K^{-1}$	*0*	*1.970*	*5.460*	*9.387*	*15.33*	*19.49*	*26.17*
T (contd.)		*248.4*	*273.0*	*288.1*			
$C_{p(white)}$ *(contd.)*		*26.71*	*26.84*	*26.88*			

(*B.Sc., Wales*)

To calculate ΔG, the entropy change for the grey/white tin transformation is required, but first it is necessary to calculate the absolute entropy (S_{298}) for white tin, from the heat capacities given. This can be done using the relationship

$$S_{298} = \int_0^{298} \frac{C_p\,\mathrm{d}T}{T} = 2.303 \int_0^{298} C_p\,\mathrm{d}\,(\log T)$$

The integral is usually evaluated graphically by plotting the C_p data versus $\log T$ or C_p/T versus T, and determining the area under the curve. Since the area is equal to the integral, the entropy for the C_p versus $\log T$ plot is given by

$$S_{298} = 2.303 \Big[\text{Area}\Big]_{T=0}^{T=298}$$

The C_p and $\log T$ values given are plotted in Fig. 1.

log T	1.301	1.477	1.602	1.778	1.903	2.295	2.395
C_p	1.970	5.460	9.387	15.33	19.49	26.17	26.71
log T (contd.)		2.436	2.460				
C_p (contd.)		26.84	26.88				

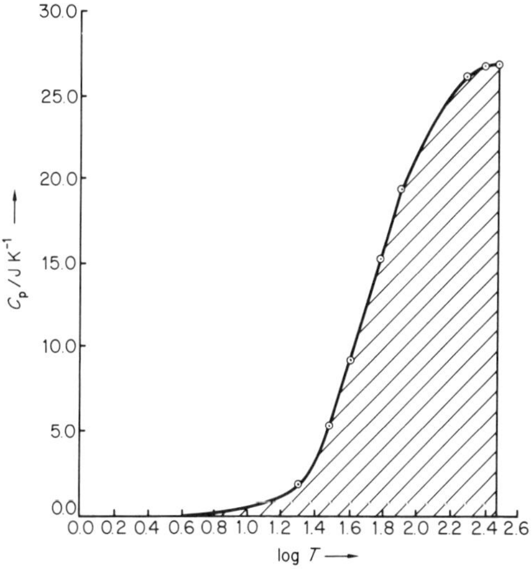

Fig. 1 Heat capacity of white tin at various temperatures

The area under the curve is shaded.

Therefore
$$S_{298} = 2.303 \times \text{area J K}^{-1}$$
$$= 2.303 \times 20.37 = 46.91 \text{ J K}^{-1}$$

The entropy change for the grey/white tin transformation at 298K is given by

$$S_{298(\text{white})} - S_{298(\text{grey})} = 46.91 - 38.77 \text{ J K}^{-1}$$
$$= 8.14 \text{ J K}^{-1}$$

ΔG at 298K for the transformation, is now easily calculated by substitution of the data in

$$\Delta G = \Delta H - T\Delta S$$
$$= 2234 - 298 \times 8.14 \text{ J}$$
$$= -191 \text{ J}$$

ΔG at 298K for the transformation $Sn_{(\text{grey})} \rightarrow Sn_{(\text{white})}$ is $\underline{-191 \text{ J}}$.

Example 2.18 The Clausius-Clapeyron equation

Calculate the latent heat of vaporization of water from the following data, expressing the result in joules per gram:

Temperature	= *100°C*
dp/dT	= *2.717 cmHg* K^{-1}
Density of water	= *0.962 g* cm^{-3}
Density of water vapour	= 5.973×10^{-4} *g* cm^{-3}
Density of mercury	= *13.59 g* cm^{-3}
Acceleration due to gravity	= *981 cm* s^{-2}

The latent heat of vaporization in joules per gram (l_{vap}) of water, can be determined from the above data by means of the following form of Clausius-Clapeyron equation:

$$\frac{dp}{dT} = \frac{l_{vap.}}{T(v_2 - v_1)}$$

where T is the boiling point of water on the absolute scale, and v_1 and v_2 are the volumes in cubic metres per gram of water and water vapour respectively. The quantity $\frac{dp}{dT}$ is expressed in Newtons per square metre ($N\ m^{-2}$) per degree as follows:

$$\frac{dp}{dT} = 2.717 \text{ cm Hg K}^{-1} = 2.717 \times 13.59 \times 981 \text{ g cm s}^{-2} \text{ cm}^{-2} \text{ K}^{-1}$$

$$= 2.717 \times 13.59 \times 981 \times 10^{-1} \text{ kg m s}^{-2} \text{ m}^{-2} \text{ K}^{-1} \qquad (\text{N m}^{-2} \text{ K}^{-1})$$

Rearrangement of the Clausius-Clapeyron equation gives

$$l_{vap.} = \frac{dp}{dT} \cdot T(v_2 - v_1)$$

Substitution of the data now gives

$$l_{vap.} = 2.717 \times 13.59 \times 981 \times 10^{-1} \times 373 \left(\frac{10^{-6}}{5.973 \times 10^{-4}} - \frac{10^{-6}}{0.962} \right) \text{ J g}^{-1}$$

$$= \underline{2258 \text{ J g}^{-1}}$$

<u>The latent heat of vaporization of water is 2.26 kJ g^{-1}</u>

Example 2.19 The Clausius-Clapeyron equation

Given that $\log p = C - \dfrac{L}{2.303\,RT}$, *determine the value of L, the molar latent heat of vaporization, from the following data for trichloromethane.*

Temp/°C	*20*	*30*	*40*	*50*
Sat. vap. press./mmHg	*160*	*248*	*369*	*535*

(University of Durham)

The equation $\log p = C - \dfrac{L}{2.303\,RT}$, is the integrated form of the Clausius-Clapeyron equation. Comparison of this with the equation of a straight line ($y = c + mx$), suggests that if values for $\log p$ are plotted against $1/T$, the resulting graph should be a straight line with slope $-L/2.303R$. Thus, from the slope, the value of L can be calculated.

It is also possible to calculate L by direct substitution of the data in the given equation, the constant c being eliminated by considering the resulting equations in pairs.

The graphical method is illustrated in Fig. 2 which is a plot of log p against $1/T$, the required data being given in the following table:

T/°C	*20*	*30*	*40*	*50*
T/K	293	303	313	323
$1/T \times 10^{-3}$	3.413	3.301	3.196	3.096
Sat. vap. press.(p)/mmHg	160	248	369	535
log p	2.204	2.395	2.567	2.728

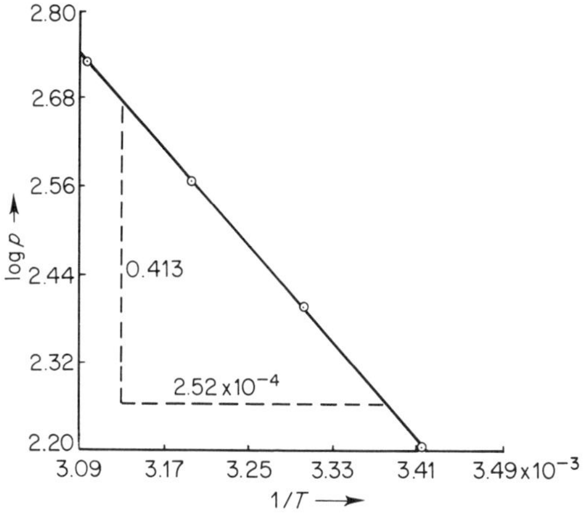

Fig. 2 Plot of log p versus $1/T$ for trichloromethane

By measurement, the slope of the line $= -\dfrac{0.413}{2.52 \times 10^{-4}}$

Therefore $$-\frac{L}{2.303\,R} = -\frac{0.413}{2.52 \times 10^{-4}}$$

And $$L = \frac{0.413 \times 2.303 \times 8.31}{2.52 \times 10^{-4}}\ \text{J mol}^{-1}$$

$$= 31.37\ \text{kJ mol}^{-1}$$

The molar latent heat of vaporization of trichloromethane is 31.4 kJ.

Additional Examples

1 Compare the theoretical efficiencies of a heat engine working with steam between (*a*) 130°C and 30°C; (*b*) 230°C and 30°C.

2 A heat engine operates with mercury vapour between (*a*) 350°C and 50°C; (*b*) 450°C and 50°C. What is the amount of heat that must be withdrawn from the hot reservoir to produce 500 J of work in each case?

3 Calculate the change in entropy when 11.21 dm^3 of a perfect gas at 0°C and 760 mmHg pressure expands isothermally until its pressure is 190 mmHg. (B.Sc., Wales)

4 A refrigerator operating in a room at 30°C converts 1 kilogram of water at 0°C into ice at 0°C. What is the minimum amount of work required? (The latent heat of fusion of ice is 334 J g^{-1} at 0°C.)
(B. Agric., Queen's University, Belfast)

5 What is the change of entropy on heating 1 g of water from 0°C to 100°C? Mean specific heat of water between 0°C and 100°C = 4.18 J g^{-1}.
(B.Pharm., London)

6 What is the entropy change for the flow of 400 J of heat from surroundings at 300 K into a 290 K system?
(Adapted from ACS Cooperative Examination: Physical Chemistry (Thermodynamics).)

7 If $\Delta G^{\ominus}$ for a chemical reaction at 298 K is 57.1 kJ mol^{-1}, what is the value of the equilibrium constant, K_p, at that temperature?
(Adapted from ACS Cooperative Examination: Physical Chemistry (Thermodynamics).)

8 Calculate the change in entropy when 1 mole of water at 0°C is heated at atmospheric pressure to form steam at 110°C. The mean specific heat of water is 4.1 J K^{-1} g^{-1}; the latent heat of vaporization is 2257 J g^{-1}. (H, 1.008; O, 16.00.) (R.S.C.)

9 Evaluate the entropy change per mole when lead is heated from 27°C to 677°C, given the following data:

Pb(s) $C_p = 23.5 + 9.61 \times 10^{-3} T\,\mathrm{J\,K^{-1}\,mol^{-1}}$ for 298 K to m.p.
Pb(l) $C_p = 32.4 + 3.14 \times 10^{-3} T\,\mathrm{J\,K^{-1}\,mol^{-1}}$ for m.p. to 1000 K.
M.p. lead 327°C; $L_f = 4.93\,\mathrm{kJ\,mol^{-1}}$.

10 Calculate the entropy change per mole, when helium at 1 atm pressure and 27°C is heated to 250°C and compressed, so that its final pressure is 5 atm. Assume that helium behaves as an ideal gas. ($C_v = 12.5\,\mathrm{J\,K^{-1}\,mol^{-1}}$.)

11 Calculate the entropy change for the reaction

$$2\mathrm{C(graphite)} + 3\mathrm{H_2(g)} \rightarrow \mathrm{C_2H_6(g)};$$

given the following standard entropies at 25°C:

	$S^{\ominus}/\mathrm{J\,K^{-1}\,mol^{-1}}$
C(graphite)	5.68
$H_2(g)$	130.5
$C_2H_6(g)$	229.3

12 Given for aluminium that

$T_{\text{fusion}} = 933\,\mathrm{K}$, $\Delta H^{\ominus}_{\text{fusion}} = 10.66\,\mathrm{kJ\,mol^{-1}}$, $C_{p(\text{liquid})} = 34.4\,\mathrm{J\,K^{-1}\,mol^{-1}}$, and $C_{p(\text{solid})} = 31.9\,\mathrm{J\,K^{-1}mol^{-1}}$

calculate the entropy change when 1 mole of metal is heated from 873 K to 973 K.

(Adapted from ACS Cooperative Examination: Physical Chemistry (Thermodynamics).)

13 Derive an expression for the molar free energy of mixing, at constant temperature and pressure, of two non-reacting ideal gases, in terms of the mole fraction of each gas in the mixture, and indicate how this calculation could have been made in terms of the partial pressure of each gas in the mixture.

A thermally insulated vessel is divided into two compartments by a partition of insulating material. One compartment contains 0.4 mole of helium at 20°C and 1 atm pressure; the other contains 0.6 mole of nitrogen at 100°C and 2 atm pressure.

The partition is removed so that the two gases mix. Calculate the final temperature and pressure of the mixture and then evaluate the magnitude of the entropy change that has occurred. The heat capacities at constant volume for helium and nitrogen are 12.5 and 20.8 $\mathrm{J\,K^{-1}\,mol^{-1}}$ respectively.

(B.Sc. (Special), London)

14 Explain why a system at constant temperature and pressure is at equilibrium when its Gibbs free energy (G) is a minimum.

The equilibrium constant for the reaction

$$\mathrm{H_2 + I_2 = 2HI}$$

may be expressed in the form:

$\ln K_p = 8.57 + 985/(T/K) + 0.90 \ln (T/K)$

at temperatures around 400 K. Evaluate $\Delta G^{\ominus}$, $\Delta H^{\ominus}$ and $\Delta S^{\ominus}$ at 400 K.

(University of Oxford)

15 Given the following data, calculate the standard free energy of formation of $Cs_2O(s)$ at 298 K. Ions are in aqueous solution.

$Cs_2O(s) + H_2O(l) \longrightarrow 2Cs^+ + 2OH^-$; $\Delta H^{\ominus} = -345.7$ kJ
$Cs(s) + H_2O(l) \longrightarrow Cs^+ + OH^- + \frac{1}{2}H_2(g)$; $\Delta H^{\ominus} = -202.9$ kJ
$H_2(g) + \frac{1}{2}O_2(g) \longrightarrow H_2O(l)$; $\Delta H^{\ominus} = -286.9$ kJ

Standard entropies/J K^{-1} mol^{-1}, are

$O_2(g)$ 205.8; $Cs(s)$ 85.7; $Cs_2O(s)$ 147.4.

(University of Toronto, Canada)

16 The following values of standard entropies and heats of combustion to gaseous CO_2 and liquid water hold for 25°C:

	$S^{\ominus}/J\,K^{-1}\,mol^{-1}$	$-\Delta H^{\ominus}/kJ\,mol^{-1}$
C(graphite)	5.88	396
$H_2(g)$	131	287
$C_2H_5OH(l)$	161	1372
$C_2H_4(g)$	220	1399
$C_2H_6(g)$	231	1566
$H_2O(l)$	66.8	—

Calculate the $\Delta H^{\ominus}$ and $\Delta G^{\ominus}$ values for the following reactions under the same temperature and pressure conditions. Which of them are thermodynamically possible, or could be made so by relatively small changes in the conditions?

$$2C+2H_2 \longrightarrow C_2H_4;$$
$$2C+3H_2 \longrightarrow C_2H_6;$$
$$C_2H_4+H_2O \longrightarrow C_2H_5OH;$$
$$C_2H_4+H_2 \longrightarrow C_2H_6;$$
$$C_2H_6+H_2O \longrightarrow C_2H_5OH + H_2.$$

(R.S.C.)

17 For the reaction $\frac{1}{2}N_2(g) + \frac{3}{2}H_2(g) = NH_3(g)$ the value of K_p is 6.59×10^{-3} at 450°C. Calculate the change in free energy at the same temperature for:

(*a*) the formation of 2 moles of ammonia at 10 atm pressure from 1 mole of nitrogen and 3 moles of hydrogen at pressures of 1 atm and 2 atm respectively, and
(*b*) the formation of 2 moles of ammonia and 1 atm pressure from 1 mole of nitrogen and 3 moles of hydrogen at pressures of 10 atm and 50 atm respectively.

18 Determine the Gibbs free energy change ($\Delta G^{\ominus}$) for the reduction of one mole of acetone at 25°C and 1 atm pressure, to propan-2-ol under the same conditions, given the following values of standard free energies of formation.

	$\Delta G^{\ominus}_{298\,K}/kJ\,mol^{-1}$
$CH_3CHOH.CH_3(l)$	-185
$CH_3.CO.CH_3(l)$	-156

19 Discuss the feasibility of reducing cadmium sulphide to the metal with hydrogen at 1100°C using the following standard free energy values at that temperature:

$$H_2(g)+\tfrac{1}{2}S_2(g) = H_2S(g); \quad \Delta G^{\ominus} = -49.10\ kJ\ mol^{-1}$$
$$Cd(g)+\tfrac{1}{2}S_2(g) = CdS(g); \quad \Delta G^{\ominus} = -127.7\ kJ\ mol^{-1}$$

(B.Sc., Wales)

20 Calculate K_p at 1000 K for the reaction:

$$C_2H_4+H_2 \rightleftharpoons C_2H_6$$

from the following data:

(i) $\Delta H^{\ominus}$ values at 298 K,

$$C_2H_4+3O_2 = 2CO_2+2H_2O(g); \quad \Delta H^{\ominus}_{298} = -1395\ kJ$$
$$C_2H_6+\tfrac{7}{2}O_2 = 2CO_2+3H_2O(g); \quad \Delta H^{\ominus}_{298} = -1550\ kJ$$
$$H_2+\tfrac{1}{2}O_2 = H_2O(g); \quad \Delta H^{\ominus}_{298} = -243\ kJ$$

(ii) Molar entropies at 298 K,

Substance	C_2H_4	C_2H_6	H_2
$S^{\ominus}_{298}$	220.7	230.4	131.1 $J\,K^{-1}\,mol^{-1}$

(iii) The average heat capacity change for the reaction (ΔC_p) over the temperature range 298–1000 K = 10.9 $J\,K^{-1}\,mol^{-1}$. (B.Sc., Durham)

21 Calculate the equilibrium constant, at 25°C, of the reaction

$$Fe_2O_3+H_2 \rightleftharpoons 2FeO+H_2O;$$

the appropriate standard free energies of formation at 25°C, in kJ mol^{-1}, are as follows:

Fe_2O_3, -744; FeO, -245; H_2O, -229;

assume that water is present as vapour.

(B.Sc.(Eng.) in Metallurgy, London)

22 The ionic product of water, $K_w = [H^+][OH^-]$, where the terms in brackets represent activities, has the values of 0.681×10^{-14} at 20°C and 1.471×10^{-14} at 30°C. Assess the heat of neutralization of one mole of hydrogen ions by one mole of hydroxyl ions at 25°C. (R.S.C.)

23 The heat of neutralization of a strong acid by a strong base in very dilute aqueous solution is 56.89 kJ mol^{-1} H_3O^+ at 20°C and the ionic product of water at this temperature is 6.81×10^{-15}. Calculate the ionic product at 30°C, stating any approximation you may find it necessary to make. (R.S.C.)

24 The dissociation constant of ethanoic acid is 1.700×10^{-5} at 5°C, 1.745×10^{-5} at 15°C, 1.750×10^{-5} at 30°C and 1.703×10^{-5} at 40°C.

Calculate the standard entropy ($\Delta S^\ominus$) of ionization of ethanoic acid in water at 10°C and 35°C. Suggest a possible reason for the direction in which $\Delta S^\ominus$ changes with temperature. (B.Sc., Birmingham)

25 Calculate from the data given below the pressure of zinc vapour in equilibrium with solid zinc oxide and hydrogen at a pressure of one atm at 1000°C. (Assume the zinc vapour and water pressures to be equal.)

$$ZnO(s)+H_2(g) \longrightarrow Zn(g)+H_2O(g);$$
$$\Delta G^\ominus \text{ (in kJ)} = 233.7-0.1607T$$

(B.Sc.(Eng.) in Metallurgy, London)

26 Over a wide temperature range the standard free energy of formation of water vapour at TK is given by the equation:

$$\Delta G_f^\ominus = -240\,800+6.95T+12.93T\log_{10} T \text{ J mol}^{-1}.$$

Using this datum, calculate

(*a*) the standard enthalpy and standard entropy of formation at 2000 K;
(*b*) the percentage dissociation of water vapour at 2000 K and 0.1 atm.

(R.S.C.)

27 For the chemical reaction

$$A(g)+B(g) \longrightarrow AB(l)$$

the standard molar entropies at 25°C and 1 atm pressure are, in J K^{-1} mol^{-1}:

A(g), 131.0; B(g), 102.9; AB(l), 69.8.

The standard enthalpy change under the same conditions of temperature and pressure is -287.5 kJ mol^{-1}. Calculate the standard Gibbs free energy change of the reaction when it proceeds:

(*a*) at 25°C and 1 atm pressure,
(*b*) at 35°C and 2 atm pressure.

The volume of AB(l) may be neglected; and A(g) and B(g) may be assumed to behave as ideal gases. ΔS for the reaction may be assumed to be independent of temperature. (B.Sc. (Special), London)

28 For the hydrogenation of benzene to cyclohexane, $C_6H_6+3H_2=C_6H_{12}$, $\Delta H_{100°C}=-193$ kJ and the partial pressures at equilibrium at 100°C and 1 atm were found to be $p_{H_2}=1$ mmHg, $p_{C_6H_6}=69$ mmHg, $p_{C_6H_{12}}=690$ mmHg.

Calculate the equilibrium constant, K_p, and the free energy of the hydrogenation reaction at 100°C, and the log K_p at 90°C, assuming ideal behaviour.

(B.Sc. in Applied Science (Chem. Eng.), Durham)

29 The following data apply to the reaction:

$$SO_2(g)+\tfrac{1}{2}O_2(g) = SO_3(g);$$

T/°C	K_p	T/°C	K_p
528	31.3	727	1.86
579	13.8	832	0.63
627	6.55	897	0.36

Calculate ΔH over the temperature range 528–897°C from these data, and comment on the value of ΔC_p for the above reaction. What is the value of ΔG and of ΔS at 727°C? (B.Sc., B.Met., Sheffield)

30 A study of the equilibrium: $CO_2+C \rightleftharpoons 2CO$ yielded the following results:

T/°K	*Total pressure/atm.*	*Per cent CO_2 in equilibrium mixture*
1073	2.57	26.45
1173	2.30	6.92

For the equilibrium: $2CO_2 \rightleftharpoons 2CO+O_2$ the value of K_p at 1173 K is 1.25×10^{-16} atm; the heat of combustion of carbon at 1173 K is 392.2 kJ.

Calculate ΔH and ΔS for the reaction: $2CO_2 = 2CO+O_2$ at 1173 K. (R.S.C.)

31 The equilibrium constant for the reaction $Ba^{2+} + Y^{4-} \rightleftharpoons BaY^{2-}$ (where H_4Y represents ethane-1,2-diamine tetra-acetic acid) is said to be $10^{8.01}$ at 0°C and $10^{7.68}$ at 30°C. Calculate the heat content change and the entropy change and comment on the values you obtain. (R.S.C.)

32 The standard free energies of formation ($-\Delta G^{\ominus}$ at 25°C and 1 atm) of solid AgCl and of Ag^+ and Cl^- ions in ideal 1 molal solution are 110.1, −77.49 and 131.5 kJ respectively. Calculate the solubility product of AgCl at 25°C. (R.S.C.)

33 Calculate the absolute entropy per mole of anhydrous sodium sulphate at 298 K from the following heat capacity data:

T/K	14	20	25	35	50	100	219	282	298
$C_p/J\,K^{-1}\,mol^{-1}$	1.89	4.96	7.98	15.12	28.22	67.54	113.9	131.0	134.1

34 Calculate the latent heat of vaporization in units of $J\,mol^{-1}$ for (*a*) ethanol, (*b*) tetrachloromethane using the following data for 77°C and 1 atm pressure:

	Ethanol	*Tetrachloromethane*
$\frac{dp}{dT}$/mmHg deg^{-1}	28.6	20.4
Volume per g of vapour/cm^3	606.0	202.5
Volume per g of liquid/cm^3	0.737	1.49
Acceleration due to gravity/cm s^{-2}	981	
Density of mercury/g cm^{-3}	13.59	

35 Determine the mean molar heat of evaporation of propanone, using the following data for its pressure:

T/°C	10	20	30	40	50
p/mmHg	115.6	184.8	282.7	421.5	612.6

(B.Sc. (Special), London)

36 It is proposed to use liquid sodium at 100°C and 120 atm pressure as the primary-stage coolant in a fast breeder reactor. At 1 atm pressure liquid sodium solidifies at 97.6°C and the densities of liquid and solid sodium at

this temperature are 0.929 and 0.952 g cm^{-3} respectively. On solidification of the sodium the heat evolution is 3.00 kJ mol^{-1}. Since the liquid sodium is less dense than the solid a large increase in pressure above atmospheric will favour solidification. Does the high pressure proposed invalidate the proposal?
(Na = 23.0).

37 Moist Ag_2CO_3 is to be dried in an air-oven at 110°C. Use the data given below to determine the minimum percentage by volume of CO_2 to be maintained in the drying-air, the pressure of which is 1 atm, in order to repress the decomposition of Ag_2CO_3.

Compound	$Ag_2CO_3(s)$	$Ag_2O(s)$	$CO_2(g)$
Standard enthalpy of formation at 298 K/kJ mol^{-1}	−501.4	−29.07	−393.3
Standard entropy of formation at 298 K/J K^{-1} mol^{-1}	167.3	121.7	213.6
Mean heat capacity/J K^{-1} mol^{-1}	109.6	68.59	40.15

38 The triple point of naphthalene is at 353 K. The vapour pressure of liquid naphthalene is 10 mm at 358.8 K and 40 mm at 392.3 K. Assume ΔH to be independent of T. Find
(a) the heat of vaporization of the liquid
(b) the normal boiling point
(c) the pressure at the triple point
(University of Washington, Seattle, USA)

3

The Gaseous State

Example 3.1 Kinetic theory

Calculate the density (in kg m^{-3}) of a gas at a pressure of 10^5 N m^{-2} when the root mean square velocity of its molecules is 3×10^2 m s^{-1}.

(*B.Pharm., London*)

From the kinetic theory $$PV = \frac{1}{3}mnu^2 \qquad \text{(i)}$$

where P and V have their usual significance of pressure and volume; m is the mass per molecule, n is the number of molecules and u the root mean square velocity.

Since P is expressed in N m^{-2}, the density will be given by mn kg m^{-3}. The volume V is expressed in cubic metres. Substituting the given data in equation (i), we have

$$10^5 = \frac{1}{3}mn\,(9 \times 10^4)$$

Hence $$\underline{mn = 3.33 \text{ kg m}^{-3}}$$

Example 3.2 Van der Waals and critical constants

The critical temperature T_c for CO_2 is 300K and its critical density is 0.45 g cm^{-3}. Calculate the van der Waals constants a and b.

(*B.Sc., Bristol*)

The van der Waals constants a and b can be expressed in terms of critical constants by means of the following equations:

(i) $b = \frac{1}{3}V_c$ where V_c is the critical volume.

(ii) $b = \frac{RT_c}{8P_c}$ where T_c is the critical temperature and P_c the critical pressure.

(iii) $a = \frac{27R^2T_c^2}{64P_c}$

The critical volume, V_c, is given by (relative molecular mass/critical density).

$$V_c = \frac{44}{0.45 \times 10^6}\ \text{m}^3.$$

Therefore, by equation (i),

$$b = \frac{44}{3 \times 0.45 \times 10^6}\ \text{m}^3\ \text{mol}^{-1}$$
$$= 3.26 \times 10^{-5}\ \text{m}^3\ \text{mol}^{-1}$$

By equation (ii)

$$P_c = \frac{RT_c}{8b}$$
$$= \frac{8.31 \times 300}{8 \times 3.26 \times 10^{-5}}\ \text{N m}^{-2}.$$
$$= 9.56 \times 10^6\ \text{N m}^{-2}.$$

Therefore by equation (iii)

$$a = \frac{27 \times (8.31)^2 \times (300)^2}{64 \times 9.56 \times 10^6}\ \text{N m}^4\ \text{mol}^{-2}$$
$$= 0.274\ \text{N m}^4\ \text{mol}^{-2}$$

The van der Waals constants for 1 mol of carbon dioxide are:
$a = 0.274$ N m^4 mol^{-2}; $b = 3.26 \times 10^{-5}$ m^3 mol^{-1}

Example 3.3 The gas laws and equations of state

Calculate the volume occupied by one mole of a slightly imperfect gas at 10 atm pressure and 0°C. The second viral coefficient is 2×10^{-5} m^3 mol^{-1}. (*B.Sc., B.Met., Sheffield*)

The product PV_m expressed as a power series gives

$$PV_m = A+BP+CP^2+\ldots$$

where P is the pressure, V_m the molar volume and the coefficients A, B and C are the first, second and third virial coefficients. In general, the order of significance of coefficients is their order in the equation. Thus at low pressures, only the first is significant and is equal to RT.

In this question the second virial coefficient is also given. Thus on substitution in

$$PV_m = RT+BP$$

we have

$$10\times 1.013\times 10^5\times V_m = 8.31\times 273+2\times 10^{-5}\times 10\times 1.013\times 10^5$$

and

$$V_m = \frac{8.31\times 273}{1.013\times 10^6}+2\times 10^{-5}\ \text{m}^3$$

$$= 2.26\times 10^{-3}\ \text{m}^3$$

The molar volume of the gas under the given conditions is 2.26×10^{-3} m^3.

Example 3.4 Van der Waals equation and molecular dimensions

The molar volume of helium at 100 atm and 0°C is 0.011075 of its molar volume at 1 atm pressure and 0°C. Assess the radius of the helium atom. (R.S.C.)

The constant 'a' in van der Waals equation is small for helium, hence the term $\frac{a}{V^2}$ can be neglected.

Therefore, for helium, the van der Waals equation is of the form

$$P(V-b) = RT$$

Set up two equations from the data given and solve for 'b':

$$100\times 1.013\times 10^5(0.011075V-b) = 8.31\times 273 \qquad \text{(i)}$$

$$1.013\times 10^5(V-b) = 8.31\times 273 \qquad \text{(ii)}$$

Substituting the value given for V by equation (ii) in (i)

$$1.013\times 10^7\left[0.011075\left(\frac{8.31\times 273}{1.013\times 10^5}+b\right)-b\right] = 8.31\times 273$$

Therefore

$$b = 2.435 \times 10^{-5}\ \mathrm{m^3\ mol^{-1}}$$

The value of $b/4$ represents the actual volume of one mole of helium atoms, hence the volume of one helium atom is

$$\frac{2.435 \times 10^{-5}}{4 \times 6.02 \times 10^{23}} = 1.011 \times 10^{-29}\ \mathrm{m^3\ atom^{-1}}$$

Assuming the atoms to be spherical

$$\frac{4}{3}\pi r^3 = 1.011 \times 10^{-29}\ \mathrm{m^3\ atom^{-1}}$$

Therefore

$$r = \left(\frac{1.011 \times 10^{-29} \times 3}{4\pi}\right)^{1/3}\ \mathrm{m}$$

$$= 1.342 \times 10^{-10}\ \mathrm{m}$$

The radius of the helium atom is 1.34×10^{-10} m.

Example 3.5 Gas viscosity, molecular diameter and mean free path

At 0°C and 1 atm pressure, the coefficient of viscosity of hydrogen is 8.41×10^{-6} Ns m^{-2}, the density is 9×10^{-2} kg m^{-3} and the root mean square velocity is 1.69×10^3 m s^{-1}. Calculate (a) the mean free path and (b) the molecular diameter.

(*a*) The relationship between the coefficient of viscosity η and the mean free path l is

$$\eta = \frac{1}{3} mnul$$

where m is the mass per molecule, u is the root mean square velocity and n the number of molecules per m^3. Hence the product $mn = d$ (the density).

Therefore

$$l = \frac{3\eta}{ud}$$

$$= \frac{3 \times 8.41 \times 10^{-6}}{1.69 \times 10^3 \times 9 \times 10^{-2}}\ \mathrm{m}$$

$$= \underline{1.66 \times 10^{-7}\ \mathrm{m}}$$

(*b*) The molecular diameter σ is calculated by substituting the relevant data in the equation

$$l = \frac{1}{\sqrt{2}\pi n\sigma^2}$$

Therefore $$\sigma = \sqrt{\frac{1}{\sqrt{2}\pi nl}}$$

$$= \sqrt{\frac{22.4 \times 10^{-3}}{\sqrt{2} \times 3.142 \times 6.02 \times 10^{23} \times 1.66 \times 10^{-7}}}\ \text{m}$$

$$= \underline{2.25 \times 10^{-10}\ \text{m}}.$$

Note (i) Where the mean free path has not been calculated, direct substitution of the data in the equation $\eta = \frac{1}{3}mu/\sqrt{2}\pi\sigma^2$ will yield the same result of 2.25×10^{-10} m for the molecular diameter.
(ii) The solution is based on the equation, $\eta = \frac{1}{3}mnul$, originally derived by Maxwell. A more precise derivation gives instead the equation, $\eta = \frac{1}{2}mnul$ (*see* E. A. Moelwyn Hughes, *Physical Chemistry*, Pergamon Press, 1957, p. 56; E. A. Guggenheim, *Elements of the Kinetic Theory of Gases*, Pergamon Press, 1960, p. 32 and 44).

Example 3.6 The gas equation and relative molecular mass determination

The ratio of density (in g dm^{-3}) to pressure (in atm) at 0°C for phosphine gas is as follows:

Pressure/atm	*1.000*	*0.750*	*0.500*	*0.250*
(d/P)/g dm^{-3} atm^{-1}	*1.5307*	*1.5272*	*1.5238*	*1.5205*

Calculate the relative atomic mass of phosphorus, taking the value of hydrogen to be 1.008.

(*B.Sc., Durham*)

The ideal gas equation in terms of n moles is written $PV = nRT$. But $n = \frac{W}{M_r}$, where W is the mass of gas and M_r the relative molecular mass. Hence the gas equation can be expressed in a form suitable for use in molecular mass determinations:

$$M_r = \frac{WRT}{PV}$$

But $$W/V = \text{density } (d).$$

Therefore $M_r = \dfrac{d}{P} \cdot RT$

Or $\dfrac{d}{P} = \dfrac{M_r}{RT} =$ constant, at constant temperature.

For real gases, d/P changes with decreasing pressure, but a plot of P against d/P is nearly linear and can be extrapolated to zero pressure.

That is $$\left(\frac{d}{P}\right)_{P=0} = \frac{M_r}{RT}$$

A plot of the values of P and d/P given in the question, gives the graph shown in Fig. 3 and extrapolation to $P = 0$ gives a value of 1.5170 g dm^{-3} atm^{-1} for d/P (i.e. 1.517×10^3 g m^{-3} atm^{-1}).

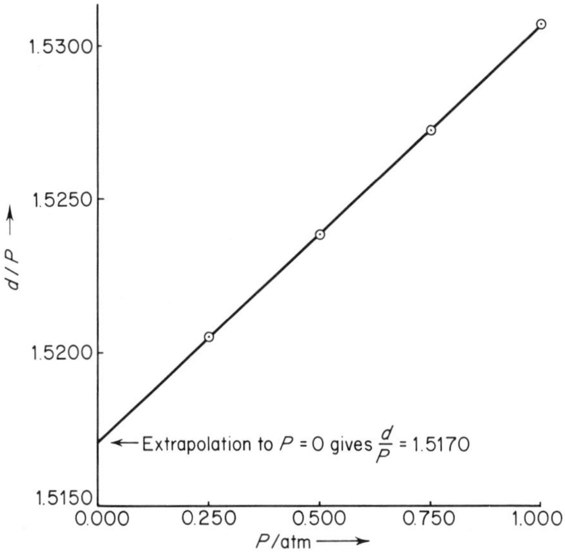

Fig. 3 Plot of P versus d/P

Therefore, M_r, the relative molecular mass of phosphine, is given by

$$M_r = \frac{8.31 \times 273 \times 1.5170 \times 10^3}{1.013 \times 10^5}$$
$$= 34.00$$

But the formula of phosphine is PH_3.
Therefore, the relative atomic mass of phosphorus is

$$34.00 - (3 \times 1.008) = \underline{30.98}$$

Example 3.7 Graphical determination of fugacity

*In studies on the properties of carbon monoxide, Bartlett et al. (J.A.C.S., **53** (1930), 1374), obtained the following data for the gas at 0°C:*

P/atm	25	50	100	200	400	800	1000
PV/RT	0.9890	0.9792	0.9741	1.0196	1.2482	1.8057	2.0819

From these data evaluate the fugacity of the gas at 100, 500, and 1000 atm.

It can be shown that

$$d\ln\frac{f}{P} = -\frac{\alpha}{RT}dP \qquad \text{(i)}$$

where f is the fugacity and $\alpha = \frac{RT}{P} - V$, that is, the difference between the ideal molar volume and the real molar volume of the gas, the remaining symbols having their usual significance.

Integration of equation (i) between zero pressure and a pressure P, at constant temperature gives

$$\ln\frac{f}{P} = -\frac{1}{RT}\int_0^P \alpha dP \qquad \text{(ii)}$$

Thus if values of α/RT are plotted against P, the integral of α/RT between zero pressure and any pressure, P, may be evaluated graphically, and is equal to $-\ln\frac{f}{P}$. The fugacity (f) can then be calculated.

The question, however, quotes values of PV/RT, that is, compressibility factors, κ, for various pressures. These can be adjusted to give α/RT values by using the relationship defining α:

$$\alpha = \frac{RT}{P} - V$$

Therefore

$$\frac{\alpha}{RT} = \left(1 - \frac{PV}{RT}\right)\frac{1}{P} \qquad \text{(iii)}$$

The calculated values of α/RT are shown in the table.

P	PV/RT	α/RT
25 atm	0.9890	$4.40\times10^{-4}\,atm^{-1}$
50	0.9792	4.16
100	0.9741	2.59
200	1.0196	− 0.98
400	1.2482	− 6.21
800	1.8057	− 10.07
1000	2.0819	− 10.82

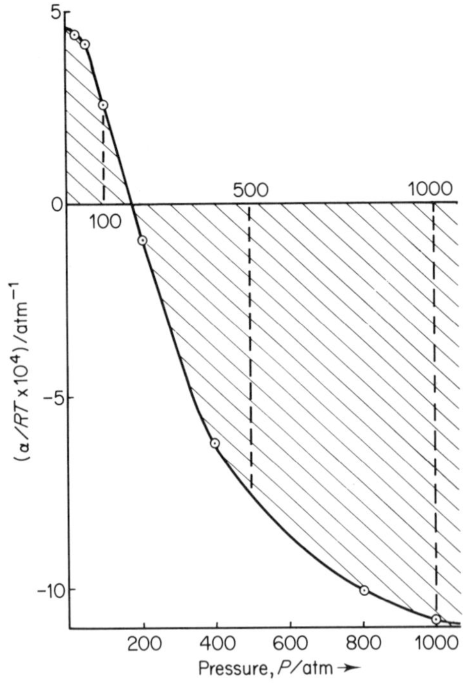

Fig. 4 Plot of P versus α/RT

From the graph (Fig. 4) the values of the integral and hence the fugacities at the required pressures, can be determined and are as shown below.

P	Integral $-\ln f/P$	f/P	f
100 atm	0.0392	0.9616	96 atm
500	−0.0940	1.098	549
1000	−0.5716	1.771	1771

Note The value of the integral is the area between the curve and the P axis at the required pressures. Allowance is made for positive and negative areas, that is, areas above the P axis (shaded) are positive and areas below the P axis (shaded) are negative.

Example 3.8 Approximate calculation of fugacity from equation of state

An approximate equation of state for hydrogen at 25°C is $P(V-b) = RT$, where $b = 2.67 \times 10^{-5}\, m^3\, mole^{-1}$ when P is in $N\, m^{-2}$. Use this information to evaluate the fugacity of hydrogen at 25°C and 100 atm pressure.

As we have seen in Example 3.3, the value of PV for a gas may be a linear function of its pressure at constant temperature:

$$PV = RT + BP \qquad \text{(i)}$$

This equation is identical to that given in the question:

$$PV = RT + bP \qquad \text{(ii)}$$

That is, the second virial coefficient, B, is equal to the van der Waals constant, b.

In Example 3.7, a function α was defined as follows:

$$\alpha = \frac{RT}{P} - V \qquad \text{(iii)}$$

By comparing equations (ii) and (iii), it is seen that $\alpha = -b$. It is now possible to calculate the fugacity of hydrogen by substitution of the data given in the question, in the integrated form of the following equation:

$$\ln \frac{f}{P} = -\frac{1}{RT}\int_0^P \alpha\, dP \quad \textit{where } f = \text{fugacity.}$$

Integrating and rearranging, remembering that $\alpha = -b$

$$\log f = \log P + \frac{Pb}{2.303RT}$$

$$= \log(100 \times 1.013 \times 10^5) + \frac{100 \times 2.67 \times 10^{-5} \times 1.013 \times 10^5}{2.303 \times 8.31 \times 298}$$

$$= 7.0055 + 0.0474$$

$$= 7.0529$$

Therefore $f = 1.129 \times 10^7$ N m^{-2}
$= 111.5$ atm

The fugacity of hydrogen at 25°C and 100 atm pressure is 112 atm.

Additional Examples

1 If the densities of helium and argon are 0.18 and 1.78 g dm^{-3} respectively, at a barometric height of 760 mmHg (density 13.6 g cm^{-3}), what are their molecular velocities? (B.Sc., Birmingham)

2 The van der Waals constants for nitrogen are $a = 0.142$ N m^4 mol^{-2}, $b = 3.9 \times 10^{-5}$ m^3 mol^{-1}. Use the given data to compare the pressures exerted by 15 mol of nitrogen, in a closed vessel of volume 2 dm^3 at 18°C, assuming (*a*) ideal behaviour, (*b*) that the gas obeys the van der Waals equation of state.

3 Oxygen has a critical temperature of 154.3 K and a critical pressure of 49.7 atm. Calculate the volume occupied by one mole of this gas at a pressure of 100 atm and a temperature of 25°C. (B.Sc., Wales)

4 Argon has a critical temperature of −122°C and a critical pressure of 48 atm. Assess the radius of the argon atom.

5 For helium at 0°C, $PV = 1$ dm^3 atm when P is 1 atm and $PV = 1.0275$ dm^3 atm when $P = 26.634$ atm. Neglecting the effects of intermolecular attraction, calculate:

(*a*) the number of moles of helium involved, *and*
(*b*) the radius of the helium molecule. (R.S.C.)

6 What do you understand by (*a*) Boyle temperature, (*b*) critical state, (*c*) virial coefficient?

The viscosity of chlorine at one atm pressure and 20°C is 147.0×10^{-7} N s m^{-2}. Calculate the mean free path of the chlorine molecule. (B.Sc., Wales)

7 The data given below refer to 1.153 g of ethene at 298.1 K

P/atm	1	5	10	15	20
PV/dm^3 atm	1.000	0.9745	0.9443	0.9198	0.8818
P/atm	30	40	50	60	70
PV/dm^3 atm	0.8143	0.7364	0.6467	0.5360	0.4076
P/atm	80	90	100	110	120
PV/dm^3 atm	0.3493	0.3466	0.3596	0.3774	0.3975

By plotting suitable graphs (*a*) comment on the behaviour and condition of the gas; (*b*) calculate the relative molecular mass of ethene as accurately as possible using four-figure logarithms. (B.Sc., Birmingham)

8 PV for nitrogen may be expressed in terms of the second virial coefficient as $PV = RT + 1.476 \times 10^{-5}P$ at 200°C when P is in N m^{-2}. Calculate the fugacity at 80 atm and 200°C.

9 In a report on studies of the compressibility of nitrogen, E. P. Bartlett (J.A.C.S., **49** (1927), 689) quotes the following values for A, B, and C at 0°C in the virial equation

$$\frac{PV}{RT} = A + BP + CP^2;$$

$A = 1.000$, $B = -5.314 \times 10^{-4}$, $C = 4.276 \times 10^{-6}$.

These figures are valid for pressures (P) up to 400 atm.

Use the given data to evaluate the fugacity of nitrogen at 350 atm.

10 In studies of the compressibility of nitrogen at 20°C Bartlett et al. (J.A.C.S., **52** (1930), 1363), obtained the following data:

Pressure/atm	25	50	150	200	400	500	800	1000
PV/RT	0.9954	0.9934	1.0210	1.0543	1.2543	1.3746	1.7528	2.0006

Evaluate the fugacity at 50, 200, 500 and 1000 atm.

4

Liquids, Vapours and Solutions

Example 4.1 Surface tension and capillary rise

How high will sap rise in a plant if the capillaries are 0.01 mm diameter, the density of the fluid 1.3 g cm^{-3}, and its surface tension 0.065 N m^{-1}, assuming that the latter property accounts for the rise?
(B.Sc., Birmingham)

The relationship between surface tension (γ) in N m^{-1} and the capillary rise (h) of a liquid in a capillary of radius r metres is given by

$$\gamma = \frac{rhdg}{2}$$

where d is the density in kg m^{-3} and g the gravitational acceleration in m s^{-2}. h represents the height the sap will rise in the plant and is given by

$$h = \frac{2\gamma}{rdg} \text{ metres}$$

Substitution of the data gives

$$h = \frac{2 \times 2 \times 0.065}{10^{-5} \times 1.3 \times 10^{3} \times 9.81} = 2.04 \text{ m}$$

For a plant with capillaries 0.01 mm diameter, the sap will rise to a height of 2.04 m.

Example 4.2 Viscosity

In an Ostwald viscometer, the time taken for the meniscus to fall between the two engraved marks at 20°C is 405 s for propane-1,2,3-triol, and 300 s for a solution of pyroxylin in propanone. The *kinematic viscosity of the pyroxylin solution is 500×10^{-4} m² s⁻¹ and the density of the propane-1,2,3-triol is 1.259 g cm⁻³ at 20°C. From the given data calculate the dynamic viscosity of propane-1,2,3-triol, and given that the normal relative molecular mass of propane-1,2,3-triol is 92, say whether or not the liquid is associated.*

The kinematic viscosities (ν) of two liquids are directly proportional to the appropriate times of fall of the meniscus between the two engraved marks of an Ostwald viscometer.

Therefore
$$\frac{\nu_P}{\nu_G} = \frac{t_P}{t_G}$$

and
$$\nu_G = \frac{\nu_P \times t_G}{t_P}$$

Substitution of the given values yields

$$\nu_G = \frac{500 \times 10^{-4} \times 405}{300}\ \mathrm{m^2\,s^{-1}}$$
$$= 6.75 \times 10^{-4}\ \mathrm{m^2\,s^{-1}}$$

The kinematic viscosity of a fluid, in $\mathrm{m^2\,s^{-1}}$, is equal to the dynamic viscosity, η, in $\mathrm{N\,s\,m^{-2}}$, divided by the density, in $\mathrm{kg\,m^{-3}}$.

Therefore $\eta_G = \nu_G \times d_G$ where d_G = density of propane–1,2,3-triol

$$= 6.75 \times 10^{-4} \times 1.259 \times 10^3 = 8.498 \times 10^{-1}\ \mathrm{kg\,m^{-1}\,s^{-1}}$$
$$= 8.498 \times 10^{-1}\ \mathrm{N\,s\,m^{-2}}$$

Dunstan's relationship states that for normal non-associated liquids

$$\frac{d}{M_r}\eta \times 10^7 = 40 \text{ to } 60$$

where M_r is the relative molecular mass, d the density in $\mathrm{g\,cm^{-3}}$, and η the coefficient of viscosity of the liquid in $\mathrm{N\,s\,m^{-2}}$.

Values greater than 40 to 60 are obtained for associated liquids. On substitution of the data for propane-1,2,3-triol, the left-hand side is given by

$$\frac{1.259 \times 8.498 \times 10^{-1} \times 10^7}{92} = 116\,200$$

This value exceeds 60 and indicates that the propane-1,2,3-triol is associated.

Summary The dynamic viscosity of propane-1,2,3-triol is $8.50 \times 10^{-1}\ \mathrm{N\,s\,m^{-2}}$. Propane-1,2,3-triol is associated.

Example 4.3 Viscosity

A metal ball of density 8.8 g cm^{-3} took 38 s to fall between the graduations of a falling sphere viscometer containing a solution of pyroxylin of density 1.6 g cm^{-3} and kinematic viscosity of 2.3×10^{-3} m^2 s^{-1} at 20°. Calculate the constant for the instrument. If a second solution of the same density under the same conditions gave a reading of 31.9 s, calculate its kinematic viscosity.

(B.Pharm., Wales)

The falling sphere method depends on the application of Stokes's law. In practice, the viscosity coefficient, in N s m^{-2}, of a liquid (η_1) relative to that of a standard (η_{st}) is determined from the relationship

$$\frac{\eta_1}{\eta_{st}} = \frac{t_1\,(d_{sph} - d_1)}{t_{st}\,(d_{sph} - d_{st})}$$

where t_1 and t_{st} are the times taken for the sphere to fall through the liquid and standard respectively, d_1 and d_{st} are the respective densities and d_{sph} is the density of the sphere. But the dynamic viscosity (η), in N s m^{-2}, is equal to the product of the kinematic viscosity (ν), in m^2 s^{-1}, and the density (d) in kg m^{-3}.

Therefore
$$\frac{\nu_1 d_1}{\nu_{st} d_{st}} = \frac{t_1\,(d_{sph} - d_1)}{t_{st}\,(d_{sph} - d_{st})}$$

Rearrangement and substitution of the data gives

$$\frac{\nu_1 d_1}{t_1} = \frac{2.3 \times 10^{-3} \times 1.6 \times 10^3}{38}\ \frac{(8.8 \times 10^3 - d_1)}{(8.8 \times 10^3 - 1.6 \times 10^3)}$$

$$= 1.1836 \times 10^{-1} - 1.345 \times 10^{-5} d_1$$

or
$$\nu_1/t_1 = 1.1836 \times 10^{-1}/d_1 - 1.345 \times 10^{-5}$$

The constant for the instrument is $\underline{1.1836 \times 10^{-1}/d_1 - 1.345 \times 10^{-5}}$.

The kinematic viscosity of the second solution is, therefore

$$\nu_1 = \frac{31.9}{1.6 \times 10^3}(1.1836 \times 10^{-1} - 1.345 \times 10^{-5} \times 1.6 \times 10^3)$$

$$= \underline{1.93 \times 10^{-3}\ \text{m}^2\ \text{s}^{-1}}.$$

Example 4.4 Calculation of miscellaneous constants

The boiling point of propanone is 56.5°C at 760 mmHg, its refractive index $n_D^{15°}$ is 1.3620, its density $d_{4°}^{15°}$ is 0.7928 g cm^{-3} and its Trouton constant is 88.

Explaining briefly the basis of each calculation, derive approximate values for (a) the critical temperature, (b) the molar refraction, (c) the molar heat of vaporization, and (d) the molal elevation of the boiling point. (M_r propanone = 58.) (*B.Sc., Wales*)

(*a*) It has been found empirically that, for different liquids at atmospheric pressure, the boiling point in K (T_b), is approximately two thirds of the critical temperature (T_c), also measured on the absolute scale:

$$T_b = \frac{2}{3} T_c$$

Therefore, the critical temperature (T_c) of propanone has the approximate value of

$$T_c = \frac{3}{2} T_b = \frac{3}{2} \times 329.5$$

$$= \underline{494.3 \text{K}}$$

(*b*) In 1880 Lorenz in Denmark and Lorentz in Holland, independently of one another, deduced the relationship

$$R_m = \left(\frac{n^2-1}{n^2+2}\right)\frac{M_r}{d}$$

where M_r is the relative molecular mass of the substance, n the refractive index for light of a definite wavelength, in this case the D light of sodium at 15°C, and d is the density of the liquid at the same temperature. R_m is called the molar refraction and for normal liquids is an additive property of the atoms and bonds present in the molecule. Substitution of the data gives

$$R_m = \left(\frac{1.3620^2-1}{1.3620^2+2}\right)\frac{58}{0.7928}$$

$$= \underline{16.23 \text{ cm}^3}$$

(*c*) In 1884 Trouton discovered that, for normal non-associated liquids, the quotient obtained by dividing the molar heat of vaporization (ΔH_v) at the boiling point, by the boiling point in K, has the approximate value of 88, that is, the entropy of vaporization is approximately 88 J K^{-1} Using this relationship, the approximate value for the molar heat of vaporization of propanone (ΔH_v) is

$$\begin{aligned}\Delta H_v &= 88 \times \text{boiling point of propanone in K}\\ &= 88 \times 329.5 \text{ J mol}^{-1}\\ &= \underline{27\,896 \text{ J mol}^{-1}}\end{aligned}$$

(*d*) The molal elevation of the boiling point (K_b) signifies the rise in boiling point of a one molal solution of a solute in a solvent (in this case propanone), provided the laws of dilute solutions are applic-able, that is,

$$K_b = \frac{RT_b^2 M_r}{\Delta H_v 1000}$$

where T_b is the boiling point of the solvent, M_r is the relative molecular mass and ΔH_v is the molar heat of vaporization.

Substitution of the data gives

$$K_b = \frac{8.31 \times (329.5)^2 \times 58}{27\,896 \times 1000} = \underline{1.88°}$$

Note K_b is referred to 1000 grams of propanone.

Example 4.5 Vaporization

36.0 g of water (H_2O) are evaporated at its boiling point, 100°C at a constant pressure of 1.00 atmosphere (1.013×10^5 N m^{-2}). The heat of vaporization of water is 2.258 kJ g^{-1}. Calculate (a) the work involved in the expansion from liquid to vapour, (b) the heat of vaporization (ΔH_v), and (c) the difference in the internal energy (ΔU_v) of vapour and liquid water. ($H = 1.01$; $O = 16.00$).

(University of Arizona, Tucson, USA)

The heat of vaporization (ΔH_v) is given by the sum of the difference between the internal energy of vapour and liquid ($\Delta U_v = U_v - U_l$) and the work involved in the expansion from liquid to vapour, that is,

$$\Delta H_v = \Delta U_v + P\Delta V \qquad \text{(i)}$$

where P is the vapour pressure (here 1 atmosphere) and $\Delta V = V_v - V_l$.

At temperatures considerably removed from the critical, V_l is quite small compared to V_g and may be neglected. Hence, $\Delta V \approx V_g$.

(a) The work involved in the expansion from liquid to vapour is

$$PV_g = P\left(2 \times 22.4\left(\frac{373}{273}\right)\right) \qquad \text{(since 36g of water = 2 moles)}$$

$$= 2RT$$
$$= 2 \times 8.31 \times 373\,\text{J}$$
$$= \underline{6.199\,\text{kJ}}$$

(b) The heat absorbed for the vaporization of 1 g of water is 2.258 kJ.
Therefore, the heat of vaporization for 36 g of water is

$$36 \times 2.258\,\text{kJ}$$
$$= \underline{81.29\,\text{kJ}}$$

(c) From equation (i) above, the difference in the internal energy (ΔU_v) of vapour and liquid water is

$$\Delta U_v = \Delta H_v - P\Delta V$$
$$= 81.29 - 6.20\,\text{kJ}$$
$$= \underline{75.09\,\text{kJ}}$$

Note Since heat added to the system (q) goes towards raising the internal energy of the system (ΔU) and to do any outside work the system may perform as a result of the absorption of heat, it follows that $\Delta H = q = 81.29$ kJ.

Example 4.6 Ideal solutions and Raoult's law

The vapour pressures of trichloromethane ($CHCl_3$) and tetrachloromethane (CCl_4) at 25°C are 199.1 and 114.5 mmHg respectively. Assuming ideal mixtures, what is (a) the total vapour pressure and (b) the mass percentage of $CHCl_3$ in the vapour in equilibrium with a liquid mixture containing 1 mole of each pure liquid?
(B.Sc. in Applied Science (Metallurgy), Durham)

(*a*) Raoult's law states that the partial vapour pressure (P_A) of any volatile constituent of a solution is equal to the vapour pressure of the pure constituent (P_A^0) multiplied by the mole fraction (x_A) of that constituent in solution:

$$P_A = P_A^0 x_A$$

For a binary liquid mixture, the total vapour pressure above the solution is

$$= P_A + P_B$$
$$= P_A^0 x_A + P_B^0 x_B$$

where P_B is the partial vapour pressure and P_B^0 the vapour pressure of the pure second constituent, x_B being the mole fraction. Hence, the total vapour pressure (P) of a liquid mixture containing 1 mole each of trichloromethane (constituent A) and tetrachloromethane (constituent B) is

$$P = 199.1 \times 0.5 + 114.5 \times 0.5$$
$$= 156.8 \text{ mmHg}$$

(*b*) Let x'_A be the mole fraction of trichloromethane (constituent A) in the vapour above the solution of composition x_A. Then, according to Dalton's law of partial pressures

$$x'_A = \frac{P_A}{P}$$

Similarly, for tetrachloromethane (constituent B)

$$x'_B = \frac{P_B}{P}$$

Therefore $$\frac{x'_A}{x'_B} = \frac{P_A}{P_B} = \frac{199.1 \times 0.5}{114.5 \times 0.5}$$

Since the mole fraction $x \propto \frac{W}{M_r}$ where W = mass of substance and M_r = relative molecular mass, then

$$\frac{x'_A M_{rA}}{x'_B M_{rB}} = \frac{W_A}{W_B}$$

Therefore $$\frac{W_A}{W_B} = \frac{199.1 \times 0.5 \times 119.5}{114.5 \times 0.5 \times 154} = 1.35$$

Therefore, the ratio by mass of trichloromethane to tetrachloromethane in the vapour phase is 1.35:1 and the percentage by mass of trichloromethane is

$$\frac{1.35}{2.35} \times 100\% = \underline{57.4\%}$$

Example 4.7 Raoult's law and vapour pressure lowering

A solution containing 25.97 g of hexanhexol per 500 g of water has a vapour pressure of 17.42 mm Hg, at 20°C. Given that the vapour pressure of water is 17.51 mm Hg, calculate the relative molecular mass of hexanhexol.

By Raoult's law the vapour pressure (P) of a solvent above a solution is given by

$$P = P^0 x_A \qquad \text{(i)}$$

where P^0 is the vapour pressure of the solvent and x_A the mole fraction of solvent.

The vapour pressure lowering (ΔP) is:

$$\begin{aligned} \Delta P = P^0 - P &= P^0 - P^0 x_A \\ &= P^0(1 - x_A) \\ &= P^0 x_B \qquad \text{(ii)} \end{aligned}$$

where x_B is the mole fraction of solute.
But x_B is given by

$$x_B = \left(\frac{W_B/M_{rB}}{W_A/M_{rA} + W_B/M_{rB}}\right) \qquad \text{(iii)}$$

where W_A and W_B are the masses of solvent and solute respectively and M_{rA} and M_{rB} the relative molecular masses.
Combining equations (ii) and (iii) we have

$$\Delta P = P^0 \left(\frac{W_B/M_{rB}}{W_A/M_{rA} + W_B M_{rB}}\right) \qquad \text{(iv)}$$

But for very dilute solutions W_B/M_{rB} is small in relation to W_A/M_{rA} so that (iv) can be reduced to

$$\Delta P = P^0 \frac{W_B M_{rA}}{W_A M_{rB}} \tag{v}$$

Substitution of the given data in equation (v) gives

$$17.51 - 17.42 = 17.51 \frac{25.97 \times 18}{500 \times M_{rB}}$$

and $$M_{rB} = \frac{17.51 \times 25.97 \times 18}{500 \times 0.09} = 181.9$$

The relative molecular mass of hexanhexol is 182

Example 4.8 Ideal solubility

From the data given below calculate the solubility of benzoic acid in ethanol at 27°C assuming the solution to be perfect.

Substance	*m.p./°C*	$\Delta H_f/kJ\,mol^{-1}$
Benzoic acid	*122*	*16.73*
Ethanol	*−114*	*8.36*

ΔH_f is the molar latent heat of fusion

For a saturated solution the chemical potential of the solute in the solution is the same as that of the pure solid solute in equilibrium with the solution so that

$$\mu_s(T, p, x_s) = \mu_{s(\text{solid})}(T, p) \tag{i}$$

where the suffix s denotes solute and T and p are the constant temperature and pressure respectively. x_s is the mole fraction of the solute in the saturated solution, and is, therefore, the solubility of the solute.

For an ideal solution

$$\mu_s(T, p, x_s) = \mu_s^\ominus + RT \ln x_s$$

Hence $$\mu_s^\ominus + RT \ln x_s = \mu_{s(\text{solid})} \tag{ii}$$

at the temperature T and pressure p.

$\mu_s^\ominus$ is the chemical potential of the pure *liquid solute* at T and p. $\mu_s^\ominus$ and $\mu_{s\,(\text{solid})}^\ominus$ are the molar free energies of pure liquid and pure solid respectively. Hence equation (ii) may be written as

$$\ln x_s = \frac{\mu_{s(\text{solid})} - \mu_s^\ominus}{RT} = \frac{-\Delta G_f}{RT} \tag{iii}$$

where ΔG_f is the molar free energy change on fusion and is equal to $\mu_s^{\ominus} - \mu_{s(\mathrm{solid})}$.
Differentiation of equation (iii) with respect to T yields

$$\frac{\mathrm{d}(\ln x_s)}{\mathrm{d}T} = \frac{-1}{R}\frac{\mathrm{d}(\Delta G_f/T)}{\mathrm{d}T}$$

at constant pressure p.
From the Gibbs-Helmholtz equation

$$\frac{\mathrm{d}(\Delta G_f/T)}{\mathrm{d}T} = -\frac{\Delta H_f}{T^2}$$

so that

$$\frac{\mathrm{d}(\ln x_s)}{\mathrm{d}T} = \frac{\Delta H_f}{RT^2} \qquad \text{(iv)}$$

Equation (iv) can be integrated from T_0, the freezing point of pure solute of mole fraction unity, to T, the temperature at which the solution of solute of mole fraction x_s is in equilibrium with pure solid solute:

$$\int_1^{x_s} \mathrm{d}(\ln x_s) = \int_{T_0}^{T} \frac{\Delta H_f \, . \, \mathrm{d}T}{RT^2} \qquad \text{(v)}$$

ΔH_f may be taken as constant if the temperature range T_0 to T is small so that equation (v) becomes

$$\ln x_s = \frac{-\Delta H_f}{R}\left(\frac{T_0 - T}{TT_0}\right) \qquad \text{(vi)}$$

Equation (vi) is an expression of the ideal law of solubility. According to this law the solubility of a substance is the same in all solvents in which it forms an ideal solution. It is seen that the solubility of the substance depends on the properties of that substance only. This ideal law of solubility will give erroneous results if the temperature of interest is a long way below the melting point of the solid since ΔH_f is temperature dependent and this has to be taken into consideration if the range T_0 to T is large.

To calculate the solubility of benzoic acid from the given data, the data for the acid only are required.

Substitution of the data in equation (vi) yields

$$\ln x_s = \frac{-16\,730}{8.31}\left(\frac{395-300}{300 \times 395}\right) = \frac{-167.3 \times 95}{8.31 \times 1185}$$

$$= -1.614$$

and $$\log x_s = -1.614/2.303 = -0.7004 = \bar{1}.2996$$

$$x_s = 0.1994$$

The mole fraction of benzoic acid in a saturated solution of benzoic acid in ethanol at 27°C is 0.199.

Example 4.9 Activity and chemical potential

A saturated solution of potassium chloride in equilibrium with pure ice at −10.7°C contains 3.30 moles of KCl in 1000 g of water.

Calculate the activity of water in this saturated solution taking pure water at 0°C as standard ($\Delta H_f = 5965$ J mol^{-1} of water).

Evaluate ΔG for the reaction:

ice (0°C)+KCl (solid at −10.7°C)

→ sat. KCl sol. (at −10.7°C) per mole of KCl.

(B.Sc. in Applied Science (Chemical Engineering), Durham)

The activity (a) of a solvent in a solution is related to the freezing point (T) of the solution at constant pressure by the expression

$$\frac{d(\ln a)}{dT} = \frac{\Delta H_f}{RT^2}$$

where ΔH_f is the molar heat of fusion of the solvent.

Assuming that the variation of ΔH_f with temperature is sufficiently small for it to be neglected, this equation may be integrated as follows:

$$\int_{\ln a_1}^{\ln a_0} d(\ln a) = \frac{\Delta H_f}{R}\int_{T_1}^{T_0}\frac{dT}{T^2} \qquad \text{(i)}$$

where, a_0 is the activity of the pure solvent at its freezing point T_0K, or 273K (0°C);

and a_1 is the activity of the solvent in the solution which freezes at T_1K, or 262.3K (−10.7°C).

Equation (i) can therefore be written

$$\ln a_0 - \ln a_1 = \frac{\Delta H_f}{R}\left[-\frac{1}{T}\right]_{262.3}^{273}$$

In a pure solvent the activity is unity, therefore $\ln a_0 = 0$,

and $$-\ln a_1 = \frac{-\Delta H_f}{R}\left[\frac{1}{273} - \frac{1}{262.3}\right]$$

Hence $$\log a_1 = -\frac{5965}{2.303\times 8.31}\left[\frac{10.7}{273\times 262.3}\right]$$
$$= -0.04659 = \bar{1}.9534$$

Therefore $$a_1 = 0.8983$$

The activity of the water in the saturated KCl solution taking pure water at 0°C as standard is 0.8983.

To evaluate ΔG, per mole of KCl, for the reaction

$$\text{ice } (0°\text{C}) + \text{KCl (solid at } -10.7°\text{C)} \rightarrow \text{sat. KCl sol. (at } -10.7°\text{C)},$$

we have to consider the chemical potential of each constituent. These are as follows:

Ice (0°C). The chemical potential is $\mu^{\ominus}_{H_2O}$, where $\mu^{\ominus}_{H_2O}$ is the chemical potential of pure liquid water at 0°C. This equality in chemical potential follows because ice at 0°C is in equilibrium with pure liquid water at 0°C.

KCl (solid at −10.7°C). The chemical potential is μ_{KCl}, that is, the chemical potential of pure solid KCl at −10.7°C.

KCl (in sat. sol. at −10.7°C). The chemical potential is μ_{KCl}, because a saturated solution of KCl at −10.7°C is in equilibrium with solid KCl at −10.7°C making the chemical potential in each phase identical.

H_2O (in the sat. sol. at −10.7°C). The chemical potential is

$$\mu^{\ominus}_{H_2O(-10.7)} + RT \ln a_1$$

The free energy change (ΔG) for any general reaction, e.g.

$$aA + bB = mM + nN$$

is given by

$$\Delta G = (m\mu_M + n\mu_N) - (a\mu_A + b\mu_B)$$

where μ_M, μ_N etc., represent the chemical potentials of the reactants and products and *m*, *n*, etc., represent the numbers of moles involved. From the data given in the question, the reaction can be written

$$n\text{H}_2\text{O (ice at } 0°\text{C)} + m\text{KCl (solid at } -10.7°\text{C)} \rightarrow (n\text{H}_2\text{O} + m\text{KCl) (in sat. sol. at } -10.7°\text{C)}$$

where $m = 3.30$ moles KCl, and $n = \frac{1000}{18} = 55.56$ moles water.

Therefore

$$-\Delta G = (55.56\mu^{\ominus}_{H_2O} + 3.30\mu_{KCl}) - [3.30\mu_{KCl} + 55.56(\mu^{\ominus}_{H_2O(-10.7)} + RT\ln a_1)]$$

$$= 55.56(\mu^{\ominus}_{H_2O} - \mu^{\ominus}_{H_2O(-10.7)}) - 55.56RT\ln a_1 \text{ J}.$$

for the reaction as written.

Therefore

$$-\Delta G = \frac{55.56}{3.30}(\mu^{\ominus}_{H_2O} - \mu^{\ominus}_{H_2O(-10.7)}) - \frac{55.56}{3.30}RT\ln a_1 \text{ J mol}^{-1} \text{ KCl}$$

$$= \frac{55.56}{3.30}(\mu^{\ominus}_{H_2O} - \mu^{\ominus}_{H_2O(-10.7)}) - \frac{55.56 \times 8.31 \times 262.3 \times 2.303}{3.30}\log 0.8983 \text{ J mol}^{-1} \text{ KCl}$$

$$= \frac{55.56}{3.30}(\mu^{\ominus}_{H_2O} - \mu^{\ominus}_{H_2O(-10.7)}) + 3937 \text{ J mol}^{-1} \text{ KCl}$$

The free energy decrease for the given reaction is

$$\underline{\frac{55.56}{3.30}(\mu^{\ominus}_{H_2O} - \mu^{\ominus}_{H_2O(-10.7)}) + 3937 \text{ J mol}^{-1} \text{ KCl}}$$

Example 4.10 Boiling point elevation of solution

Ethoxyethane boils at 34.6°C and its latent heat of vaporization is $378\,J\,g^{-1}$, nitrobenzene boils at 210.0°C, and the two liquids are miscible together in all proportions. Assuming the ideal law, calculate the composition of the solution obtained on passing ethoxyethane vapour to saturation into nitrobenzene at 35.6°C, given that the value of the gas constant is $8.31\,J\,K^{-1}$ and that the relative molecular mass of nitrobenzene is 123. (*B.Sc., Wales*)

Solutions containing non-volatile solutes boil at temperatures higher than that of the pure solvent. Nitrobenzene, with its high boiling point relative to that of ethoxyethane, can be regarded as non-volatile around the temperature of 35°C; hence the relation between the boiling point of a dilute solution and its composition can be applied to the solution of this question.

$$\Delta T_b = \frac{RT^2}{\Delta H_v} \cdot \frac{W_B M_{rA}}{1000 M_{rB}}$$

Where ΔT_b is the boiling point elevation, T the boiling point of the solvent (ethoxyethane in this case), ΔH_v the latent heat of vaporization per mole of solvent, W_B the mass of solute, and M_{rA} and M_{rB} the relative molecular mass of solvent and solute respectively. But $\Delta H_v/M_{rA}$ is the latent heat of vaporization per gram of solvent. Therefore substitution of the data gives.

$$35.6 - 34.6 = \frac{8.31 \times (307.6)^2}{378 \times 1000 \times 123} \cdot W_B$$

and $$W_B = 59.13 \text{ g nitrobenzene.}$$

The composition of solution obtained on passing ethoxyethane vapour to saturation into nitrobenzene at 35.6°C is 59.1 g nitrobenzene per 1000 g ethoxyethane

Example 4.11 Depression of freezing point of solutions

A solution of 9.20 g iodine in 1000 g benzene has a freezing point of 5.283°C. The solid which separates on freezing is a solid solution of iodine in benzene. The freezing point of pure benzene is 5.400°C and its heat of fusion is 125.4 J g^{-1}*. Calculate the ratio in which iodine is distributed between the solid and liquid phases at the freezing point of the solution.* ($I_2 = 253.8$)

If, when a dilute solution is cooled, there is solid solubility of solute in the solvent on freezing, the ratio of the mole fractions (x_1' and x_1) of solvent in the solid and liquid phases respectively is given by

$$\frac{\mathrm{d}\ln(x_1'/x_1)}{\mathrm{d}T} = \frac{-\Delta H_f}{RT^2} \qquad \text{for constant pressure conditions.}$$

ΔH_f is the molar heat of fusion of the solvent.
Assuming ΔH_f to remain constant over the temperature range between the freezing points of the solution (T) and pure solvent (T_0), the equation may be integrated

$$\int_{\ln\left(\frac{x_1'}{x_1}\right)T}^{\ln\left(\frac{x_1'}{x_1}\right)T_0} \mathrm{d}[\ln(x_1'/x_1)] = \frac{-\Delta H_f}{R}\int_T^{T_0} \frac{\mathrm{d}T}{T^2} \qquad \text{(i)}$$

The ratio, x_1'/x_1, of the mole fractions of solvent in the solid and liquid phases of pure solvent on freezing is unity, hence

$$\ln\left(\frac{x_1'}{x_1}\right)_{T_0} = 0$$

Therefore equation (i) can be written

$$-\ln\left(\frac{x_1}{x_1'}\right)_T = \frac{\Delta H_f}{R}\left[\frac{T_0 - T}{T_0 T}\right] \qquad \text{(ii)}$$

Since the liquid and solid solutions are dilute

$$\ln x_1 \approx -x_s \quad \text{and} \quad \ln x_1' \approx -x_s'$$

where x_s is the mole fraction of solute in the liquid phase, and x_s' the mole fraction of solute in the solid phase.
The difference (ΔT) between T and T_0 for dilute solutions is so small that it can be neglected without causing significant error. Therefore, equation (ii) may be rewritten

$$x_s - x_s' = \frac{\Delta H_f \Delta T}{R T_0^2}$$

and

$$\Delta T = \frac{R T_0^2 x_s}{\Delta H_f}\left[1 - \frac{x_s'}{x_s}\right] \qquad \text{(iii)}$$

x_s'/x_s is the ratio required by the question, that is, the ratio of the mole fraction of I_2 in the solid phase to that in the liquid phase at the freezing point of the solution.
The mole fraction of iodine in the solution (x_s) at the freezing point is given by

$$x_s = \frac{\dfrac{9.20}{253.8}}{\dfrac{9.20}{253.8} + \dfrac{1000}{78}} = \frac{0.0363}{12.86}$$

Substitution of the relevant data in equation (iii) gives

$$5.400 - 5.283 = \frac{8.31 \times (278.4)^2 \times 0.0363}{125.4 \times 78 \times 12.86}\left[1 - \frac{x_s'}{x_s}\right]$$

$$(1 - x_s'/x_s) = 0.630$$

and

$$x_s'/x_s = 0.37 = \frac{1}{2.7}$$

Therefore the ratio in which iodine is distributed between the solid and liquid phases at the freezing point of a solution of 9.20 g of iodine in 1000 g of benzene is 1:2.7.

Example 4.12 Activity coefficient from freezing data

The following data for aqueous solutions of sodium chloride are quoted by Lewis and Randall (J.A.C.S., **43** *(1921), 1112):*

Molality	*0.01*	*0.02*	*0.05*	*0.10*	*0.20*
Depression of freezing point/°C	*0.0361*	*0.0714*	*0.1758*	*0.3471*	*0.6850*

Calculate the mean ionic activity coefficient of sodium chloride in a 0.10 m solution.

(The molal freezing point depression for water is 1.858.)

The activity (a) of the solvent in a solution, referred to the pure solvent at its freezing point as standard, is related to the freezing point of the solution (T_f) by the expression:

$$\frac{d(\ln a)}{dT} = \frac{\Delta H_f}{RT_f^2} \qquad \text{(i)}$$

where ΔH_f is the molar heat of fusion of the solvent.

Furthermore, the Gibbs-Duhem equation relates the activity of the solvent to that of the solute (a_s):

$$n_s d(\ln a_s) + n d(\ln a) = 0$$

and

$$d(\ln a_s) = -\frac{n}{n_s} d(\ln a) \qquad \text{(ii)}$$

n and n_s are the numbers of moles of solvent and solute respectively. In equation (i), for small depressions (ΔT) of freezing point

$T_f^2 \approx T_0^2$, where T_0 is the freezing point of pure solvent.

Also, since $\Delta T = T_0 - T_f$, $\quad dT_f = -d(\Delta T)$

Therefore

$$-d(\ln a) = \frac{\Delta H_f}{RT_0^2} d(\Delta T)$$

Substitution for d(ln a) in equation (ii) yields

$$d(\ln a_s) = \frac{n}{n_s}\frac{\Delta H_f}{RT_0^2} d(\Delta T)$$

Let the relative molecular mass of the solvent be M_r and let n_s be set equal to the molality (m), that is, the number of moles of solute per 1000 g of solvent.

Hence $$n = \frac{1000}{M_r}, \quad \text{and} \quad \frac{n}{n_s} = \frac{1000}{mM}.$$

Therefore $$d(\ln a_s) = \frac{1000}{mM_r}\frac{\Delta H_f}{RT_0^2}\,d(\Delta T)$$

$$= \frac{1}{mK}\,d(\Delta T) \qquad \text{(iii)}$$

where K is the molal freezing point depression constant.

For a solute which dissociates into ν ions $a_s = a_\pm^\nu$ where $a_\pm$ = mean ionic activity and is given by $a_\pm = \gamma_\pm m_\pm$, where $\gamma_\pm$ is the mean activity coefficient.

Therefore $$d(\ln a_s) = \nu d(\ln a_\pm)$$

The mean molality $m_\pm$ is related to the molality m by

$$m_\pm^\nu = m^\nu(\nu_+^{\nu+} \, . \, \nu_-^{\nu-})$$

Therefore $$a_s = a_\pm^\nu = \gamma_\pm^\nu m^\nu(\nu_+^{\nu+} \, . \, \nu_-^{\nu-})$$

Hence $$\nu \ln a_\pm = \nu \ln \gamma_\pm + \nu \ln m + \ln(\nu_+^{\nu+} \, . \, \nu_-^{\nu-})$$

Therefore $$\nu\, d(\ln a_\pm) = \nu\, d(\ln \gamma_\pm) + \nu\, d(\ln m) = d(\ln a_s)$$

Substitution for $d(\ln a_s)$ in equation (iii) yields

$$\nu\, d(\ln \gamma_\pm) + \nu\, d(\ln m) = \frac{1}{mK}\,d(\Delta T)$$

Therefore $$d(\ln \gamma_\pm) = \frac{1}{\nu mK}\,d(\Delta T) - d(\ln m) \qquad \text{(iv)}$$

Let $1 - \dfrac{\Delta T}{\nu mK} = j$ to represent the departure of the real solution from ideal behaviour.

j becomes zero at infinite dilution (when $\Delta T = \nu mK$).

On differentiating $$dj = -\frac{d(\Delta T)}{\nu mK} + \frac{\Delta T}{\nu m^2 K}\,dm$$

Therefore $$\frac{d(\Delta T)}{\nu mK} = -dj + (1-j)\,d(\ln m)$$

Substitution for $\frac{d(\Delta T)}{\nu m K}$ in equation (iv) yields

$$d(\ln \gamma_{\pm}) = -dj - j\, d(\ln m)$$

which on integration from 0 to m, with correspondingly $\gamma_{\pm}$ from 1 to $\gamma_{\pm}$ and j from 0 to j, gives

$$\ln \gamma_{\pm} = -j - \int_0^m \frac{j}{m}\, dm$$

or

$$\log \gamma_{\pm} = -\frac{j}{2.303} - \frac{1}{2.303}\int_0^m \frac{j}{m}\, dm$$

This integral is evaluated graphically from a set of measurements of the depression of freezing point in solutions of low concentrations, that is, j/m values are plotted against m values, and the area under the curve is determined after extrapolation to zero concentration.

The various j and j/m values are calculated from given data as follows by substitution in

$$j = 1 - \frac{\Delta T}{\nu m K} \qquad \text{where } K = 1.858.$$

Molality (m) $= 0.01$; $\Delta T = 0.0361°C$

$$j = 1 - \frac{0.0361}{2 \times 0.01 \times 1.858}$$

$$= 1 - 0.9714 \qquad = 0.0286$$

$$\frac{j}{m} = 2.860$$

Similarly when molality (m) $= 0.02$ and $\Delta T = 0.0714°C$

$$j = 0.0393 \qquad \text{and} \qquad \frac{j}{m} = 1.965.$$

When molality (m) $= 0.05$ and $\Delta T = 0.1758°C$

$$j = 0.0538 \qquad \text{and} \qquad \frac{j}{m} = 1.076.$$

When molality (m) $= 0.10$ and $\Delta T = 0.3471°C$

$$j = 0.0659 \qquad \text{and} \qquad \frac{j}{m} = 0.659.$$

When molality (m) $= 0.20$ and $\Delta T = 0.6850°C$

$$j = 0.0783 \qquad \text{and} \qquad \frac{j}{m} = 0.3915.$$

A plot of the above j/m values against the corresponding molalities gives the curve shown in Fig. 5, from which it can be shown that the area under the curve between $m = 0$ and $m = 0.1$ is 0.1412. Substitution in the relationship

$$\log \gamma_\pm = -\frac{j}{2.303} - \frac{1}{2.303}\int_0^m \frac{j}{m}\,dm$$

gives

$$\log \gamma_\pm = -\frac{0.0659+0.1412}{2.303}$$

$$= -0.0899$$

$$= \bar{1}.9101$$

Therefore $\gamma_\pm = 0.8130$

The mean ionic activity coefficient of sodium chloride in a 0.10 m solution is <u>0.813.</u>

Note Since the freezing points of the solutions vary with concentration, the activity coefficients calculated for different concentrations will not refer to the same temperature. For concentrations up to about 0.10 m, however, the activity coefficients are hardly altered by changes in temperature, and the results obtained will be valid for temperatures not too far from the freezing point of the water, e.g. the value for $\gamma_\pm$ obtained in the above problem would be valid for 25°C.

Example 4.13 Chemical potential and activity coefficient

A solution of 1 mole NaOH in 4.6 moles of water has a vapour pressure of 4.474 mmHg at 15°C whereas the vapour pressure of pure water is 12.788 mmHg. Assuming that the activity coefficient of pure water is unity, calculate (a) the activity coefficient of water in the solution, and (b) the difference between the chemical potential of water in the solution and in pure water.

(*B.Sc. in Applied Chemistry, Glasgow*)

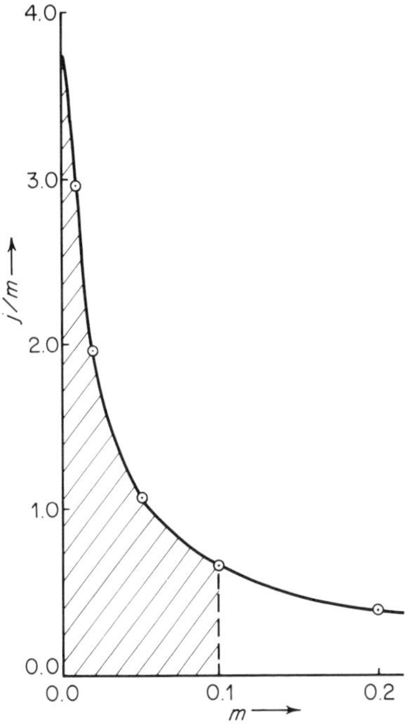

Fig. 5 Plot of j/m values versus molalities

For a gas in a mixture of non-ideal gases the fugacity (f) is defined by

$$\mu = \mu^{\ominus} + RT \ln \frac{f}{f^{\ominus}}$$

μ is the chemical potential of the gas, $\mu^{\ominus}$ the chemical potential in its standard state, and $f^{\ominus}$ the fugacity in the standard state.

The fugacity of a constituent in solution may be defined by the same equation, because the chemical potential of a constituent in the solution will be the same as that of the constituent in the vapour phase in equilibrium with the solution. In order to evaluate the free energy change, $\mu - \mu^{\ominus}$, it is necessary to know the value of the ratio $\frac{f}{f^{\ominus}}$. For substances in solution, it is frequently impossible to determine this ratio by direct measurement of f and $f^{\ominus}$. However, we may consider the ratio between the fugacity (f) of the substance in a given state and its fugacity ($f^{\ominus}$) in some state, chosen as standard for its convenience. This ratio of fugacities is called the activity (a). That is,

$$a = \frac{f}{f^{\ominus}}.$$

In the standard state chosen (chemical potential $= \mu^{\ominus}$), the activity will be taken as unity; in any other state it will be given by

$$\mu = \mu^{\ominus} + RT \ln a$$

For the water in an aqueous solution, pure liquid water at one atm pressure may be taken as the standard state. The activity of pure water will therefore be taken as unity, and the activity of the water in any solution will be given by the ratio of its fugacity to that of liquid water at the same temperature.

Since the vapour pressure of water is not very high, the fugacity of water may be taken as equal to its vapour pressure to a very good approximation.

Therefore the activity (a) of the water is given by

$$a = \frac{p}{p^0}$$ where p is the vapour pressure over the solution, and p^0 is the vapour pressure of pure water at the same temperature.

In the given problem, the vapour pressures are low and may be taken as equal to the fugacities.

Therefore $$a_{H_2O} = \frac{p}{p^0} = \frac{4.474}{12.788} = 0.3499$$

The activity of the water in the solution is <u>0.350.</u>

The mole fraction of water in the solution is given by

$$x_{H_2O} = \frac{4.6}{1+4.6} = 0.8214$$

The activity coefficient of water in the solution is given by

$$\gamma_{H_2O} = \frac{a_{H_2O}}{x_{H_2O}} = \frac{0.3499}{0.8214} = 0.426$$

(*a*) The activity coefficient of water in the solution is <u>0.426.</u>

The chemical potential (μ) of the water in the solution is given by

$$\mu = \mu^{\ominus} + RT \ln a_{H_2O}$$

where $\mu^{\ominus}$ is the chemical potential of pure water at temperature

$$T = 288\text{K}.$$

The difference between the chemical potential of the water in the solution and that of pure water, $\mu - \mu^{\ominus}$, is given by

$$\begin{aligned} \mu - \mu^{\ominus} &= 8.31 \times 288 \times 2.303 \log 0.3499 \text{ J mol}^{-1} \\ &= -8.31 \times 288 \times 2.303 \times 0.4561 \text{ J mol}^{-1} \\ &= -2514 \text{ J mol}^{-1} \end{aligned}$$

(*b*) The difference between the chemical potential of the water in the solution and that of pure water is $\underline{-2514 \text{ J mol}^{-1}}$.

Example 4.14 Dipole moments

For water vapour, E. C. Hurdis and C. P. Smyth (J.A.C.S., ***64*** *(1942) 2829) quote the values of the molar polarizations, P_M, tabulated below. Determine the dipole moment for water in the vapour state, and estimate the dipole moment of each O—H bond if the angle between these bonds is 105°.*

P_M/cm^3	57.4	53.6	50.1	46.8	43.4
T/K	384.3	420.1	444.7	484.1	522.0

The molar polarization, P_M, is related to the relative permittivity, ε_r, of a substance by the equation

$$P_M = \frac{\varepsilon_r - 1}{\varepsilon_r + 2} \cdot \frac{M_r}{\rho}$$

in which M_r is the relative molecular mass and ρ is the density of the substance. For a vapour, values of P_M may be determined for a series of temperatures by measuring the density and relative permittivity of the vapour at each temperature.

The Debye equation in the MKS system*

* The reader is referred to the following texts for discussion on conversion from the cgs system to the MKS system.

D. H. Trevena: *Static fields in electricity and magnetism,* Butterworth, London, 1961.

B. I. Bleaney and B. Bleaney: *Electricity and Magnetism*, O.U.P., 1959.

$$P_M = \frac{L}{3\varepsilon_0}\left(\alpha + \frac{\mu^2}{3kT}\right)$$

relates the molar polarization to the dipole moment, μ, and polarizability, α, of a substance. L is the Avogadro constant, k is the Boltzmann constant, ε_0 is the absolute permittivity of free space which is equal to 8.85×10^{-12} coulomb^2 newton^{-1} metre^{-2} ($C^2\,N^{-1}\,m^{-2}$), and T is the absolute temperature.

For a substance in the liquid or solid state, measurements are made on solutions of the substance in an inert non-polar solvent, e.g benzene or tetrachloromethane. Inherent in the derivation of the Debye equation is the assumption that the molecules of substance behave independently of each other. Any molecules which possess a dipole moment inevitably must interact with their neighbours and for this reason the Debye equation is strictly applicable only to dilute solutions in non-polar solvents in which these interactions are considerably reduced.

For substances in the gaseous state, intermolecular distances are usually large enough for the interactions to be neglected.

The Debye equation has the form $P_M = A + B/T$ in which A and B are constants for a specific substance. Therefore, a plot of the molar polarization against the reciprocal of absolute temperature should be linear. The slope of this plot will equal $L\mu^2/9k\varepsilon_0$ from which the dipole moment, μ, may be calculated. This procedure is valid provided that the molecules of the substance are not associated to varying extents at different temperatures and that the configuration of the molecules does not alter with variation in temperature.

For the values of P_M given, the corresponding values of $1/T$ are as follows:

P_M/cm^3	57.4	53.6	50.1	46.8	43.4
$\frac{10^3}{T}\Big/K^{-1}$	2.602	2.381	2.249	2.065	1.915

Fig. 6 shows the linear plot of P_M against $\frac{1}{T} \times 10^3$ from which the slope is found to be 2.08×10^4 cm^3 K,

$$= 2.08 \times 10^{-2}\ m^3\ K.$$

Hence
$$\frac{L\mu^2}{9k\varepsilon_0} = 2.08 \times 10^{-2}\ m^3\ K$$

ε_0 has the units, $C^2\,N^{-1}\,m^{-2}$, and k, the units $J\,K^{-1}$ ($=N\,m\,K^{-1}$), so that

$$\mu^2 = \frac{2.08\times10^{-2}\times9\times1.381\times10^{-23}\times8.85\times10^{-12}}{6.02\times10^{23}}\ \mathrm{C^2\,m^2}$$

$$= 38\times10^{-60}\ \mathrm{C^2\,m^2}$$

Therefore, $\mu = 6.165\times10^{-30}$ C m = $\underline{1.85\ \mathrm{D}}$

(1 Deybe (D) = 3.336×10^{-30} C m).

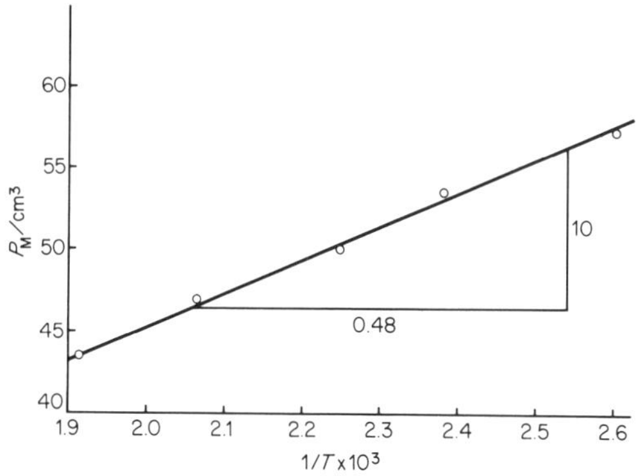

Fig. 6 Molar polarization of water vapour versus reciprocal of temperature

In general, when a molecule contains two dipoles of moments, μ_1 and μ_2, in fixed relative positions the resultant dipole moment, μ, of the molecule is given by

$$\mu = (\mu_1^2+\mu_2^2+2\mu_1\mu_2\cos\theta)^{1/2} \tag{i}$$

in which θ is the angle between two moments. The dipole moment μ of water is the resultant of two O—H moments acting at an angle of 105° to each other. For water, therefore, equation (i) becomes

$$\mu = (2\mu_{\mathrm{OH}}^2+2\mu_{\mathrm{OH}}^2\cos\theta)^{1/2}$$

$$= \mu_{\mathrm{OH}}(2(1+\cos\theta))^{1/2} = \mu_{\mathrm{OH}}(4\cos^2\theta/2)^{1/2}$$

(since $(1+\cos\theta) = 2\cos^2\theta/2$)

Hence $\mu = 2\mu_{\mathrm{OH}}\cos\theta/2$.

From the given value of θ and the calculated value of μ

$$1.85 = \mu_{\mathrm{OH}}2\cos 52.5°$$

$$\mu_{\mathrm{OH}} = \frac{1.85}{2\times0.6088}\ \mathrm{D} = 1.52\ \mathrm{D}$$

<u>The dipole moment of water in the vapour state is 1.85 D and the dipole moment of each OH bond is 1.52 D.</u>

Example 4.15 Bond angles from dipole moments

For 4-nitro(chloromethyl)benzene the dipole moment is 3.59 D when measured in dilute solution in benzene. If the dipole moments of nitrobenzene and (chloromethyl)benzene measured in dilute solutions in benzene are 3.98 D and 1.85 D respectively, estimate the angle between the C—Cl and C—C_6H_5 bonds in 4-nitro(chloromethyl) benzene.

In 4-nitro(chloromethyl)benzene the effective dipole moment, μ, is given by vector addition of the dipole moments, μ_1 μ_2, for nitrobenzene and (chloromethyl)benzene respectively. The angle, θ, between the two moments is the required bond angle:

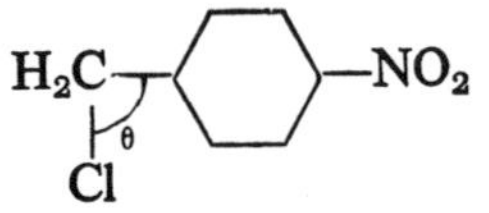

By equation (i) in example 4.13, cos θ is given by

$$\begin{aligned}\cos\theta &= (\mu^2-\mu_1^2-\mu_2^2)/2\mu_1\mu_2 \\ &= (3.59^2-3.98^2-1.85^2)/(2\times3.98\times1.85) \\ &= (12.89-15.84-3.423)/14.72 = -0.4329\end{aligned}$$

Hence, $\theta = 115°\ 39'$

The C—C—Cl bond angle is estimated to be 115° 39′ from the given dipole moments.

Additional Examples

1 The surface tension of tetrachloromethane ($M_r = 153.8$) at 20°C is 0.02568 N m^{-1} and at 80°C, 0.01871 N m^{-1}. The density/kg m^{-3}, at 20°C is 1594 and at 80°C 1470. Show that tetrachloromethane is not associated.

2 A viscometer as standardized by means of benzene which has a dynamic viscosity of 6.47×10^{-4} N s m^{-2} and density 0.8794 g cm^{-3} at 20°C; the time of flow was found to be 183 s. The time of flow for ethanol, density 0.7893 g cm^{-3} at 20°C, was 378 s. What is the dynamic viscosity of ethanol at this temperature? (B.Pharm., Wales)

3 A steel ball having a diameter of 0.1588 cm took 16.7 s to fall a distance of 15 cm through an oil in a tube 2 cm in diameter. The height of liquid was

25.4 cm, the density of oil was $0.96\,g\,cm^{-3}$ and the density of the ball $7.65\,g\,cm^{-3}$. Find the coefficient of dynamic viscosity of the oil at the temperature of the experiment.

4 A liquid of relative molecular mass 112.0 has a refractive index 1.347, relative permittivity 4.285 and density $1.108\,g\,cm^{-3}$ at 25°C. What are the values of its molar refraction and molar polarization? (B.Sc., Wales)

5 0.20 moles of liquid benzene is evaporated at its normal boiling point, 80.2°C, at a constant pressure of 1 atmosphere ($1.013 \times 10^5\,N\,m^{-2}$). ΔH_v for benzene is $30.7\,kJ\,mol^{-1}$. Calculate (*a*) the work involved in the expansion from liquid to vapour, (*b*) the heat of vaporization (ΔH_v), (*c*) the difference in the internal energy (ΔU_v) of vapour and liquid benzene, (*d*) heat (q) added to the system, (*e*) entropy change (ΔS), and (*f*) free energy change (ΔG). (University of Connecticut, Storrs, USA)

6 The heat of vaporization of methylbenzene at its boiling point, 111°C, is $33.28\,kJ\,mol^{-1}$. For the evaporation of 1 mole at 1 atmosphere pressure calculate (*a*) the work involved, (*b*) the heat (q) added to the system, (*c*) ΔH of vaporization, (*d*) the internal energy difference (ΔU), (*e*) free energy change (ΔG), and (*f*) the entropy change (ΔS).
(University of Arizona, Tucson, USA)

7 How much work is done on condensing 500 g of steam at its boiling point under a constant pressure of 1 atmosphere? What are the values of q, ΔH, and ΔU for the process? Assume that the heat of vaporization of water is $2.26\,kJ\,g^{-1}$. (H = 1.008; O = 16.00.)

8 Mixtures of 1,2-dibromoethane and 1,2-dibromopropane behave ideally at 85°C. At this temperature, the vapour pressure of pure 1,2-dibromoethane is 172 mmHg, and that of pure 1,2-dibromopropane 126 mmHg. What is (*a*) the total vapour pressure, and (*b*) the mass percentage composition of 1,2-dibromoethane in the vapour in equilibrium with a liquid mixture consisting of 3 moles of 1,2-dibromopropane and 2 moles of 1,2-dibromoethane? (C = 12; Br = 80; H = 1.)

9 The vapour pressure of ethoxyethane at 20°C is 442 mmHg. 12.2 g of a non-electrolyte dissolved in 100 g ethoxyethane caused a reduction in the vapour pressure to 410 mmHg. Calculate the relative molecular mass of the solute.

10 From the following data calculate the solubility of 1,4-dibromobenzene ($M_r = 236$) and 1,4-dichlorobenzene ($M_r = 147$) in ethanol at 25°C assuming ideal behaviour.

Substance	*m.p./°C*	$\lambda_f / J\,g^{-1}$
1,4-dibromobenzene	86.0	86
1,4-dichlorobenzene	52.7	124
Ethanol	−114	182

λ_f is the latent heat of fusion per gram.

11 5 g of an organic compound dissolved in 100 g of water ($M_r = 18$) gives a solution with a boiling-point of 100.40°C at 1 atm. What is the relative molecular mass of the compound, and what is the molal boiling-point elevation constant for water?

(b.p. water at 1 atm = 100.00°C; molar heat of vaporization of water = 40.6 kJ.)

12 A solution containing 0.5 g of an organic hydrocarbon in 20 g benzene freezes at 4.94°C. Pure benzene freezes at 5.40°C and its latent heat of fusion is 21.4 kJ mol^{-1}. What is the relative molecular mass of the compound? ($M_r(C_6H_6) = 78$.) (B.Sc., Durham)

13 0.20 mol of non-volatile solute are added to 0.80 mol of a liquid solvent to form a liquid solution. The vapour pressure of the solvent above the solution is 5.33 kN m^{-2}. The vapour pressure of the pure liquid solvent at the same temperature is 11.73 kN m^{-2}. Assuming the vapour is ideal, what is the activity coefficient of the solvent in the liquid solution?

(Adapted from ACS Cooperative Examination: Physical Chemistry (Thermodynamics).)

14 Derive an expression for the solubility of a substance in a solvent in which it forms an ideal solution.

Calculate the solubility of benzoic acid in the ideal solution at 300 K given that it melts at 395 K and has a heat of fusion of 17.3 kJ mol^{-1}. The solubility of benzoic acid (measured as a mole fraction) is 0.0006 in water, 0.014 in hexane, 0.082 in benzene, 0.105 in chlorobenzene and 0.19 in ethanol. Comment on these values. (University of Oxford)

15 Randall and Young (J.A.C.S., **50** (1928), 989) quote the following values of the freezing point depression, θ, for solutions of hydrochloric acid of molality m.

m	θ	m	θ
0.001	0.003675	0.10	0.35209
0.002	0.007318	0.20	0.7064
0.005	0.018152	0.30	1.0689
0.01	0.036028	0.50	1.8225
0.02	0.07143	0.70	2.5801
0.05	0.17666	1.00	3.5172

Determine the mean ionic activity coefficients of the hydrochloric acid in the various solutions. (Molal freezing point depression for water = 1.858.)

16 The vapour pressure of mercury in equilibrium with a thallium amalgam containing 20.06 g of mercury and 11.30 g of thallium is 9.60×10^{-4} mmHg at 26°C. The vapour pressure of pure mercury at the same temperature is 20.1×10^{-4} mmHg. Taking the activity coefficient of pure mercury to be unity, calculate (*a*) the activity and activity coefficient of the mercury in the amalgam, (*b*) the difference between the chemical potential of the mercury in the amalgam and that of pure liquid mercury. (Hg = 200.6; Tl = 204.4.)

17 The pressure of water vapour above a saturated solution of sodium nitrate, containing 92 g of the salt per 100 g of water, at 25°C is 17.53 mmHg, and the vapour pressure of pure water at the same temperature is 23.76 mmHg.

Use the data to evaluate the following:

(*a*) The activity of the water in the solution, referred to pure water as standard.
(*b*) The activity coefficient of the water in the solution.
(*c*) The change in free energy per mole of sodium nitrate for the process:

$$NaNO_3 \text{ (crystalline at 25°C)} + H_2O \text{ (at 25°C)} \longrightarrow NaNO_3 \text{ (saturated solution at 25°C.)}$$

(Na = 23.00; N = 14.01; O = 16.00; H = 1.008.)

18 Discuss briefly the effect of an alternating electric field on a polar molecule and describe one method for determining the dipole moment of the molecule.

The molar polarization P_M of nitroethane vapour has been measured at a series of temperatures and the results are given below.

Temperature/K	397.5	413.6	421.1	484.3
P_M/cm^3	225.9	218.4	214.7	188.6

Calculate the dipole moment of nitroethane. (B.Sc., Wales)

19 The relative permittivities (ε_r) and densities (p) of a vapour of a substance of relative molecular mass 50.5 at a series of temperatures are:

T/°C	70	90	114
ε	1.00843	1.00736	1.00653
ρ/g dm^{-3}	2.023	1.891	1.793

Calculate the molar polarizations at these temperatures. Does the substance have a dipole moment? If so, how would you use these data to estimate its value? (B.Pharm., London)

20 The following results have been obtained for the relative permittivity ε_r, of gaseous HCl at one atm pressure as a function of temperature:

T/K	201.4	359.2	588.8
$(\varepsilon_r - 1) \times 10^3$	7.452	2.672	1.182

Estimate the dipole moment, μ, and the polarizability, α, of the molecule assuming ideal gas behaviour. Comment briefly on the values of μ and α obtained in terms of the chemical bonding in HCl. (B.Sc., Bristol)

21 The dipole moments of chlorobenzene and nitrobenzene are 1.58 and 3.98 *D* respectively. From purely geometrical considerations estimate the approximate dipole moments of 1,3-dinitrobenzene, 1,2-dichlorobenzene and chloro-3-nitrobenzene. The observed moments are 3.89, 2.27 and 3.40 *D* respectively. How would you explain any discrepancies bigger than 0.1 *D*? (R.S.C.)

22 The vapour phase dipole moment of water is 1.84 *D* and that of dimethyl ether is 1.29 *D*. If the OH moments are at an angle of 105° to each other in water and the CO moments are at an angle of 110° to each other in the ether, estimate the oxygen valence angle in methanol for which the dipole moment is 1.69 *D*.

5

Surface Chemistry and Macromolecular Systems

Example 5.1 Adsorption isotherm

Test graphically the applicability of the Langmuir isotherm to the following data referring to the adsorption of a gas on charcoal.

Pressure/mmHg	*100*	*200*	*500*	*900*
Gas adsorbed/mg g^{-1}	*1.56*	*1.97*	*2.29*	*2.41*

From your graph, calculate the Langmuir constants.

The Langmuir adsorption isotherm may be written in the form

$$\frac{p}{x/m} = \frac{1}{k_1 k_2} + \frac{p}{k_2}$$

where p is the gas pressure, x the amount of gas adsorbed by a definite mass (m) of adsorbent, and k_1 and k_2 are constants.

This is a straight line relationship between $p/(x/m)$ and p, the slope being $1/k_2$ and the intercept on the $p/(x/m)$ axis $1/k_1k_2$.

Fig. 7 is a plot of the following $p/(x/m)$ and p values calculated from the given data. The straight line obtained shows that the Langmuir adsorption isotherm is applicable to the data.

$\frac{p}{x/m}$	64.10	101.5	218.4	373.5
p/mmHg	100	200	500	900

From the graph, the slope is

$$\frac{284}{730} = \frac{1}{k_2}$$

Therefore $\quad k_2 = 2.57 \text{ mg g}^{-1}$

The intercept on the $p/(x/m)$ axis is

$$25 = \frac{1}{k_1 k_2}$$

Therefore $$k_1 = \frac{1}{25 \times 2.57} = 1.56 \times 10^{-2}\ (\text{mmHg})^{-1}$$

The values of the Langmuir constants are $k_1 = \underline{1.56 \times 10^{-2}\ (\text{mmHg})^{-1}}$

and $k_2 = \underline{2.57\ \text{mg g}^{-1}}$.

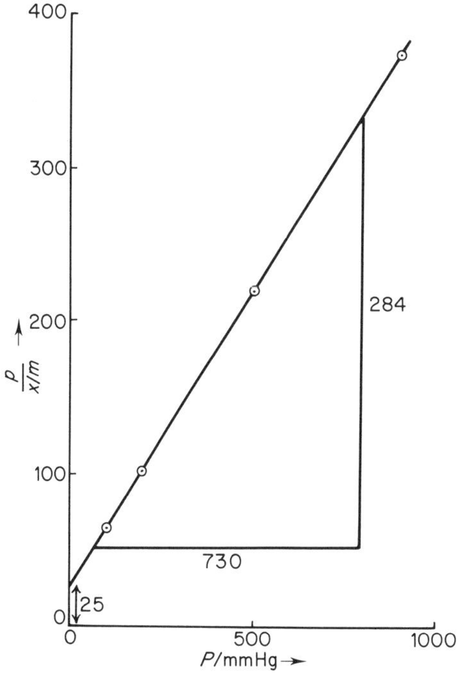

Fig. 7 Langmuir adsorption isotherm

Example 5.2 Surface area of adsorbents

The following data have been obtained for the adsorption of nitrogen on silica at 77K. P_0 is the vapour pressure of liquid nitrogen at this temperature.

Relative pressures P/P_0	*cm^3 adsorbed per gram of silica (reduced to standard state)*
0.05	*30*
0.10	*34*
0.15	*38*
0.20	*40*
0.25	*42.5*
0.30	*45*
0.40	*48*
0.5	*52*
0.6	*55*
0.7	*72*
0.8	*108*

Calculate the surface area of the silica, in terms of square metres per gram, by (a) the BET method and (b) the Harkins and Jura method. *Assume the area of the nitrogen molecule to be 1.62×10^{-19} m^2 and the Harkins–Jura constant (k) to be 4.06 at the temperature of the experiment.*

Much use is made of low temperature gas adsorption in determining surface areas, the results obtained being of importance in assessing the catalytic activity of solid catalysts. This example illustrates the application of two methods of calculation of surface areas from adsorption data.

(a) The BET method

The adsorption isotherm for the given data, obtained by plotting the relative pressure P/P_0 against the volume of the gas adsorbed is shown in Fig. 8. From the isotherm (of Brunauer type II) the adsorbed volume corresponding to a monolayer of gas on the surface may be determined. This can be done by reading directly the amount adsorbed (V_m m^3 g^{-1}) at the first inflexion point (point B in Fig. 8). It is assumed that the adsorbate covers the solid as a monolayer at this point. Finally, the area per gram of adsorbent is given by

Area (in m^2) = (Number of moles in volume V_M)LS'

$$= \left(\frac{P'V_m}{RT_0}\right) LS' \qquad \text{(i)}$$

where $P' = 1.013 \times 10^5$ N m^{-2}, $T_0 = 273$ K, R is the gas constant, L is Avogadro's constant and S' is the area of surface occupied by a single gas molecule. Alternatively, V_m may be determined using the BET equation, this latter method being superior to the more subjective 'point B' method.

Brunauer, Emmett and Teller (J.A.C.S., **60**, (1938), 309), postulated multilayer adsorption, in which layers of adsorbate molecules are adsorbed on those already on the surface of the adsorbent. They make two simplifying assumptions:
(i) the molecules or atoms in successive layers are in dynamic equilibrium, and the amount adsorbed in each layer when full is the same;

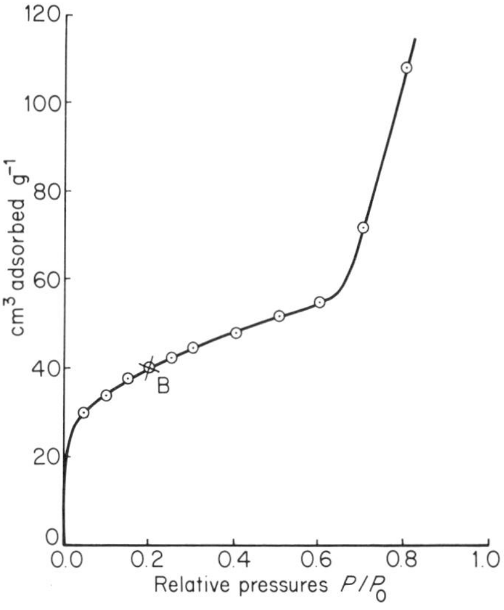

Fig. 8 Plot of relative pressures versus amount adsorbed

(ii) the heats of adsorption for all but the first layer are equal to each other and to E_L, the heat of liquefaction of the adsorbate. This is equivalent to saying that the evaporation/condensation properties of the second and higher adsorbed layers are the same as those of the liquid state.

Using these postulates Brunauer, Emmett and Teller derived an equation, now called the BET equation, which fits the data for types II and III adsorption:

$$v = \frac{V_m c}{(1-f)} \cdot \frac{f}{(1+(c-1)f)} \tag{ii}$$

v = volume reduced to standard conditions of gas adsorbed per unit mass of adsorbent at a given pressure, P, and constant temperature, T.

$f = P/P_0$ where P_0 is the saturated vapour pressure at the experimental temperature.

V_m = volume, reduced to standard conditions, of gas adsorbed per unit mass of adsorbent when the surface is covered by a unimolecular layer of adsorbate.

$c \doteq e^{(E_1 - E_L)/RT}$ where E_1 is the heat of adsorption in the first layer and E_L is the heat of liquefaction of adsorbate.

Type II isotherms are given by equation (ii) when $E_1 > E_L$, i.e. $c > 1$.

Type III isotherms are given by equation (ii) when $E_1 < E_L$, i.e., $c < 1$.

$E_1 > E_L$ when the attractive forces between the adsorbent and adsorbate are greater than those between the adsorbate molecules in the liquefied state.

$E_1 < E_L$ when the attractive forces between the adsorbent and adsorbate are small in comparison with those between the adsorbate molecules in the liquid state.

The BET equation can be rearranged:

$$\frac{f}{v(1-f)} = \frac{1}{V_m c} + \frac{(c-1)f}{V_m c} \qquad \text{(iii)}$$

Thus, a plot of $f/v(1-f)$ against f should be linear. From the slope of this plot the value of $(c-1)/V_m c$ can be obtained, and from the intercept on the ordinate a value for $1/V_m c$ is obtained.

From these two quantities the value V_m can be obtained.

Plots of equation (iii) obtained with type II isotherms are linear up to values of the relative pressure, f, of about 0.35. An advantage of using equation (iii) is that only a few experimental points are needed in the range of $f = 0.05$ to 0.35.

For the data provided the values of f and $f/v(1-f)$ are as follows:

f	0.05	0.10	0.15	0.20	0.25	0.30	0.40
$\frac{f}{v(1-f)}$	0.00176	0.00327	0.00464	0.00625	0.00784	0.00952	0.0139

Figure 9 shows the plot of $\frac{f}{v(1-f)}$ against f, for which the slope $(S) = 0.0095/0.33 = 0.0288$ and the intercept $(I) = 0.0003$.

$$S = \frac{c-1}{V_m c} \quad \text{(iv)}; \qquad I = \frac{1}{V_m c} \quad \text{(v)}$$

From equation (v) $c = \dfrac{1}{IV_m}$. Substitution of this value for c in equation (iv) yields:

$$S = \frac{\dfrac{1}{IV_m} - 1}{V_m \times \dfrac{1}{IV_m}} = \frac{1}{V_m} - I, \text{ from which } V_m = \frac{1}{S+I}.$$

$$\text{Hence } V_m = \frac{1}{0.0288+0.0003} = \frac{1}{0.0291} = 34.4 \text{ cm}^3 = 3.44 \times 10^{-5} \text{ m}^3.$$

Substitution of the data into equation (i) gives

$$\text{Area} = \left(\frac{1.013 \times 10^5 \times 3.44 \times 10^{-5}}{8.31 \times 273}\right) 6.02 \times 10^{23} \times 1.62 \times 10^{-19} \text{ m}^2 \text{ g}^{-1}$$

$$= \underline{150 \text{ m}^2 \text{ g}^{-1}}.$$

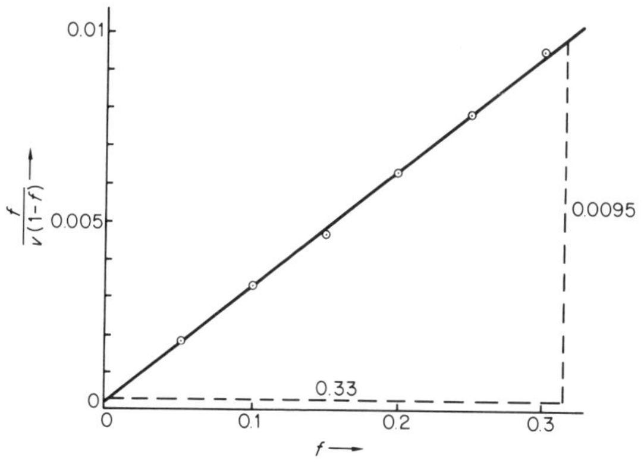

Fig. 9 Plot of f versus $f/v(1-f)$

Note The BET equation is theoretically unsound, in that it is based on the improbable assumptions that all the adsorption sites on the adsorbent surface are exactly equivalent energetically and that lateral interactions between the adsorbed molecules in the layers are negligible, the latter assumption invalidating the postulate that the heats of adsorption for all but the first layer are equal to the heat of liquefaction. However, the equation provides a good analytical method for locating point B and gives reasonable values of V_m. (Halsey, G. D., Disc. Faraday Soc., **8**, (1950), 54.)

(b) The Harkins and Jura method

Harkins and Jura (J.A.C.S., **68** (1946), 1941) deduced that the area of a solid can be obtained from a plot of log P/P_0 versus $1/V^2$ by means of the equation

$$\text{Area (in m}^2\,\text{g}^{-1}) = k(-S)^{\frac{1}{2}} \qquad \text{(ii)}$$

where S is the slope of the linear portion of the plot of the equation

$$\log \frac{P}{P_0} = B - \frac{C}{V^2} \quad (B \text{ and } C \text{ are constants; } V \text{ in cm}^3)$$

and k is a constant that has to be evaluated by independent means.

Fig. 10 is a plot of the following log P/P_0 and $1/V^2$ values calculated from the data given in the question.

$\log \frac{P}{P_0}$	−1.301	−1.000	−0.824	−0.699	−0.602	−0.523	−0.398
$\frac{1}{V^2} \times 10^4$	11.11	8.65	6.93	6.25	5.54	4.94	4.34

$\log \frac{P}{P_0}$ (contd.)	−0.301	−0.222	−0.155	−0.097
$\frac{1}{V^2} \times 10^4$ (contd.)	3.70	3.31	1.93	0.858

From the graph, the slope of the linear portion is

$$-\frac{0.55}{3.35 \times 10^{-4}} = -1643.$$

Substitution of this value in equation (ii) (the value of k having been given as 4.06), gives

$$\text{Area} = 4.06 \times (1643)^{\frac{1}{2}}\,\text{m}^2 = 165\,\text{m}^2$$

The surface area per gram of silica is (*a*) 150 m^2 by the BET method and (*b*) 165 m^2 by the Harkins and Jura method.

Note The Harkins and Jura method is not as convenient as the BET method because data have to be plotted over a wider range of values of relative pressure in order to locate the linear portion of the graph, and the value of $1/V^2$ is sensitive to small errors in V, which, therefore, must be determined very accurately.

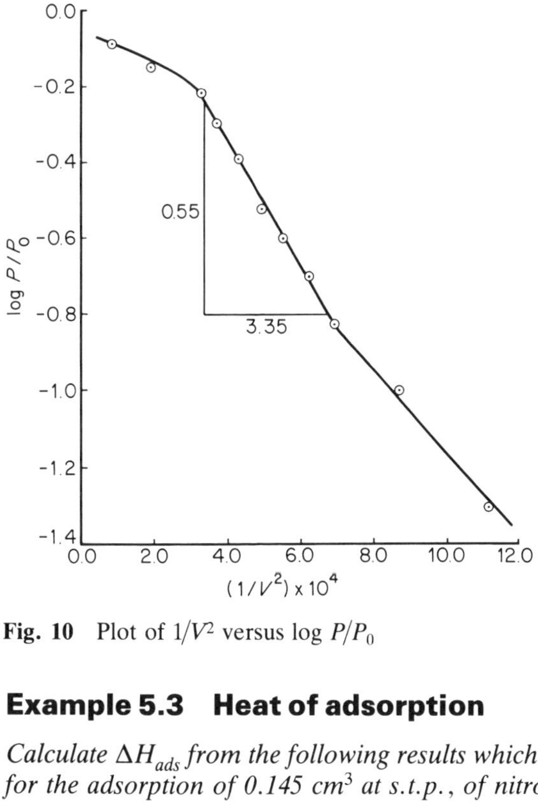

Fig. 10 Plot of $1/V^2$ versus $\log P/P_0$

Example 5.3 Heat of adsorption

Calculate ΔH_{ads} from the following results which have been obtained for the adsorption of 0.145 cm³ at s.t.p., of nitrogen on charcoal:

Temperature/K	*Pressure/atm*
195	*1.5*
244	*3.75*
273	*5.6*

It is possible to calculate, by means of the Clausius-Clapeyron equation, the heat of adsorption from measurement of the pressures required to produce a given amount of adsorption at different temperatures.

The curves showing the variation of the pressure (p) with temperature (T) are called *isosteres*, and the isostere for $\log p$ plotted against $1/T$ is linear. The heat of adsorption obtained by this method is referred to as the 'isosteric' heat of adsorption.

The integrated form of the Clausius-Clapeyron equation applicable to the above data, gives $\Delta H_{\text{desorption}}$ which is equal to $-\Delta H_{\text{adsorption}}$

$$\log p = -\frac{\Delta H_{\text{des}}}{2.303R}\frac{1}{T}+\text{constant.}$$

The slope of the isostere obtained for $\log p$ against $1/T$ is equal to $-\dfrac{\Delta H_{\text{des}}}{2.303R}$ from which ΔH_{des} can be calculated and hence ΔH_{ads}.

The isostere in Fig. 11 is obtained by plotting the following values of $\log p$ against $1/T$.

$\log p$	0.1761	0.5740	0.7482
$1/T$	0.005129	0.004099	0.003663

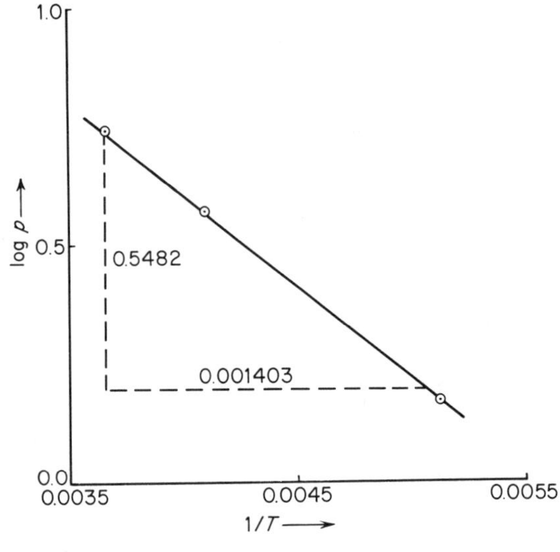

Fig. 11 Isostere for nitrogen on charcoal

The slope of the isostere is $-\dfrac{0.5482}{0.001403}$

Therefore $$-\frac{0.5482}{0.001403} = \frac{\Delta H_{\text{ads}}}{2.303\times R}$$

And $$\Delta H_{\text{ads}} = -\frac{0.5482\times 2.303\times 8.31}{0.001403}\text{ J}$$
$$= -7480\text{ J}$$

$\Delta H_{\text{adsorption}}$ for nitrogen is -7.5 kJ mol^{-1}.

Example 5.4 Gibbs adsorption isotherm

The data tabulated below have been obtained in studies of monolayer formation by butan-1-ol on water (W. D. Harkins and R. W. Wampler, J.A.C.S., **53,** *(1931), 850). The surface tensions (γ) of the solutions are given for molalities (m) and activities (a) at 25°C.*

m	0.00329	0.00658	0.01320	0.0264	0.0536	0.1050	0.2110	0.4330	0.8540
a	0.00328	0.00654	0.01304	0.0258	0.0518	0.0989	0.1928	0.3796	0.7119
$\gamma/\mathrm{N\,m^{-1}}$	0.07280	0.07226	0.07082	0.06800	0.06314	0.05631	0.04808	0.03887	0.02987

Calculate the excess surface concentrations of the butan-1-ol at the molalities 0.0536 and 0.2110 and for each concentration evaluate the area per molecule in the monolayer.

The excess surface concentration (Γ) is related to the surface tension (γ) of the solution and the activity (a) of the solute by the Gibbs adsorption isotherm

$$\Gamma = -\frac{1}{RT}\left(\frac{\partial \gamma}{\partial \ln a}\right)_T \qquad \text{(i)}$$

The excess surface concentration is the excess amount per unit area of surface.

Equation (i) may be rewritten as

$$\Gamma = -\frac{a}{RT}\left(\frac{\partial \gamma}{\partial a}\right)_T \qquad \text{(ii)}$$

For dilute solutions the activity (a) may be replaced by the molality (m) of the solution.

Equation (ii) shows that if an increase in concentration causes the surface tension of the solution to decrease, that is, $\left(\frac{\partial \gamma}{\partial a}\right)_T$ is negative, the excess surface concentration will be positive, so that there is an excess of solute in the surface and adsorption may be said to have occurred. If $\left(\frac{\partial \gamma}{\partial a}\right)_T$ is positive, Γ is negative and the surface of the solution is deficient in solute molecules. This phenomenon is referred to as negative adsorption and is observed for ionic solutes in water.

To determine Γ from the given data at the concentrations specified γ must be plotted against a (Fig. 12) and $\left(\frac{\partial \gamma}{\partial a}\right)_T$ evaluated by measuring the slope at the values of the corresponding activities.

For $m = 0.0536$ $\left(\frac{\partial \gamma}{\partial a}\right)_T = -0.160 \text{ N m}^{-1}$, and

for $m = 0.2110$ $\left(\frac{\partial \gamma}{\partial a}\right)_T = -0.072 \text{ N m}^{-1}$.

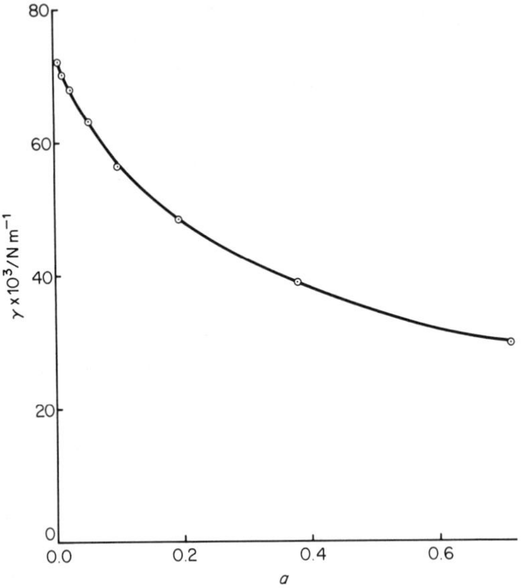

Fig. 12 Surface tension of butan-1-ol-water solutions

By equation (ii) for $m = 0.0536$

$$\Gamma = -\frac{0.0518}{8.31 \times 298} \times (-0.160) \text{ mol m}^{-2}$$

$$= 3.347 \times 10^{-6} \text{ mol m}^{-2},$$

and for $m = 0.2110$

$$\Gamma = -\frac{0.1928}{8.31 \times 298} \times (-0.072) \text{ mol m}^{-2}$$

$$= 5.606 \times 10^{-6} \text{ mol m}^{-2}.$$

The area per mole is given by $1/\Gamma$, and division of this quantity by the Avogadro constant yields the area (α) per molecule.

$$m = 0.0536: \alpha = \frac{1}{6.02\times10^{23}\times3.347\times10^{-6}} = 4.964\times10^{-19}\ \text{m}^2$$

$$m = 0.2110: \alpha = \frac{1}{6.02\times10^{23}\times5.606\times10^{-6}} = 3.375\times10^{-19}\ \text{m}^2$$

The excess surface concentrations and areas per molecule are:

$m = 0.0536$; $\Gamma = 3.35\times10^{-6}$ mol m^{-2}; $\alpha = 4.96\times10^{-19}$ m^2

$m = 0.2110$; $\Gamma = 5.61\times10^{-6}$ mol m^{-2}; $\alpha = 3.38\times10^{-19}$ m^2

Note The areas are calculated for the excess butan-1-ol molecules in the monolayer. The small percentage of molecules normally in the surface layer as solute molecules has been neglected.

Example 5.5 Centrifugal method of determining particle size

The sedimentation constant of the spherical haemocyanin molecule in water is 17.4 × 10^{-13} s, and its density is 1.35 g cm^{-3}. Calculate the radius of the molecule and its relative molecular mass. (Coefficient of viscosity of water = 10^{-3} N s m^{-2}.) (*B.Sc., Bristol*)

The determination of particle size or molecular mass can be made from a knowledge of the velocity of sedimentation in an ultracentrifuge.

In an infinitesimally small time interval ($\mathrm{d}t$), the particle will move a very short distance ($\mathrm{d}x$) and the sedimentation velocity is $\mathrm{d}x/\mathrm{d}t$ which is given by

$$\frac{\mathrm{d}x}{\mathrm{d}t} = \frac{2r^2\omega^2x(d-d_m)}{9\eta} \qquad \text{(i)}$$

where r is the radius of the particle, ω is the angular velocity of rotation, x the distance of the particle from the axis of rotation, d the density of the disperse phase, d_m the density of the medium and η the viscosity of the medium.

Integration of this equation between the limits of $x = x_1$ at $t = t_1$ and $x = x_2$ at $t = t_2$ gives

$$\ln\frac{x_2}{x_1} = \frac{2r^2\omega^2(d-d_m)}{9\eta}(t_2-t_1) \qquad \text{(ii)}$$

The quantity $\dfrac{\ln \dfrac{x_2}{x_1}}{\omega^2(t_2-t_1)}$ is a constant for the given particle in the particular medium used and is called the *sedimentation constant*, *S*. Hence

$$S=\frac{2r^2(d-d_m)}{9\eta} \tag{iii}$$

Substitution of the data in equation (iii) gives

$$17.4\times10^{-13}=\frac{2r^2(1.35-1)\times10^3}{9\times10^{-3}}$$

$$r^2=\frac{9\times17.4\times10^{-19}}{2\times0.35}\,\text{m}^2$$

$$\underline{r=4.731\times10^{-9}\text{ m}}$$

To express the result as the relative molecular mass of the particle:

$$\text{Relative molecular mass}=mL\times10^3$$

where m is the mass of the particle in kg, and L the Avogadro constant.

But $$m=\frac{4}{3}\pi r^3 d$$

Therefore

$$\text{Relative molecular mass}=\frac{4}{3}\pi r^3 dL\times10^3$$

$$=\frac{4}{3}\times3.142(4.731\times10^{-9})^3 1.35\times10^3 \times6.02\times10^{23}\times10^3$$

$$=\underline{3.603\times10^5.}$$

The radius of the molecule is $\underline{4.73\times10^{-9}\text{ m}}$ and its relative molecular mass $\underline{3.60\times10^5}$.

Example 5.6 Osmometric determination of relative molecular mass of polymers

The following results have been obtained in the course of osmotic pressure experiments on a series of solutions of polypropenonitrile in dimethylformamide:

$\dfrac{10\pi}{c}\Big/ \text{N m g}^{-1}$	0.6316	0.6909	0.7500	0.8093
$c\times10^3/\text{g cm}^{-3}$	1	2	3	4

From this information, calculate the relative molecular mass of the polypropenonitrile. The temperature of the experiments is 25°C.

As a result of statistical considerations of the entropy of mixing, expressions of the following type have been deduced for the osmotic pressure (π) of polymer solutions of concentration c:

$$\frac{\pi}{c} = RT\left[\frac{1}{M_r} + Ac + Bc^2 + \ldots\right] \qquad \text{(i)}$$

where R is the gas constant, M_r the relative molecular mass of the solute, and A and B are constants.

At sufficiently low concentrations of polymer, the third and higher terms on the right-hand side can be neglected. Therefore a plot of π/c against concentration is linear, with an intercept on the ordinate from which the relative molecular mass of the polymer may be obtained, that is,

$$\left(\frac{\pi}{c}\right)_{c=0} = \frac{RT}{M} \qquad \text{(ii)}$$

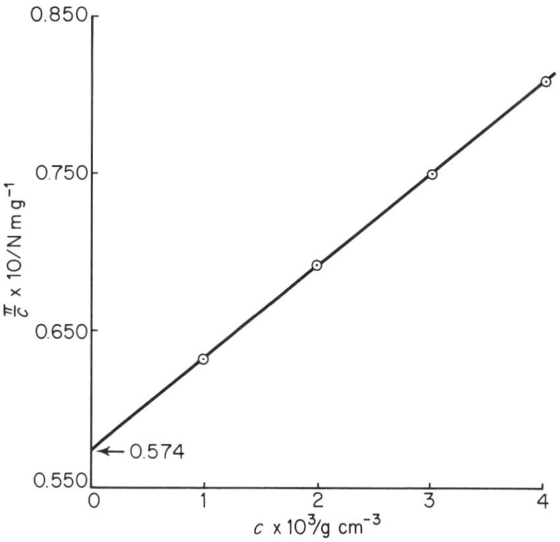

Fig. 13 Plot of π/c versus concentration for polypropenonitrile in dimethylformamide at 25°C

Fig. 13 shows a plot of π/c versus c for the data given in the question. Extrapolation to $c = 0$ gives a value of 0.574×10^{-1} N m g^{-1} for π/c.

Substitution of this value for π/c in equation (ii) permits the evaluation of the relative molecular mass, M_r:

$$M_r = \frac{8.31 \times 298}{0.574 \times 10^{-1}} = 43\,140$$

The relative molecular mass of the polypropenonitrile is 43 140.

Note Polymers usually contain molecules of varying relative molecular mass so that the value of M_r, the relative molecular mass, is an average given by

$$\bar{M}_n = \Sigma n_i M_i / \Sigma n_i$$

where n_i is the number of molecules of the ith species—all of relative molecular mass M_i.

The relative molecular mass determined by osmometry is the so-called *number-average* relative molecular mass ($\bar{M}_n$), because the osmotic pressure is proportional to the number of solute molecules in unit volume of solution.

If, however, the relative molecular mass is determined by light scattering methods, quite a different mean molecular mass is obtained. This is because the light is scattered according to the size of the molecules. Light scattering measurements give the *weight-average* relative molecular mass ($\bar{M}_w$), given by

$$\bar{M}_w = \frac{\Sigma M_i^2 n_i}{\Sigma M_i n_i}.$$

Of course, for monodisperse colloids, all methods should give the same result for $\bar{M}_w$ and $\bar{M}_n$.

Example 5.7 Viscosity and relative molecular mass of high polymers

For polymethyl-2-methylpropenoate in trichloromethane at sufficient dilution,

$$\frac{\eta_{sp}}{c} = 3.3 \times 10^{-6}\, M_r^{0.85}$$

where η_{sp} is the specific viscosity of the polymer solution of concentration, c, in g dm^{-3}, and M_r the relative molecular mass of the polymer.

What is the relative molecular mass of this polymer whose solution of concentration 2.5 g dm^{-3} in trichloromethane has a specific viscosity of 0.11?

The equation quoted in the question is a form of the general equation

$$\frac{\eta_{sp}}{c} = KM_r^a \text{ dm}^3 \text{ g}^{-1}$$

proposed as a result of the work of Staudinger, Kuhn, Mark, Meyer, Flory and others. The constants 'K' and 'a' vary with the macromolecular substance and the solvent and $\eta_{sp} = \left(\frac{\eta}{\eta_0} - 1\right)$ where η = viscosity of the solution and η_0 = viscosity of pure solvent. Substitution of the data gives

$$\frac{0.11}{2.5} = 3.3 \times 10^{-6} M_r^{0.85} \text{ dm}^3 \text{ g}^{-1}$$

Hence

$$M_r = \sqrt[0.85]{\frac{0.11}{2.5 \times 3.3 \times 10^{-6}}} = 71\ 290.$$

The relative molecular mass of the polymethyl-2-methylpropenoate is 71 290.

Example 5.8 Membrane equilibrium

1.3 g of a monobasic colloidal acid, which was fully dissociated, were dissolved in 100 cm³ of very dilute hydrochloric acid in a collodion bag, and allowed to come to equilibrium at 25°C with 100 cm³ of pure water outside the membrane. The pH outside was then found to be 3.26, and the membrane potential was 34.9 mV. Assuming that the solutions were ideal, calculate

(*a*) *the pH inside the membrane;*
(*b*) *the relative molecular mass of the colloidal acid.*
($2.303RT/F = 0.0592$ *V at 25°C*) (*B.Sc., Bristol*)

For equilibrium to be attained across the collodion membrane, hydrogen and chloride ions will migrate from the acid solution to the water. The colloidal negative ion (R^-) of the monobasic acid is unable to diffuse through the membrane and hence the condition for equilibrium will be that the sum of the chemical potentials of the diffusible ions inside the collodion bag shall equal that of the ions outside the bag.

Therefore $\mu_H^\ominus + \mu_{Cl}^\ominus + RT \ln [H^+]_I + RT \ln [Cl^-]_I$

$$= \mu_H^\ominus + \mu_{Cl}^\ominus + RT \ln [H^+]_O + RT \ln [Cl^-]_O,$$

the assumption being made that the activity coefficients are unity.

$\mu^\ominus$ represents the chemical potential in the reference state at infinite dilution. The symbols in square brackets ($[]_I$ and $[]_O$), indicate concentrations (mol dm^{-3}) inside and outside the bag respectively. Therefore, at equilibrium

$$[H^+]_I\,[Cl^-]_I = [H^+]_O\,[Cl^-]_O \qquad \text{(i)}$$

Let x and y mol dm^{-3} be the initial concentrations of colloidal acid and hydrochloric acid respectively.
The equilibrium condition may be depicted:

	Inside			*Outside*	
Ionic species	R^-	H^+	Cl^-	H^+	Cl^-
Concentrations	x	$(x+y-z)$	$(y-z)$	z	z

Applying equation (i):

$$(x+y-z)(y-z) = z^2 \qquad \text{(ii)}$$

z may be determined from the pH of the outer solution, which is given as 3.26:

Therefore $\log\,[H^+]_O = -3.26$

$= \bar{4}.74$

And $z = [H^+]_O = 5.50\times10^{-4}$ mol dm^{-3}

The pH of the inner solution is related to that of the outer solution and the membrane potential (E_m) as follows:

$$E_m = 2.303\,\frac{RT}{F}\log\frac{[H^+]_I}{[H^+]_O}$$

$$= 0.0592\,(\text{pH}_{\text{outer}} - \text{pH}_{\text{inner}})\ \text{V}$$

Therefore $-\dfrac{34.9\times10^{-3}}{0.0592} + 3{\cdot}26 = \text{pH}_{\text{inner}}$

And $\text{pH}_{\text{inner solution}} = 2.67.$

(*a*) The pH inside the membrane is 2.67.

The relationship in equation (ii) may now be solved for $(y-z)$:

$$\log\,(x+y-z) + \log\,(y-z) = 2\log z$$

$$-\log\,(x+y-z) = -\log\,[H^+]_I = \text{pH}_{\text{inner}} = 2.67$$

$$-\log z = -\log\,[H^+]_O = \text{pH}_{\text{outer}} = 3.26$$

Therefore

$$2.67 - \log(y-z) = 2 \times 3.26$$

And

$$\log(y-z) = 2.67 - 6.52$$
$$= -3.85 = \bar{4}.15$$

Therefore $(y-z) = 1.414 \times 10^{-4}\ \text{mol dm}^{-3}$

But $\log(x+y-z) = -2.67$

Therefore $(x+y-z) = 2.138 \times 10^{-3}\ \text{mol dm}^{-3}$

And $x = (21.38 - 1.414) \times 10^{-4}\ \text{mol dm}^{-3}$

$$= 1.997 \times 10^{-3}\ \text{mol dm}^{-3}$$

The concentration of the acid is 13 g dm^{-3}, therefore

$$\text{Relative molecular mass} = \frac{13}{0.001997} = 6.507 \times 10^3$$

(*b*) The relative molecular mass of the colloidal acid is 6510.

Additional Examples

1 What are the essential features of the Freundlich and Langmuir isotherms?

Test graphically the applicability of these to the following data, and, from your graph, calculate the constants of the Langmuir isotherm.

Pressure/N m^{-2}	*Mass of gas adsorbed/g m^{-2}*
2.8×10^{-1}	14.0×10^{-2}
4.0	17.6
6.1	22.1
9.5	27.8
17.0	32.8
34.0	38.4

(B.Sc. and B.Met., Sheffield)

2 Give a brief account of gas–solid adsorption isotherms.

The volume of a gas (measured at 1 atm pressure and 298 K) adsorbed on 1 g charcoal at various pressures was:

P/cmHg	1.0	2.0	3.0	5.0	10.0
V/cm^3	45.0	55.9	60.2	64.7	68.4

The diameter of the gas molecules is approximately 0.5 nm. Estimate the surface area of the charcoal. (The volume of one mole of perfect gas at 298 K and 1 atm is $0.0244\,m^3$.) (University of Oxford)

3 The following data have been obtained in studies of the absorption of nitrogen on TiO_2 at 77 K. P_0 is the vapour pressure of liquid nitrogen at 77 K.

Relative pressures P/P_0	cm^3 *adsorbed* g^{-1} *(reduced to standard state)*
0.01	1.0
0.04	2.0
0.1	2.5
0.2	2.9
0.4	3.6
0.6	4.3
0.8	5.0
0.9	7.5
0.98	18

Using the BET method, determine the surface area in square metres g^{-1} of TiO_2. Assume the area of the nitrogen molecule to be $1.62 \times 10^{-19}\,m^2$.

4 Assuming the Harkins-Jura constant for nitrogen at 77 K to be 4.06, use the data in question 3 to calculate the surface area of the TiO_2 by the Harkins-Jura method.

5 Plot the isostere ($\log p$ against $1/T$) for nitrogen, from the following data for the adsorption of $0.895\,cm^3$ at s.t.p. on charcoal:

Temperature/K	*Pressure/atm*
194	4.6
225	11.5
273	35.4

Hence calculate ΔH_{ads}, for nitrogen, corresponding to the extent of adsorption for which the above data are applicable.

6 The surface tension $\gamma/N\,m^{-1}$ at 20°C of aqueous solutions of phenol of molality m are given by the approximate relationship $\gamma = 0.071–0.075\,m$ for values of m in the range 0.03 to 0.30. For solutions of molality 0.11 and 0.28, estimate the excess surface concentration of phenol and the area per molecule at each concentration.

7 The surface tension $\gamma/N\,m^{-1}$ at 19°C for aqueous solutions of n-hexanoic acid of molality m are given by the approximate relationship $\gamma = 62.5 \times 10^{-3} - 5.5 \times 10^{-1}\,m$ for values of m in the range 0.01 to 0.05. Estimate the molality at which the area occupied per molecule is $3.5 \times 10^{-19}\,m^2$.

8 A protein molecule has a sedimentation constant of $2.01 \times 10^{-12}\,s$. If the density of the protein is $1.32\,g\,cm^{-3}$, calculate the radius of the molecule and its relative molecular mass, assuming the molecule is spherical. (Coefficient of viscosity of water $= 10^{-3}\,N\,s\,m^{-2}$.)

9 Osmotic pressure studies on solutions of haemoglobin at 7°C yielded the following data:

Haemoglobin concn./$g\,dm^{-3}$	10	20	30	60	90
Osmotic pressure/cm H_2O	3.47	7.2	11.17	24.6	40.5

Calculate the relative molecular mass of the haemoglobin.

10 In an Ostwald viscometer at 25°C, the time of flow for a solution containing $5\,g\,dm^{-3}$ of poly(chloroethene) in cyclohexanone was 125 s and for cyclohexanone was 100 s. Assuming the equation

$$\frac{\eta_{sp}}{c} 1.0 \times 10^{-6} M_r$$

is obeyed, estimate the relative molecular mass (M_r) of the poly(chloroethene).

($\eta_{sp} = \frac{\eta}{\eta_0} - 1$ where η is the viscosity of the solution and η_0 is the velocity of the pure solvent.)

11 The relative viscosity number, η_r, of a polymer solution containing 10.00 g polymer in $1\,dm^3$ is 2.800. A solution half as concentrated has a relative viscosity number of 1.800.

(*a*) Determine the limiting viscosity number, $[\eta]$. (*b*) If $[\eta] = 5.00 \times 10^{-5} \times M_r^{0.600}$, what is the polymer's relative molecular mass, M_r? (University of Connecticut, Storrs, USA)

12 A 5% aqueous solution of a protein (free from ionic material) gave an osmotic pressure of 18.62 mmHg at 20°C. Calculate the relative molecular mass of the protein and the temperature at which the solution would freeze. (Molar depression constant $kg^{-1}\,H_2O = 1.85$°C.) (B.Sc., Bristol)

13 $100\,cm^3$ of a $0.1\,mol\,dm^{-3}$ solution of congo red, which is fully dissociated as follows

$$NaR \longrightarrow Na^+ + R^-$$

are contained in a collodion bag and equilibriated, at 25°C, with $100\,cm^3$ water outside the membrane.

Assuming ideal behaviour of the solutions, calculate

(*a*) the pH on each side of the membrane.
(*b*) the membrane potential.

6

Transport Numbers, Conductance and Ionic Equilibria

Example 6.1 Transport numbers—Hittorf method

A solution of hydrochloric acid was electrolysed in a transport cell between platinum electrodes. The cathode compartment contained 0.177 g of chloride ions before electrolysis and 0.163 g afterwards. A silver coulometer in series had a deposit of 0.2508 g of silver. What are the transport numbers of H^+ *and* Cl^-*?*

The transport number of an ion is that fraction of the current it carries. Thus if n is the fraction carried by the anions, then $(1-n)$ is the fraction carried by the cations. n and $(1-n)$ are the transport numbers of the anion and cation respectively.

The current passed through the cell is proportional to 0.2508 g of silver, and to

$$0.2508 \times \frac{35.5}{107.9} \text{ g of chloride ions.}$$

The loss of chloride ions in the cathode compartment represents the current conveyed by the chloride ions, and is given by

$$0.177 - 0.163 = 0.014 \text{ g chloride ions.}$$

As a direct consequence of Hittorf's rule we have

$$\frac{\text{Loss of anion equivalents in cathode compartment}}{\text{Equivalents of current passed}}$$

$$= \text{transport number of anion } (n).$$

$$\text{Hence transport number of } Cl^- \ (n) = \frac{0.014}{0.2508 \times \dfrac{35.5}{107.9}} = \underline{0.170.}$$

And transport number of H^+ $(1-n) = \underline{0.830.}$

Note One equivalent is the mass in grams of any charged species liberated by the passage of one Faraday during electrolysis.

Example 6.2 Transport numbers—moving boundary method

The velocity of a boundary of hydrochloric acid with lithium chloride is followed in aqueous solution. It moves 15.0 cm in a tube 1 cm diameter in 22 min when the current is 11.54 mA. If the concentration of the hydrochloric acid is 0.01065 mol dm^{-3}*, what is the transport number of the hydroxonium ion?*

In the moving boundary method, the observation made is the motion of the ions under the influence of an applied potential, and not concentration changes, as in the Hittorf method.

During the passage of q coulombs of electricity, the number of equivalents transported is q/F of which t_+q/F are carried by the cation. F is the Faraday and t_+ the transport number of the cation. If c is the concentration in equivalents cm^{-3}, then the volume of solution swept out by the boundary during the passage of q coulombs is t_+q/Fc. If a is the cross-sectional area of the tube and x the distance the boundary has moved for the passage of q coulombs, then

$$xa = \frac{t_+q}{Fc}, \qquad \text{or} \qquad t_+ = \frac{Facx}{q}$$

Substitution of the given data gives

$$t_+ = \frac{96\,500 \times 1.065 \times 10^{-5} \times 3.142 \times (0.5)^2 \times 15}{11.54 \times 10^{-3} \times 22 \times 60}$$
$$= 0.7949.$$

The transport number of the hydroxonium ion is <u>0.795.</u>

Example 6.3 Molar conductance at infinite dilution

Find graphically the molar conductance at infinite dilution (Λ_∞) *for sodium fluoride at 18°C from the following values of concentration,* c/*mol cm*$^{-3}$*, and corresponding conductance,* Λ/*ohm*$^{-1}$ *cm*^{2} *mol*$^{-1}$*.*

c	10^{-4}	10^{-5}	10^{-6}	10^{-7}
Λ	73.7	83.4	87.8	89.2

The dissociation of an electrolyte increases with dilution to become complete at infinite dilution (zero concentration). Experiments by Kohlrausch supported this idea. Kohlrausch expressed the product

$$\kappa \,.\, V = \Lambda$$

where κ is the specific conductance per cm^3, V the volume in cm^3 containing one mole of electrolyte, and Λ is the molar conductance.

Λ is not a constant, but increases asymptotically with dilution towards a limiting value Λ_∞. By plotting Λ against c, a value can be obtained for Λ_∞ by extrapolation to zero concentration. However, due to the nature of the curve obtained, this is a very uncertain method of determining Λ_∞. It was Kohlrausch who pointed out that a straight line (nearly so) can be obtained by plotting Λ against $\sqrt{c}$ for dilute solutions, that is, the variation of Λ with concentration can be represented by the equation

$$\Lambda = \Lambda_\infty - b\sqrt{c} \quad \text{where } b \text{ is a constant.}$$

The value of Λ_∞ can be obtained by extrapolating to $\sqrt{c} = 0$ and reading the intercept.

Proceeding in the manner described for sodium fluoride, Fig. 14 shows a plot of the following Λ and $\sqrt{c}$ values.

Λ	73.7	83.4	87.8	89.2
$\sqrt{c}$	0.01000	0.00316	0.00100	0.00032

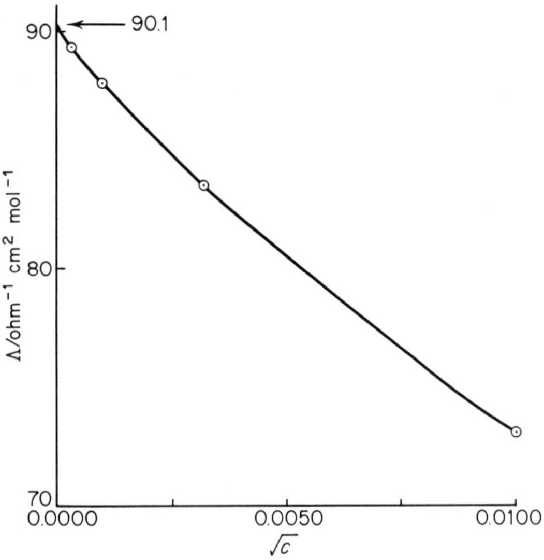

Fig. 14 Plot of Λ against $\sqrt{c}$

Extrapolation of the curve to $\sqrt{c} = 0$ gives $\Lambda_\infty = 90.1$ ohm^{-1} cm^2 mol^{-1}. The conductance at infinite dilution of sodium fluoride at 18°C is 90.1 ohm^{-1} cm^2 mol^{-1}.

Example 6.4 Molar conductance and transport numbers

The conductance of sodium fluoride in 0.1 mol dm^{-3} solution is 83.5 ohm^{-1} cm^{-2} mol^{-1}. The salt may be taken as 92% dissociated. If the transport number of the sodium ion is 0.45, what are the mobilities of the sodium and fluoride ions? (*B.Sc., Durham*)

By Kohlrausch's law of independent migration of ions, the molar conductance (Λ_∞), at infinite dilution of a uni-univalent electrolyte is given by

$$\Lambda_\infty = l_+^\infty + l_-^\infty$$

where l_+^∞ and l_-^∞ are the molar conductances at infinite dilution of the cation and anion respectively.
The absolute mobilities of the ions, in cm^2 v^{-1}s^{-1}, are given by dividing l_+^∞, or l_-^∞, by the value of the Faraday.
For a solution of finite concentration, the molar conductance (Λ) is given by

$$\Lambda = \alpha F \mu_+ + \alpha F \mu_- \qquad \text{(i)}$$

and

$$\Lambda = l_+ + l_- \qquad \text{(ii)}$$

where α is the degree of dissociation, μ_+ and μ_- the mobilities of the ions, l_+ and l_- the molar ionic conductances for the concentration to which Λ corresponds, and F the Faraday.
The value of the molar ionic conductance represents the contribution to the total conductance, due to the ion and is given by the product of the transport number of the ion and the molar conductance:

$l_{Na^+} = t_{Na^+}\Lambda$ where t_{Na^+} is the transport number of the sodium ion
$= 0.45 \times 83.5$

and

$l_{F^-} = t_{F^-}\Lambda$ where t_{F^-} is the transport number of the fluoride ion
$= 0.55 \times 83.5$

By a comparison of equations (i) and (ii) it follows that the following procedures can be adopted in calculating the mobilities, μ_{Na^+} and μ_{F^-},

$$\mu_{Na^+} = \frac{l_{Na^+}}{\alpha F}$$

$$= \frac{0.45 \times 83.5}{0.92 \times 96\,500}\ \text{cm}^2\,\text{V}^{-1}\,\text{s}^{-1}$$

$$= 0.0004233\ \text{cm}^2\,\text{V}^{-1}\,\text{s}^{-1}$$

And

$$\mu_{F^-} = \frac{l_{F^-}}{\alpha F}$$

$$= \frac{0.55 \times 83.5}{0.92 \times 96\,500} \text{ cm}^2 \text{ V}^{-1} \text{ s}^{-1}$$

$$= 0.0005174 \text{ cm}^2 \text{ V}^{-1} \text{ s}^{-1}$$

The mobilities of the sodium and fluoride ions in a 0.1 mol dm^{-3} solution are 4.23×10^{-4} and 5.17×10^{-4} cm^2 V^{-1} s^{-1} respectively.

Example 6.5 Application of Kohlrausch's law

The following table gives conductance data at infinite dilution at 25°C:

Electrolyte	$\Lambda_\infty/ohm^{-1}\,cm^2\,mol^{-1}$
Sodium butanoate	*82.6*
Hydrochloric acid	*426.2*
Sodium chloride	*126.5*

Calculate the molar conductance of butanoic acid at infinite dilution at 25°C.

As indicated in Example 6.4, the molar conductance of a uni-univalent electrolyte at infinite dilution is given by

$$\Lambda_\infty = l_+^\infty + l_-^\infty$$

Use is made of this in determining Λ_∞, the molar conductance at infinite dilution (zero concentration), for weak electrolytes. This is because the plot of Λ versus $\sqrt{c}$ for a weak electrolyte, such as butanoic acid, does not approach linearity, even for very dilute solutions.

Thus Λ_∞ values for weak electrolytes can be obtained by direct addition and subtraction of the appropriate Λ_∞ values for other electrolytes. Hence, Λ_∞ for butanoic acid is given by:

$$\Lambda_{\infty\,(NaBu)} + \Lambda_{\infty\,(HCl)} - \Lambda_{\infty\,(NaCl)}$$

$$= l_{Na^+}^\infty + l_{Bu^-}^\infty + l_{H^+}^\infty + l_{Cl^-}^\infty - l_{Na^+}^\infty - l_{Cl^-}^\infty$$

$$= l_{H^+}^\infty + l_{Bu^-}^\infty \qquad = \Lambda_{\infty\,(HBu)}$$

Substitution of the relevant data from the question gives

$$\Lambda_{\infty\,(HBu)} = 82.6 + 426.2 - 126.5 \text{ ohm}^{-1} \text{ cm}^2$$

$$= 382.3 \text{ ohm}^{-1} \text{ cm}^2$$

The conductance of butanoic acid at infinite dilution at 25°C is 382.3 $ohm^{-1} cm^2 mol^{-1}$.

Example 6.6 Conductance and dissociation of a weak acid

The specific conductance of a 0.25 mol dm^{-3} solution of ethanoic acid at 18°C is 4.4×10^{-4} ohm^{-1} cm^{-1}. The mobilities of the hydrogen and ethanoate ions at the same temperature are 310 and 77 $ohm^{-1} cm^2 mol^{-1}$ respectively.

Calculate the dissociation constant of ethanoic acid.

(*B.Sc., Bristol*)

By Kohlrausch's law of independent migration of ions

$$\Lambda_\infty = l_+^\infty + l_-^\infty \quad \text{for a uni-univalent electrolyte.}$$

Therefore, the conductance at infinite dilution of ethanoic acid at 18°C is given by

$$\begin{aligned}\Lambda_{\infty\,(HAc)} &= 310+77 \text{ ohm}^{-1}\text{ cm}^2\text{ mol}^{-1}\\ &= 387 \text{ ohm}^{-1}\text{ cm}^2\text{ mol}^{-1}\end{aligned}$$

The molar conductance (Λ) of a solution of an electrolyte is given by (specific conductance)/(concentration in mol cm^{-3}). Therefore, the conductance of 0.05 mol dm^{-3} ethanoic acid at 18°C is

$$\begin{aligned}&4.4\times10^{-4}/(0.05\times10^{-3}) \text{ ohm}^{-1}\text{ cm}^2\text{ mol}^{-1}\\ &= 8.8 \text{ ohm}^{-1}\text{ cm}^2\text{ mol}^{-1}.\end{aligned}$$

The dissociation of ethanoic acid can be represented thus

$$HAc \rightleftharpoons H^+ + Ac^-$$

and the dissociation constant, K_a, by

$$K_a = \frac{[H^+][Ac^-]}{[HAc]}$$

But, both $[H^+]$ and $[Ac^-]$ are equal to αc, where α is the degree of dissociation and c the concentration in mol dm^{-3}. [HAc] is equal to $(1-\alpha)c$.

Therefore $$K_a = \frac{\alpha^2 c}{(1-\alpha)}$$

But by the Arrhenius ratio

$$\alpha = \frac{\Lambda}{\Lambda_\infty}$$

Therefore
$$K_a = \frac{\left(\frac{8.8}{387}\right)^2 \times 0.05}{\left(1-\frac{8.8}{387}\right)}$$

$$= \frac{(8.8)^2 \times 0.05}{387(387-8.8)}$$

$$= 2.646 \times 10^{-5}$$

The dissociation constant of ethanoic acid is 2.65×10^{-5}.

Example 6.7 Conductance and solubility

The specific conductance of a saturated aqueous solution of silver chloride at 25°C is 3.41×10^{-6} ohm^{-1} cm^{-1} and that of the water used is 1.60×10^{-6} ohm^{-1} cm^{-1}. The ionic mobilities of Ag^+ ion and Cl^- ion at 25°C are 61.92 ohm^{-1} cm^2 mol^{-1} and 76.34 ohm^{-1} cm^2 mol^{-1} respectively. Calculate the solubility of silver chloride in water at 25°C. (*Ph.C.*)

Conductance measurements find wide application, e.g. in analysis, concentration control, etc. The application illustrated in this example is to the determination of solubility of a difficultly soluble salt.

The specific conductance of the saturated solution of silver chloride ($\kappa_{\text{sol.}}$) is the sum of the specific conductance of the salt (κ_{AgCl}) and of the water (κ_{H_2O}) used to dissolve the salt:

$$\kappa_{\text{sol.}} = \kappa_{\text{AgCl}} + \kappa_{H_2O}$$

Therefore
$$\kappa_{\text{AgCl}} = \kappa_{\text{sol.}} - \kappa_{H_2O}$$

$$= (3.41-1.60) \times 10^{-6} \text{ ohm}^{-1} \text{ cm}^{-1}$$

$$= 1.81 \times 10^{-6} \text{ ohm}^{-1} \text{ cm}^{-1}$$

Hence the molar conductance is

$$\Lambda = \frac{1000\kappa_{\text{AgCl}}}{[\text{AgCl}]}$$

where [AgCl] is the concentration of silver chloride in mol dm^{-3} and hence the solubility. Since the solution is dilute, and since salts are strong electrolytes, Λ is taken as equal to Λ_∞.

But by Kohlrausch's law

$$\Lambda_\infty = 61.92 + 76.34 \text{ ohm}^{-1}\text{ cm}^2\text{mol}^{-1}.$$

Therefore $$138.26 = \frac{1000 \times 1.81 \times 10^{-6}}{[\text{AgCl}]}$$

And $$[\text{AgCl}] = \frac{1000 \times 1{\cdot}81 \times 10^{-6}}{138{\cdot}26}$$

$$= 1.308 \times 10^{-5} \text{ mol dm}^{-3}$$

The solubility of silver chloride in water at 25°C is $\underline{1.31 \times 10^{-5}\text{ mol dm}^{-3}}$.

Example 6.8 Calculation of pH and buffer solutions

If the dissociation constant of ethanoic acid in aqueous solution is 1.8×10^{-5} at 25°C, calculate the approximate pH at the same temperature of (a) 2 mol dm^{-3} acetic acid solution, (b) a mixture of 100 cm^3 0.2 mol dm^{-3} ethanoic acid and 100 cm^3 0.5 mol dm^{-3} sodium ethanoate solution. (*B.Pharm., Wales*)

(*a*) The dissociation of ethanoic acid is represented by

$$\text{HAc} \rightleftharpoons \text{H}^+ + \text{Ac}^-$$

The concentrations of the undissociated acid and the ions produced from it, at equilibrium, are

$(1-\alpha)c$ mol dm^{-3} of HAc,
αc mol dm^{-3} of H^+,
and αc mol dm^{-3} of Ac^-.

By the law of mass action, the dissociation constant (K_a) of ethanoic acid is given by

$$K_a = \frac{[\text{H}^+][\text{Ac}^-]}{[\text{HAc}]} = \frac{\alpha^2 c}{(1-\alpha)}$$

Since ethanoic acid is a weak acid, α, the degree of dissociation is small and $(1-\alpha)$ can be approximated to unity.

Therefore $K_a = \alpha^2 c$ and $\alpha = \sqrt{K_a/c}$

But $\text{pH} = -\log [\text{H}^+]$

Therefore
$$pH = -\log \alpha c \qquad = -\log\sqrt{K_a c}$$
$$= -\log\sqrt{1.8\times10^{-5}\times2} = -(\bar{3}.7782)$$
$$= +2.222$$

The pH of 2 mol dm^{-3} ethanoic acid solution at 25°C is 2.22.

(*b*) We have a solution of ethanoic acid and its salt—sodium ethanoate. Such a solution possesses the ability to resist changes in pH when some acid, or base, is added. Solutions possessing the property of opposing a change in pH are called *buffer solutions*, and are used whenever solutions of known pH are required. The method of calculating the pH of buffer solutions is illustrated by this example.

The dissociation constant of ethanoic acid is given by (see above)

$$K_a = \frac{[H^+][Ac^-]}{[HAc]}$$

In the presence of a salt of the acid, the concentration of the anion is taken as equal to the concentration of the salt (which is completely ionized), and the unionized acid concentration is taken as the total acid concentration.

Therefore, for a buffer solution,

$$[H^+] = K_a \frac{[acid]}{[salt]}$$

or
$$pH = \log\left(\frac{1}{K_a}\frac{[salt]}{[acid]}\right) \quad \text{(Henderson equation)}$$

Substitution of the data given in the question gives

$$pH = \log\left(\frac{1}{1.8\times10^{-5}} \times \frac{0.25}{0.1}\right) = 5.143$$

The pH of a mixture of 100 cm^3 each of 0.2 mol dm^{-3} acetic acid and 0.5 mol dm^{-3} sodium ethanoate solution is 5.14.

Example 6.9 Hydrolysis of salts (weak acid—strong base)

Given that sodium phenate is hydrolysed to the extent of 3% in 0.1 mol dm^{-3} solution at 25°C and that the dissociation constant of phenol at this temperature is 1.3×10^{-10}, calculate the value of the ionic product of water at 25°C. (*B.Pharm., London*)

For sodium phenate, the equation and concentrations for the hydrolysis equilibrium are

$$\underset{(1-\alpha)c}{Na^{+}+\text{Phenate}^{-}}+H_2O \rightleftharpoons Na^{+}+\underset{\alpha c}{OH^{-}}+\underset{\alpha c}{\text{Phenol}}$$

where α is the degree of hydrolysis and c the molar concentration. The hydrolysis constant (K_h) is given by

$$K_h=\frac{[\text{NaOH}][\text{Phenol}]}{[\text{Sodium phenate}]}=\frac{[OH^-][\text{Phenol}]}{[\text{Sodium phenate}]}$$

$$=\frac{\alpha^2c}{(1-\alpha)}=\frac{(0.03)^2\times0.1}{0.97}$$

$$=9.28\times10^{-5}.$$

But $$K_h=\frac{K_w}{K_a}$$

Therefore $$K_w=9.28\times10^{-5}\times1.3\times10^{-10}$$

$$=12.06\times10^{-15}$$

$$=1.21\times10^{-14}.$$

The ionic product of water at 25°C is $\underline{1.21\times10^{-14}}$.

Example 6.10 Hydrolysis of salts (weak acid—weak base)

At 18°C the dissociation constants of ethanoic acid and phenylamine are 1.8×10^{-5} and 4.2×10^{-10} respectively. Determine (a) the degree of hydrolysis, (b) the pH of a solution of phenylamine ethanoate.

($K_w = 1.0\times10^{-14}$)

(*a*) For phenylamine ethanoate, the equation and concentrations for the hydrolysis equilibrium are

$$\begin{array}{cccc} An^+ + & Ac^- + H_2O \rightleftharpoons & \text{Free base} + & \text{Free acid} \\ & & \text{(phenylamine)} & \text{(ethanoic acid)} \\ (1-\alpha)c & (1-\alpha)c & \alpha c & \alpha c \end{array}$$

where α is the degree of hydrolysis and c the concentration (mol dm^{-3}). The hydrolysis constant (K_h) is given by

$$K_h = \frac{[\text{Free base}][\text{Free acid}]}{[\text{Unhydrolysed salt}]^2} = \frac{\alpha^2}{(1-\alpha)^2} = \frac{K_w}{K_a K_b}$$

Therefore $$\frac{\alpha^2}{(1-\alpha)^2} = \frac{10^{-14}}{1.8\times10^{-5}\times4.2\times10^{-10}} = \frac{10}{7.56}$$

And $$\alpha = 0.54$$

The degree of hydrolysis of phenylamine ethanoate is <u>0.54.</u>

(*b*) The dissociation constant (K_a) of ethanoic acid is given by

$$K_a = \frac{[H^+][Ac^-]}{[HAc]}$$

Therefore $$[H^+] = K_a\frac{[HAc]}{[Ac^-]} = K_a\frac{[\text{Free acid}]}{[Ac^-]} = K_a\frac{\alpha}{(1-\alpha)}$$

But $$\frac{\alpha}{(1-\alpha)} = \sqrt{\frac{K_w}{K_a K_b}}$$

Therefore $$[H^+] = K_a\sqrt{\frac{K_w}{K_a K_b}} = \sqrt{\frac{K_w K_a}{K_b}}$$

$$= \sqrt{\frac{10^{-14}\times1.8\times10^{-5}}{4.2\times10^{-10}}}$$

$$= 2.07\times10^{-5}$$

But $$pH = -\log[H^+] = -\log(2.07\times10^{-5})$$

$$= -(-5+0.3160) = 4.684$$

The pH of phenylamine ethanoate solution is <u>4.68.</u>

Example 6.11 Hydrolysis constant and partition

The distribution coefficient of phenylamine between benzene and water at 20°C is 11.3, the phenylamine being more soluble in benzene. 15 g of phenylamine hydrochloride were shaken with 1000 cm³ water and 100 cm³ benzene. On analysis, 25 cm³ of the benzene layer were found to contain 0.1180 g of phenylamine. Deduce the hydrolysis constant of phenylamine hydrochloride at 20°C.

Two equilibria have to be considered:

$$\text{salt} + \text{water} \underset{}{\overset{\text{hydrolysis}}{\rightleftharpoons}} \underset{\text{(in water layer)}}{\text{base}} + \text{acid}$$

$$\text{base (in water layer)} \overset{\text{partition}}{\rightleftharpoons} \text{base (in benzene layer)}$$

Neglecting the mutual solubility of water and benzene, a general expression for the hydrolysis constant of the salt can be derived as follows:

Let c_1 mol dm^{-3} be the concentration of the base in the aqueous layer. Let c_2 mol dm^{-3} be the original concentration of the salt. Then, if k is the partition coefficient of the base between benzene and water and V the volume of benzene (in dm³) taken to 1000 cm³ of water, the number of moles of the base in the benzene layer is given by

$$c_1 \times k \times V.$$

This makes the total acid concentration

$$= c_1 + c_1 \times k \times V \text{ mol dm}^{-3}$$
$$= c_1(1 + kV) \text{ mol dm}^{-3}$$

The unhydrolysed salt concentration therefore

$$= c_2 - c_1(1 + kV) \text{ mol dm}^{-3}$$

Since

$$K_h \text{ (hydrolysis constant)} = \frac{\left[\begin{matrix}\text{base}\\ \text{in water layer}\end{matrix}\right][\text{acid}]}{[\text{salt}]},$$

we have on substitution
$$K_h = \frac{c_1^2(1+kV)}{c_2 - c_1(1+kV)} \tag{i}$$

From the given data, the number of moles of phenylamine (base) in 100 cm^3 benzene layer is

$$\frac{4 \times 0.1180}{93}$$

Therefore, the number of moles of phenylamine in 1000 cm^3 aqueous layer is

$$\frac{4 \times 10 \times 0.1180}{93 \times 11.3} = 0.004491 = c_1.$$

The original concentration (c_2) of phenylamine hydrochloride is

$$\frac{15}{129.5} = 0.1158 \text{ mol dm}^{-3}$$

Since k is 11.3 and $V = 0.1$, we have on substitution of the relevant data in equation (i)

$$K_h = \frac{(0.004491)^2(1+11.3\times 0.1)}{0.1158 - 0.004491(1+11.3\times 0.1)}$$

$$= \frac{4.296\times 10^{-5}}{1.062\times 10^{-1}} = 4.045\times 10^{-4}.$$

The hydrolysis constant of phenylamine hydrochloride at 20°C is 4.05×10^{-4}.

Example 6.12 Indicators and hydrolysis of salts

If a very small amount of phenolphthalein were added to a 0.1 mol dm^{-3} solution of sodium ethanoate at 25°C, what fraction of the indicator would exist in the coloured form? (At 25°C K_a ethanoic acid = 1.80×10^{-5}; $K_w = 1.01 \times 10^{-14}$; $K_{phenolphthalein} = 3.16 \times 10^{-10}$)
(R.S.C.)

It is first of all necessary to determine the hydrogen ion concentration of the sodium ethanoate.

The equation and concentrations for the hydrolysis equilibrium are

$$\underset{}{Na^+} + \underset{(1-\alpha)c}{Ac^-} + H_2O = Na^+ + \underset{\alpha c}{OH^-} + \underset{\alpha c}{HAc}$$

where α is the degree of hydrolysis and c the concentration (mol dm^{-3}). For the above equilibrium

$$K_h = \frac{K_w}{K_a} = \frac{[OH^-][HAc]}{[NaAc]} = \frac{\alpha^2 c}{(1-\alpha)} \simeq \alpha^2 c \text{ (see Example 6.8)}$$

Therefore
$$\alpha = \sqrt{\frac{K_w}{K_a c}}$$
$$= \sqrt{\frac{1.01\times 10^{-14}}{1.80\times 10^{-5}\times 0.1}}$$
$$= 7.49\times 10^{-5}$$

Therefore $[OH^-] = 7.49\times 10^{-5}\times 0.1 = 7.49\times 10^{-6}$

But $[OH^-][H^+] = K_w$

Therefore $[H^+] = \dfrac{1.01\times 10^{-14}}{7.49\times 10^{-6}} = 1.348\times 10^{-9}$

It can be shown that
$$[H^+] = K_{Ind}\frac{[\text{colourless form}]}{[\text{coloured form}]}$$

where K_{Ind} is the indicator constant.

Therefore
$$\frac{[\text{coloured form}]}{[\text{colourless form}]} = \frac{3.16\times 10^{-10}}{1.348\times 10^{-9}}$$
$$= \frac{0.2343}{1}$$

The fraction of the indicator existing in the coloured form is therefore

$$\frac{0.234}{1.234} = \underline{0.19}$$

Example 6.13 Buffer solutions

Calculate the volume of 0.1 mol dm^{-3} sodium hydroxide that must be added to 500 cm^3 of 0.1 mol dm^{-3} ethanoic acid to produce a buffer *solution with a hydrogen ion concentration of 2×10^{-6} mol dm^{-3}. (The thermodynamic dissociation constant of ethanoic acid is 1.75×10^{-5}, and the value $\gamma = 0.83$ may be assumed for the mean ionic activity coefficient.)* (R.S.C.)

The dissociation equilibrium of ethanoic acid is represented by

$$HAc \rightleftharpoons H^+ + Ac^-,$$

for which the thermodynamic dissociation constant, K_a, is given by

$$K_a = \frac{a_{H^+}a_{Ac^-}}{a_{HAc}},$$ the 'a' terms indicating activities,

$$= \frac{[H^+][Ac^-]}{[HAc]} \cdot \frac{\gamma_{H^+}\gamma_{Ac^-}}{\gamma_{HAc}}$$

where the terms in brackets represent concentrations (mol dm^{-3}), and the γ terms represent the activity coefficients. But $\gamma_{H^+} \cdot \gamma_{Ac^-} = \gamma^2$ and γ_{HAc} is the activity coefficient of the unionized molecule, which is taken as unity. Therefore, for the buffer solution we have

$$K_a = \frac{[H^+][\text{salt}]}{[\text{acid}]} \cdot \gamma^2$$

that is, $$1.75 \times 10^{-5} = \frac{2 \times 10^{-6}\left(\dfrac{0.1x}{0.5+x}\right)}{\left(\dfrac{\frac{1}{2} \times 0.1}{0.5+x}\right) - \left(\dfrac{0.1x}{0.5+x}\right)} \cdot (0.83)^2$$

where x is the number of dm^3 of sodium hydroxide required. Therefore

$$1.75 \times 10^{-5} = \frac{2 \times 10^{-6} \times 0.1x \times 0.83^2}{0.1(\frac{1}{2} - x)}$$

And $$\frac{x}{(\frac{1}{2} - x)} = \frac{1.75 \times 10^{-5}}{2 \times 10^{-6} \times 0.83^2} = 12.70$$

Solving for x

$$x = \frac{6.35}{13.70}\ \text{dm}^3 \qquad = 0.4635\ \text{dm}^3 \qquad = 463.5\ \text{cm}^3$$

464 cm^3 of 0.1 mol dm^{-3} sodium hydroxide are required to produce the buffer solution.

Example 6.14 Activities from solubility measurements and the Debye-Hückel limiting law

The solubilities of thallium(I) chloride in water and in various aqueous solutions of potassium nitrate are as follows:

Solubility TlCl/mol dm⁻³	*0.01607*	*0.01716*	*0.01826*	*0.01961*
Concentration KNO_3/mol dm⁻³	*0*	*0.02*	*0.05*	*0.10*

Determine the mean activity coefficient of thallium (I) chloride in pure water, the solubility product and the value of the constant A in the Debye-Hückel limiting law for activities. (*B.Sc., Wales*)

The relationship between the solubility (s) of a sparingly soluble salt, in the presence of other electrolytes in aqueous solution, and the ionic strength of the solution, is given by the Debye-Hückel theory as:

$$\log\frac{s}{s_p} = Az_+z_-\sqrt{\mu} - Az_+z_-\sqrt{\mu_p} \quad \text{(i)}$$

where A is the constant in the Debye-Hückel limiting law, z_+, z_- are the valencies of the cation and anion respectively, μ is the ionic strength of the solution of the sparingly soluble salt in the presence of another electrolyte, μ_p is the ionic strength of the solution of the sparingly soluble salt in pure water only, and s_p is the solubility of the salt in pure water.

A plot of $\log s/s_p$ against $\sqrt{\mu}$ should be a straight line of slope Az_+z_-, since μ_p is constant for a particular temperature.

From the given data, the following table may be constructed:

Solubility (s) TlCl/mol dm⁻³	*Concentration (c) KNO_3/mol dm⁻³*	$\log\frac{s}{s_p}$	$\mu = \frac{1}{2}\Sigma c_i z_i^2$	$\sqrt{\mu}$
0.01607	0.00	0	0.01607	0.1267
0.01716	0.02	0.0285	0.03716	0.1928
0.01826	0.05	0.0555	0.06826	0.2613
0.01961	0.10	0.0865	0.1196	0.3459

The graph obtained by plotting $\log s/s_p$ against $\sqrt{\mu}$ is shown in Fig. 15. A good approximation to a straight line is obtained. This is extrapolated to zero ionic strength to obtain the value of $\log s_0/s_p$, whence s_0, the ideal solubility in a solution of zero ionic strength, may be calculated.

From the graph $$Az_+z_- = \frac{0.08}{0.2} = 0.4.$$

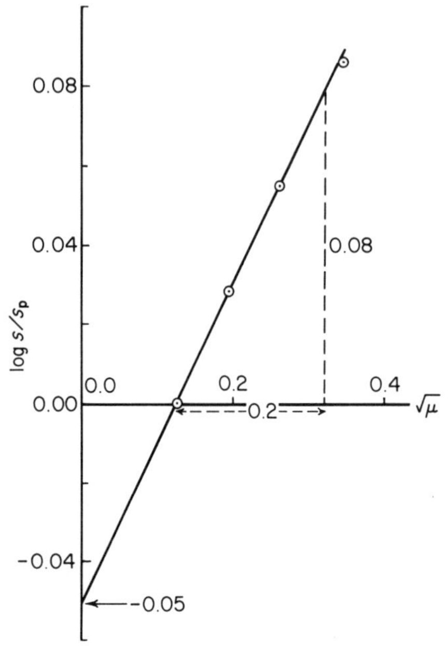

Fig. 15 Plot of $\log \frac{s}{s_p}$ versus $\sqrt{\mu}$

Since for thallium (I) chloride, $z_+ = z_- = 1$, the value of the Debye-Hückel constant A is 0.4.

From the graph $$\log \frac{s_0}{s_p} = -0.05 = \bar{1}.9500$$

Therefore $$\log s_0 = \bar{1}.9500 + \bar{2}.2060 = \bar{2}.1560.$$

And $$s_0 = 0.01432.$$

The solubility product $K = \gamma_\pm^2 s_p^2$, where $\gamma_\pm$ is the mean activity coefficient. For a solution of zero ionic strength, the solubility product $K_s = s_0^2$, because the activity coefficients are now unity.

Therefore $$\gamma_{\pm} = \frac{K_s^{1/2}}{s_p} = \frac{0.01432}{0.01607} = 0.8912.$$

The mean activity coefficient $\gamma_{\pm} = \underline{0.8912}$.

The solubility product of TlCl is $(0.01432)^2 = \underline{2.05 \times 10^{-4}}$.

Summary The mean ionic activity coefficient of thallium (I) chloride in pure water is 0.891. The solubility product of thallium (I) chloride is 2.05×10^{-4}. The constant A in the Debye-Hückel limiting law is 0.4.

Note The plot of log s/s_p against $\sqrt{\mu}$ has a slight curvature, due to the fact that deviations from the Debye-Hückel limiting law, on which equation (i) is based, become observable at ionic strengths approaching 0.1. Thus the value of A determined on the assumption that the plot is a straight line, is low.

Example 6.15 Onsager equation, dissociation of electrolytes and ionic strength

The conductance of a solution containing 2.5×10^{-3} mol dm^{-3} of copper sulphate is 188.14 ohm^{-1} cm^2 mol^{-1} at 25°C. The limiting Onsager equation for this electrolyte at 25°C is,

$$\Lambda = 267.20 - 485.84\,\mu^{1/2} \text{ where } \mu \text{ is the ionic strength.}$$

The mean activity coefficient of the free ions of valency z is given, at 25°C, by the relation

$$-\log \gamma_{\pm} = \frac{0.509\,z^2\mu^{1/2}}{1+\mu^{1/2}} - 0.20\,\mu.$$

Calculate the dissociation constant of copper sulphate.

(B.Sc., Wales)

The ionic strength (μ) of an electrolyte solution is defined by $\mu = \frac{1}{2}\Sigma c_i z_i^2$, where c_i is the concentration (mol dm^{-3}), and z_i the valency of the ith species of ion.

For complete dissociation, therefore, the ionic strength of the given copper sulphate solution would be:

$$\begin{aligned}\mu &= \tfrac{1}{2}(c_{Cu^{2+}} \times 4 + c_{SO_4^{2-}} \times 4)\\ &= \tfrac{1}{2}(2.5 \times 10^{-3} \times 4 + 2.5 \times 10^{-3} \times 4)\\ &= 10^{-2}\end{aligned}$$

Since Cu^{2+} and SO_4^{2-} are bivalent their concentrations (mol dm^{-3}) are each equal to the concentration of the copper sulphate.

The conductance (Λ_c) of such a fully ionized solution of copper sulphate would be given by the limiting Onsager equation as

$$\begin{aligned}\Lambda_c &= 267.20 - 485.84\mu^{1/2}\ \text{ohm}^{-1}\ \text{cm}^2\,\text{mol}^{-1}\\ &= 267.20 - 485.84 \times 10^{-1}\ \text{ohm}^{-1}\ \text{cm}^2\,\text{mol}^{-1}\\ &= 218.62\ \text{ohm}^{-1}\ \text{cm}^2\,\text{mol}^{-1}.\end{aligned}$$

The degree of dissociation (α) is given to a first approximation by the ratio of the observed value of the molar conductance for a particular concentration, to that calculated assuming complete dissociation.

Therefore $$\alpha = \frac{\Lambda}{\Lambda_c} = \frac{188.14}{218.62} = 0.8606$$

This value of α may be used to obtain a more accurate value as follows. Because of the ion association, the actual concentration of free ions will be αc, where c is the concentration (mol dm^{-3}). Thus the ionic strength of the copper sulphate solution is given by

$$\mu = \tfrac{1}{2}[2^2\alpha c + 2^2\alpha c] = 4\alpha c$$

For incomplete dissociation, the Onsager equation takes the form

$$\Lambda = \alpha(267.20 - 485.84\sqrt{4\alpha c})$$

Therefore $$\alpha = \frac{\Lambda}{267.20 - 485.84\sqrt{4\alpha c}}$$

Substitution of the approximate value for α into the right-hand side of this equation enables a more accurate value of α to be calculated:

$$\begin{aligned}\alpha &= \frac{188.14}{267.20 - 485.84\sqrt{4 \times 2.5 \times 10^{-3} \times 0.8606}}\\ &= \frac{188.14}{222.12} = 0.8470\end{aligned}$$

Repeating the calculation with successive values of α until a constant value is obtained, it can be shown that for the next three approximations, the values of α are 0.8459, 0.8457 and 0.8457. Therefore $\alpha = 0.8457$.

The equilibrium under consideration is

$$\underset{\text{(undissociated)}}{CuSO_4} \rightleftharpoons \underset{\text{(free ions)}}{Cu^{2+} + SO_4^{2-}}$$

Hence the dissociation constant, K, is given by

$$K = \frac{a_{Cu^{2+}} \times a_{SO_4^{2-}}}{a_{CuSO_4}} = \frac{[Cu^{2+}][SO_4^{2-}]}{[CuSO_4]} \times \frac{\gamma_{Cu^{2+}} \times \gamma_{SO_4^{2-}}}{\gamma_{CuSO_4}} \quad \text{(i)}$$

where a represents activity, γ represents activity coefficient and the terms in square brackets represent concentrations (mol dm^{-3}) at equilibrium.

At equilibrium, for each mole of copper sulphate originally taken, there will be $(1 - \alpha)$ mole undissociated and α mole each of free Cu^{2+} and SO_4^{2-} ions. Furthermore, in the dilute solution under consideration, the activity coefficient of the undissociated copper sulphate, γ_{CuSO_4}, may be taken as unity.

From the given data

$$[Cu^{2+}] = [SO_4^{2-}] = \alpha \times 2.5 \times 10^{-3}\,\text{mol dm}^{-3},$$

and

$$[CuSO_4] = (1-\alpha) \times 2.5 \times 10^{-3}\,\text{mol dm}^{-3}.$$

Taking the logarithm of equation (i) and substituting for α and the concentration terms:

$$\log K = \log\left[\frac{(0.8457)^2 \times 2.5 \times 10^{-3}}{0.1543}\right] + \log \gamma_{Cu^{2+}} + \log \gamma_{SO_4^{2-}}$$

The logarithms of the activity coefficients of the ions are given by the equation

$$-\log \gamma_{\pm} = \frac{0.509 z^2 \mu^{1/2}}{1+\mu^{1/2}} - 0.20\mu$$

where μ is the ionic strength of the free ions and is given by

$$\mu = 4\alpha c = 0.8457 \times 10^{-2}$$

Therefore

$$\log \gamma_{Cu^{2+}} = \log \gamma_{SO_4^{2-}} = \frac{-0.509 \times 4 \times \sqrt{0.8457 \times 10^{-2}}}{1 + \sqrt{0.8457 \times 10^{-2}}} + 0.20 \times 0.8457 \times 10^{-2}$$

$$= -0.1715 + 0.0017$$

$$= -0.1698$$

Therefore

$$\log K = \log\left[\frac{(0.8457)^2 \times 2.5 \times 10^{-3}}{0.1543}\right] - 2 \times 0.1698$$

$$= -1.9361 - 0.3396 = -2.2757$$

$$= \bar{3}.7243$$

And $K = 5.3 \times 10^{-3}$

The dissociation constant of copper sulphate is $\underline{5.3 \times 10^{-3}}$.

Additional Examples

1 A solution of silver nitrate was contained in a transport cell between two silver electrodes. A current was passed through the cell and 0.048 g of copper was deposited in a coulometer in series with the transport cell.

Calculate (*i*) the change in mass of each of the silver electrodes, (*ii*) the change in mass of the silver in the solution surrounding the anode.

The transport number of the silver ion in this case is 0.47. The relative atomic mass of copper is 63.57 and silver 107.9. (B.Pharm., London)

2 In a moving boundary experiment to determine the cation transport number in 0.02 mol dm^{-3} sodium chloride solution, a current of 0.001600 A caused the boundary to move a distance of 7.00 cm in 2414 s; the cross section of the transport tube was 0.1115 cm^2. Calculate the transport numbers of both ions. (R.S.C.)

3 For aqueous HCl solutions at 25°C:

Conc./mol dm^{-3}	0.0005	0.001	0.005	0.01
Conductance/ohm^{-1} cm^2 mol^{-1}	422.74	421.36	415.80	412.00

Determine the molar conductance at zero concentration, graphically or otherwise. Briefly indicate the theoretical basis of the method you use. (R.S.C.)

4 Describe either the Hittorf or the moving boundary method for determining the transport number of an ion.

Calculate the ionic mobility of the cation (cm s^{-1}) in a 0.1 mol dm^{-3} solution of sodium chloride at 25°C, given that its transport number is 0.385, that the conductance at infinite dilution is 126.45 ohm^{-1} cm^2 mol^{-1} and that the Faraday is 96 500 coulombs. (B.Pharm., London)

5 At 25°C the conductance of a 0.027 mol dm^{-3} solution of a weak monobasic acid is 10 ohm^{-1} cm^2 mol^{-1}. Given that at infinite dilution the conductance of the hydrogen ion is 350 ohm^{-1} cm^2 mol^{-1} and of the anion of the acid is 41 ohm^{-1} cm^2 mol^{-1}, calculate the ionization constant of the acid.

6 The limiting conductances of some ions in water at 25°C have the following values, in $cm^2\,ohm^{-1}\,mol^{-1}$:

$$H^+, 349.81; \quad Na^+, 50.10; \quad Cl^-, 76.35; \quad OH^-, 198.3$$

100 cm^3 of a solution of 0.01 mol dm^{-3} hydrochloric acid is titrated with 0.01 mol dm^{-3} sodium hydroxide solution at this temperature. Calculate the specific conductances and the pH values after the addition of 50, 100 and 150 cm^3 of titrant. (R.S.C.)

7 The specific conductance of a saturated aqueous solution of lead sulphate at 18°C is $1.84 \times 10^{-5}\,ohm^{-1}\,cm^{-1}$ and that of the water used $1.40 \times 10^{-6}\,ohm^{-1}\,cm^{-1}$. The ionic mobilities of Pb^{2+} and SO_4^{2-} ions at 18°C are 122 and 136 $ohm^{-1}\,cm^2\,mol^{-1}$ respectively. Calculate the solubility of lead sulphate at 18°C. (B.Pharm., Wales)

8 The specific conductance of a sample of water was found to be $4.3 \times 10^{-7}\,ohm^{-1}\,cm^{-1}$. When saturated with silver chloride at the same temperature, the specific conductance was found to be $1.550 \times 10^{-6}\,ohm^{-1}\,cm^{-1}$. If, in a field of $1\,V\,cm^{-1}$, the absolute velocities of the silver and chloride ions at infinite dilution are 5.6×10^{-4} and $6.8 \times 10^{-4}\,cm\,s^{-1}$, what is the solubility product of silver chloride at this temperature?

(B.Sc., Bristol)

9 A sample of distilled water had, at 25°C, a pH of 5.75 and a specific conductance of $1.15 \times 10^{-6}\,ohm^{-1}\,cm^{-1}$. Given that at 25°C the equilibrium constant of the reaction

$$CO_2(aq) + H_2O = H^+ + HCO_3^-$$

is $4.31 \times 10^{-7}\,mol\,dm^{-3}$ and that the limiting conductances of H^+ and HCO_3^- are 349.8 and 44.5 $ohm^{-1}\,cm^2\,mol^{-1}$, respectively, calculate:

(i) the percentage of the specific conductance of the water due to dissolved carbon dioxide;
(ii) the concentration of dissolved carbon dioxide.

(B.Sc., London)

10 A 0.1 mol dm^{-3} solution of a monobasic organic acid having a dissociation constant K, of 4.17×10^{-4} is titrated with 0.1 mol dm^{-3} sodium hydroxide. Calculate the pH of the solution (*a*) before the addition of alkali, (*b*) when 50% of the alkali equivalent has been added, and (*c*) at the equivalence. (Ionic product for water = 10^{-14}.) (B.Pharm., Wales)

11 The pH of human blood is regulated chiefly by the carbonic acid and the bicarbonate ion content. Bicarbonate ions are present to the extent of about 0.025 mol dm^{-3}, and carbonic acid to the extent of about 0.00125 mol dm^{-3}. The pK_a value for the first dissociation constant of carbonic acid is 6.1. Calculate the approximate pH of blood.

(G.C.E. 'S' Level (Nuffield), London)

12 At 25°C the conductances at infinite dilution of hydrochloric acid, sodium formate and sodium chloride are 425.5, 104.9 and 126.5

$ohm^{-1} cm^{-2} mol^{-1}$ respectively. The conductance of $0.1 mol dm^{-3}$ formic acid is $18.6 ohm^{-1} cm^{-2} mol^{-1}$ at the same temperature. Using formic acid and sodium formate how would you make up a buffer solution having a pH of 3.8? (B.Pharm., London; Ph.C.)

13 Calculate the pH value of a $0.05 mol dm^{-3}$ solution of sodium benzoate, given that the dissociation constant of benzoic acid is 6.3×10^{-5} and that the ionic product of water is 1×10^{-14}. (B.Pharm., Wales)

14 If the dissociation constant of ammonium hydroxide is $1.8 \times 10^{-5} mol dm^{-3}$, what is the degree of hydrolysis of ammonium sulphate in $0.05 mol dm^{-3}$ solution? (B.Sc., Durham)

15 Phenylamine ethanoate is extensively hydrolysed in aqueous solution. The equation $C_6H_5.NH_3^+ + CH_3CO_2^- \rightleftharpoons C_6H_5NH_2 + CH_3COOH$ leads to the formula $x/(1-x) = (K_w/K_AK_B)^{1/2}$, where x is the fraction of salt converted into phenylamine and ethanoic acid, and K_w ($=1 \times 10^{-14}$), K_A ($=1.75 \times 10^{-5}$) and K_B ($=4.5 \times 10^{-10}$) are, respectively, the ionic product of water, and the conventional dissociation constants of ethanoic acid and phenylamine.

(*a*) Derive the above formula, and point out the approximations involved.

(*b*) Explain the appearance in it of K_w.

(*c*) Calculate the approximate pH of an aqueous solution of phenylamine ethanoate.

(*d*) Describe briefly how you would check this calculated value experimentally, given a supply of phenylamine, ethanoic acid, standard sodium hydroxide and a suitable indicator. (R.S.C.)

16 A solution containing 12.95 g of phenylamine hydrochloride in $100 cm^3$ of $0.01 mol dm^{-3}$ hydrochloric acid is brought into equilibrium with $100 cm^3$ of benzene. If the amount of phenylamine in the benzene is found to be 0.1 g, what is the hydrolysis constant of phenylamine hydrochloride? What is the basic dissociation constant of phenylamine? (The partition coefficient for phenylamine between benzene and water is given by $C_B/C_W = 10$; H = 1, C = 12, N = 14, Cl = 35.5; $K_w = 10^{-14}$.)
(B.Sc., Queen's University, Belfast)

17 The indicator constant of phenolphthalein is approximately 10^{-10}. A solution is prepared by adding $100.01 cm^3$ of $0.1 mol dm^{-3}$ sodium hydroxide to $100.00 cm^3$ of $0.1 mol dm^{-3}$ hydrochloric acid. If a few drops of phenolphthalein are now added, what fraction of the indicator is converted to its coloured form?

18 An aqueous solution contains $0.01 mol dm^{-3}$ iron(III) chloride and $0.06 mol dm^{-3}$ perchloric acid. What is its ionic strength?
(Adapted from ACS Cooperative Examination: Physical Chemistry (Graduate Level).)

19 Studies of the solubility of silver iodate in water and aqueous solutions of potassium nitrate, have been made by Kolthoff and Lingane (*J. Phys. Chem.*, **42** (1938), 133) who quote the following data for 25°C:

KNO_3 concentration mol dm^{-3}/10^{-3}	0.0	1.301	3.252	6.503	14.1
$AgIO_3$ solubility mol dm^{-3}/10^{-3}	1.771	1.823	1.870	1.914	1.994

From these data determine:
(*a*) the constant A in the Debye-Hückel limiting equation,
(*b*) the solubility product of silver iodate,
(*c*) the mean activity coefficient of silver iodate in pure water.

20 The conductance, Λ, of a 1.66×10^{-4} mol dm^{-3} solution of lanthanum hexacyanoferrate(III) at 25°C is 336.3 ohm^{-1} cm^2 mol^{-1}. The limiting Onsager equation for this salt is $\Lambda = \alpha(506.7 - 2750\sqrt{3\alpha c})$ where α is the degree of dissociation and c represents mol dm^{-3}.

The corresponding limiting Debye-Hückel equation is $-\log \gamma_i = 7.94\sqrt{3\alpha c}$ where γ_i represents ion activity coefficients.

Use these data to derive the dissociation constant of lanthanum hexacyanoferrate(III) (B.Sc., Wales)

21 The conductance, Λ, of a solution of magnesium sulphate of concentration 0.810×10^{-4} mol dm^{-3} is 254.6 ohm^{-1} cm^2 mol^{-1} at 25°C.

The limiting Onsager equation for this salt is $\Lambda = 266.2 - 484.2\sqrt{\mu}$, where μ is the ionic strength.

The form of the limiting Debye-Hückel equation is $\log \gamma = -2.88\sqrt{2\alpha c}$, where α is the degree of dissociation and c is the concentration mol dm^{-3}.

From these data, calculate the dissociation constant of magnesium sulphate.

7

Electrochemical Cells

Example 7.1 Change of heat content in cell reaction

The Clark cell consists of a zinc amalgam electrode in a saturated solution of zinc sulphate and a mercury electrode covered with mercury(I) sulphate. Formulate the cell and cell reaction, and calculate the heat of reaction at 25°C, given that at T K the e.m.f. of the cell (E_T) is

$$E_T = 1.4328 - 0.00119(T-288) - 0.000007(T-288)^2 \text{ V}$$

(*B.Sc.* (*Special*), *London*)

The Clark cell is formulated thus:

Zn (10% in Hg)	$ZnSO_4 \cdot 7H_2O(s)$, $Hg_2SO_4(s)$	Hg
−ve pole	saturated solution	+ve pole

When the cell gives current, zinc dissolves from the amalgam and mercury deposits on the mercury electrode according to the equation for the cell reaction:

$$Zn_{(amalgam)} + Hg_2SO_4(s) + 7H_2O = ZnSO_4.7H_2O(s) + 2Hg(l)$$

According to the Gibbs-Helmholtz equation:

$$\Delta G = \Delta H + T\left[\frac{\partial(\Delta G)}{\partial T}\right]_P \qquad \text{(i)}$$

The free energy change (ΔG) is given by $-nFE$, where F is the Faraday, E the e.m.f. of the cell, n the number of Faradays required for the cell reaction and T the absolute temperature. Therefore, equation (i) can be rewritten to give

$$-nFE = \Delta H - TnF\left[\frac{\partial E}{\partial T}\right]_P \qquad \text{(ii)}$$

From the equation for E_T given in the question

$$\left[\frac{\partial E}{\partial T}\right]_P = -0.00119-2\times0.000007T+0.000014\times288 \text{ V K}^{-1}$$

At 25°C (298K)

$$E = 1.4328-0.00119\times10-0.000007\times10^2 \text{ V}$$
$$= 1.4202 \text{ V}$$

And

$$\left[\frac{\partial E}{\partial T}\right]_P = -0.00119-0.000014\times298+0.000014\times288 \text{ V K}^{-1}$$
$$= -0.00133 \text{ V K}^{-1}.$$

Substitution of the data for 25°C in equation (ii), remembering that the reaction requires two Faradays of electricity, gives the following value for the heat of reaction, ΔH:

$$\Delta H = -(2\times96\,500\times1.4202)-(298\times2\times96\,500\times0.00133) \text{ J}$$
$$= -350.6 \text{ kJ}.$$

The heat of the Clark cell reaction at 25°C is $\underline{\Delta H = -351 \text{ kJ}}$.

Example 7.2 Change of heat content, free energy and entropy in cell reaction

What cell would you set up to determine the energy changes for the reaction

$$Cd(s) + Hg_2^{2+}(aq) = Cd^{2+}(aq)+2Hg(l)?$$

If the e.m.f. of the cell is given by

$$E = 0.6708-1.02\times10^{-4}(T-298)-2.4\times10^{-6}(T-298)^2 \text{ V}$$

where T is the temperature in K, what are the values of ΔG, ΔH and ΔS at 45°C? *(B.Sc., Durham)*

The energy changes for the given reaction can be determined by means of the cell:

Cd	$CdSO_4$(s), Hg_2SO_4(s)	Hg
−ve pole	(saturated solution)	+ve pole

Calculation of ΔG

$$\Delta G = -nFE \text{ (see Example 7.1)}$$

Therefore, at 45°C,

$$\begin{aligned}\Delta G &= -2\times 96\,500\times(0.6708-1.02\times10^{-4}\times20-2.4\times10^{-6}\times400)\ \text{J}\\ &= \underline{-128.9\ \text{kJ}.}\end{aligned}$$

Calculation of ΔS

The entropy change of a reaction may be expressed in terms of the temperature coefficient of the e.m.f. of the cell in which the reaction occurs:

$$\Delta S = nF\left(\frac{\partial E}{\partial T}\right)_p$$

But

$$\left(\frac{\partial E}{\partial T}\right)_p = -1.02\times10^{-4}-2\times2.4\times10^{-6}T+2\times298\times2.4\times10^{-6}\ \text{V K}^{-1}$$

At 45°C $$\left(\frac{\partial E}{\partial T}\right)_p = -1.98\times10^{-4}\ \text{V K}^{-1}$$

Therefore $$\begin{aligned}\Delta S &= -2\times96\,500\times1.98\times10^{-4}\ \text{J K}^{-1}\\ &= \underline{-38.22\ \text{J K}^{-1}}\end{aligned}$$

Calculation of ΔH

By the electrical form of the Gibbs-Helmholtz equation

$$\Delta H = -nFE+TnF\left(\frac{\partial E}{\partial T}\right)_p$$

and also $\Delta H = \Delta G+T\Delta S.$

Substitution of the relevant data in either of these equations gives

$$\begin{aligned}\Delta H &= -128\,900-318\times38.22\ \text{J}\\ &= \underline{-141.1\ \text{kJ}}\end{aligned}$$

$\underline{\Delta G = -129\ \text{kJ};\ \Delta H = -141\ \text{kJ};\ \Delta S = -38.2\ \text{J K}^{-1}.}$

Example 7.3 Concentration cells and activities

The electromotive force of a cell consisting of two copper electrodes dipping respectively in 0.5 mol dm^{-3} and 0.005 mol dm^{-3} copper sulphate solutions at 18°C is 0.0391V. Given that the value of 2.303 RT/F at 18°C is 0.058V, calculate the ratio of the activities of the copper ions in the two solutions. Assume there is no potential difference at the liquid junction.

The electromotive force (E) of a concentration cell is given by

$$E = \frac{RT}{nF} \ln \frac{a}{a'}$$

where a/a' represents the ratio of the activities of the ions (in this case copper ions) in the two solutions, n is the valency, and R, T and F have their usual significance.
Substitution of the relevant values gives

$$0.0391 = \frac{0.058}{2} \log \frac{a}{a'}$$

Therefore $$\log \frac{a}{a'} = 1.348 \text{ and } \frac{a}{a'} = 22.28$$

The ratio of the activities of the copper ions in the two solutions is <u>22.3 : 1.</u>

Note a is greater than a' so that the electrode in this (more concentrated) solution forms the positive pole of the cell.

Example 7.4 Concentration cells with transport

The e.m.f. of the following concentration cell is 0.0118V at 25°C:

$$Pb(s)|PbSO_4(s),\ CuSO_4(0.2M)|CuSO_4(0.02M),\ PbSO_4(s)|Pb(s)$$

Given that the activity coefficient of the sulphate ion in 0.2 mol dm^{-3} copper sulphate solution is 0.110 and in 0.02 mol dm^{-3} solution is 0.320, calculate the transport number of the copper(II) ion.

The cell shown is a concentration cell 'with transport' in which the electrodes are reversible with respect to the anion. The e.m.f. (E) of such a cell, for a bi-bivalent electrolyte, is given by

$$E = 2n_c \times 2.303 \frac{RT}{2F} \log \frac{a}{a'}$$

where n_c is the transport number of the cation, a and a' are the activities of the anion, R, T and F having their usual significance.
Therefore

$$n_c = \frac{E}{2\times 2.303\dfrac{RT}{2F}\log\dfrac{a}{a'}}$$

$$= \frac{0.0118}{2\times 2.303\times\dfrac{8.31\times 298}{2\times 96\,500}\log\dfrac{0.2\times 0.110}{0.02\times 0.320}}$$

$$= 0.372.$$

The transport number of the copper (II) ion is 0.372.

Note The electrode on the right is positive, and when the circuit is closed positive electricity passes through the cell from left to right. When the cell is written in this way, the e.m.f. is positive.

Example 7.5 Standard electrode potentials

When metallic copper is shaken with a solution of a copper salt, the reaction $Cu(s) + Cu^{2+} \rightleftharpoons 2Cu^{+}$ *proceeds. When equilibrium is established at 20°C,* $[Cu^{2+}]/[Cu^{+}]^2 = 2.02\times 10^4$. *If the standard potential of the* Cu/Cu^{2+} *electrode on the hydrogen scale is 0.33 V, what is the standard potential of the* Cu/Cu^{+} *electrode?* (*B.Sc., Liverpool*)

According to the van't Hoff isotherm

$$\Delta G^{\ominus} = -RT\ln K \qquad \text{(i)}$$

Replacing $\Delta G^{\ominus}$ by $-nFE^{\ominus}$, where $E^{\ominus}$ is the standard cell e.m.f., we have

$$nFE^{\ominus} = RT\ln K \qquad \text{(ii)}$$

The standard potential, $E^{\ominus}_{Cu^{2+}}$ of the Cu/Cu^{2+} electrode corresponds to the reduction potential of the reaction:

(*a*) $Cu^{2+} + 2e = Cu(s)$; $E_{Cu^{2+}} = 0.33V$.

The standard potential of the Cu/Cu^{+} electrode, which is required, corresponds to the reduction potential of the reaction:

(*b*) $Cu^{+} + e = Cu(s)$; $E^{\ominus}_{Cu^{+}} = ?$ V.

Multiply equation (*b*) by 2 and subtract equation (*a*) from the result:

(*c*) 2 $Cu^+ = Cu(s) + Cu^{2+}$. For this reaction which involves 2 Faradays

$$E^\ominus = \frac{8.31 \times 293 \times 2.303}{2 \times 96\,500} \log 2.02 \times 10^4 \text{ V}$$
$$= 0.1251 \text{ V.}$$

If equation (*c*) is added to (*a*) and the result divided by 2, we get equation (*b*) and hence

$$E^\ominus_{Cu^+} = E^\ominus_{Cu^{2+}} + E^\ominus$$
$$= 0.33 + 0.1251 = 0.455 \text{ V.}$$

The standard (reduction) potential of the Cu/Cu$^+$ electrode is 0.46 V.

Example 7.6 Determination of solubility by the e.m.f. method

The standard e.m.f. of the cell

$$\overset{+}{Pt} \;|\; H_2(g) \;|\; HNO_3(aq), Pb(NO_3)_2(aq) \;|\; \overset{-}{Pb}(s)$$

is $E^\ominus = -0.126$ *V, while that of the cell*

$$\overset{+}{Pt} \;|\; H_2(g) \;|\; H_2SO_4(aq) \;|\; PbSO_4(s) \;|\; \overset{-}{Pb}(s)$$

is $E^\ominus = -0.351 V$, *the temperature being 25°C and all the concentrations in solution measured in mol* dm^{-3}. *Calculate the solubility product of lead sulphate.* (*B.Sc., Bristol*)

The standard e.m.f. of the first cell is the standard reduction potential ($E_1^\ominus$) of the Pb/Pb^{2+} electrode, and that of the second cell is the standard reduction potential ($E_2^\ominus$) of the Pb/PbSO$_4$(*s*), SO_4^{2-} electrode. The reduction potential (*E*) of the Pb/PbSO$_4$(*s*), SO_4^{2-} electrode is given by

$$E = E_2^\ominus + \frac{RT}{2F} \ln \frac{1}{a_{SO_4^{2-}}} \qquad \text{(i)}$$

where *a* represents activity.

The solubility product (K_s) of lead sulphate is given by

$K_s = a_{Pb^{2+}} a_{SO_4^{2-}}$ so that $1/a_{SO_4^{2-}}$ in equation (i) may be replaced by $a_{Pb^{2+}}/K_s$ to give

$$E = E_2^{\ominus} + \frac{RT}{2F} \ln \frac{a_{Pb^{2+}}}{K_s}$$

$$= \left[E_2^{\ominus} - \frac{RT}{2F} \ln K_s\right] + \frac{RT}{2F} \ln a_{Pb^{2+}} \qquad \text{(ii)}$$

The $Pb/PbSO_4(s)$, SO_4^{2-} electrode may also be regarded as a Pb/Pb^{2+} electrode in which the activity of Pb^{2+} is governed by the SO_4^{2-} concentration and the solubility product of lead sulphate. The quantity enclosed by the brackets in equation (ii) is constant at constant temperature and equals the standard reduction potential ($E_1^{\ominus}$) of the Pb/Pb^{2+} electrode.

Therefore $E_1^0 = E_2^0 - \dfrac{RT}{2F} \ln K_s$

$$-0.126 = -0.351 - \frac{2.303 \times 8.31 \times 298}{2 \times 96\,500} \log K_s$$

And $$\log K_s = -\frac{0.225 \times 2 \times 96\,500}{2.303 \times 8.31 \times 298} = \bar{8}.386$$

Hence $$K_s = 2.432 \times 10^{-8}$$

The solubility product of lead sulphate at 25°C is $\underline{2.43 \times 10^{-8}}$.

Example 7.7 Application of e.m.f. measurements to the determination of activity coefficients

The galvanic cell

$$\overset{-}{H_2(1\ atm), Pt} \quad | \quad HCl(m) \quad | \quad Hg_2Cl_2 \quad | \quad \overset{+}{Hg}$$

has, at 25°C, the following values of e.m.f. for the given molalities, m, of hydrochloric acid:

m/mol kg^{-1}	*0.07508*	*0.03769*	*0.01887*	*0.00504*
E/V	*0.4119*	*0.4452*	*0.4787*	*0.5437*

By a simple graphical method determine the standard e.m.f. of this cell and calculate the activity coefficient of hydrochloric acid in the most concentrated of the four solutions mentioned. (2.3026RT/F = 0.05916V at 25°C.) (R.S.C.)

The e.m.f. of the cell is given by

$$E_{\text{cell}} = E^{\ominus}_{\text{Hg-Hg}_2\text{Cl}_2} - \frac{RT}{F} \ln a_{\text{H}^+}a_{\text{Cl}^-}$$

where a_{H^+} and a_{Cl^-} are the activities of the ions contained in the cell, R, T and F having their usual significance, and $E^{\ominus}_{\text{Hg-Hg}_2\text{Cl}_2}$ is the standard e.m.f. of the cell when the ionic activities in the solution are unity.

a_{H^+} may be set equal to $m_+\gamma_+$ and a_{Cl^-} to $m_-\gamma_-$, where m_+ and m_- are molalities of the hydrogen ion and chloride ion respectively and γ_+ and γ_- are the respective activity coefficients.
Therefore

$$E_{\text{cell}} = E^{\ominus}_{\text{Hg-Hg}_2\text{Cl}_2} - \frac{RT}{F} \ln m_+m_- - \frac{RT}{F} \ln \gamma_+\gamma_-$$

$$= E^{\ominus}_{\text{Hg-Hg}_2\text{Cl}_2} - \frac{2RT}{F} \ln m_\pm - \frac{2RT}{F} \ln \gamma_\pm \qquad \text{(i)}$$

$\gamma_\pm$ is the mean ionic activity coefficient of the hydrochloric acid solution of mean molality $m_\pm$ (equal to m).
Rearranging equation (i)

$$E_{\text{cell}} + \frac{2RT}{F} \ln m = E^{\ominus}_{\text{Hg-Hg}_2\text{Cl}_2} - \frac{2RT}{F} \ln \gamma_\pm \qquad \text{(ii)}$$

The quantities on the left-hand side of equation (ii) are available from the data in the question. Hence if $E^{\ominus}_{\text{Hg-Hg}_2\text{Cl}_2}$ is known $\gamma_\pm$ may be calculated.

The experimental quantity on the left-hand side of equation (ii) is plotted against a function of the molality ($\sqrt{m}$) as abscissa and the plot extrapolated to $\sqrt{m} = 0$. Since at $m = 0$, $\gamma_\pm = 1$, the last term on the right-hand side of equation (ii) is zero and the value of the extrapolated ordinate gives $E^{\ominus}_{\text{Hg-Hg}_2\text{Cl}_2}$.

Fig. 16 shows a plot of the $\left(E_{\text{cell}} + \frac{2RT}{F} \ln m\right)$ versus $\sqrt{m}$ values shown in the table:

$\left(E_{\text{cell}} + \frac{2RT}{F} \ln m\right)$	0.2790	0.2767	0.2747	0.2719
$\sqrt{m}$	0.2747	0.1941	0.1374	0.07099

Extrapolation to $\sqrt{m} = 0$ gives $E^{\ominus}_{\text{Hg-Hg}_2\text{Cl}_2} = 0.2685$ V

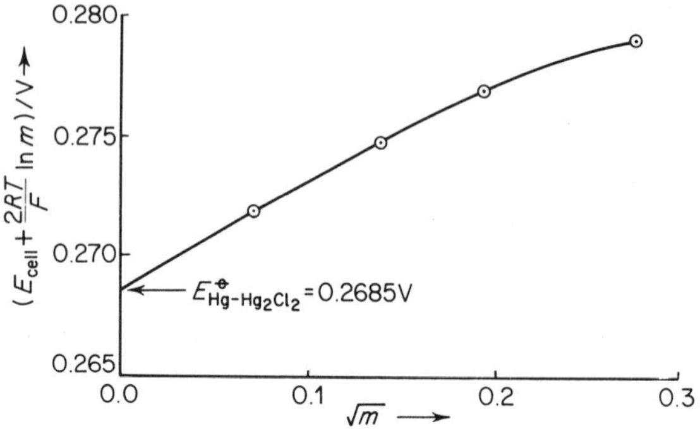

Fig. 16 Plot of $\left(E_{cell} + \dfrac{2RT}{F} \ln m\right)$ versus $\sqrt{m}$,

To determine the mean ionic activity coefficient of the hydrochloric acid for the 0.07508*m* solution, substitution of the relevant data in equation (ii) gives

$$0.2790 = 0.2685 - \frac{2RT}{F} \ln \gamma_{\pm}$$

Therefore
$$\log \gamma_{\pm} = -\frac{0.0105}{0.05916 \times 2}$$

$$= -0.08876 = \bar{1}.9112$$

And
$$\gamma_{\pm} = 0.8151.$$

The mean ionic activity coefficient of hydrochloric acid in the solution of molality 0.07508 is 0.815.

Example 7.8 Standard electrode potentials from equilibrium constants

If at 25°C the standard electrode potential of the Ag, Ag^+ electrode is +0.799V, and the equilibrium constant for the reaction $Fe^{3+} + Ag \rightleftharpoons Fe^{2+} + Ag^+$ is 0.531 mol dm^{-3}, calculate the standard iron(II)–iron(III) electrode potential.

At 25°C the equation giving the relationship between the standard e.m.f. of a cell and the equilibrium constant of the cell reaction may be written in the form

$$E^{\ominus}_{\text{cell}} = \frac{RT}{nF} \ln K$$

$E^{\ominus}_{\text{cell}}$ can also be derived from standard redox potentials as follows: The reaction given in the question can take place in the cell.

$$\underset{+\text{ve pole}}{\text{Ag}} \left| \; \text{Ag}^+(\text{aq}) \; \right\| \; \text{Fe}^{3+}(\text{aq}),\ \text{Fe}^{2+}(\text{aq}) \; \left| \; \underset{-\text{ve pole}}{\text{Pt}} \right.$$

If $E^{\ominus}_{\text{Ag}}$ is the standard (reduction) electrode potential of the Ag, Ag^+ electrode and $E^{\ominus}_{\text{Fe}^{2+}/\text{Fe}^{3+}}$ is the standard (reduction) potential of the Pt-Fe^{2+}, Fe^{3+} electrode then the standard potential, $E^{\ominus}_{\text{cell}}$, of the cell is given by

$$E^{\ominus}_{\text{cell}} = E^{\ominus}_{\text{Fe}^{2+}/\text{Fe}^{3+}} - E^{\ominus}_{\text{Ag}}$$

(the expression being written in this way since both the cell and the cell reaction are written in the non-spontaneous manner).
But from the data given in the question

$$E^{\ominus}_{\text{cell}} = \frac{8.31 \times 298}{96\,500} \ln 0.531 \text{ V}$$

$$= -\frac{8.31 \times 298 \times 2.303 \times 0.2749}{96\,500} \text{ V}$$

$$= -0.0162 \text{ V}$$

Therefore

$$E^{\ominus}_{\text{Fe}^{2+}/\text{Fe}^{3+}} = 0.799 - 0.0162\text{V}$$
$$= 0.7828\text{V}$$

The standard iron(II)–iron(III) electrode potential (exposed as a reduction potential) is +0.783V.

Example 7.9 Reversible electrodes involving oxidized and reduced states

The reduction potential, referred to the hydrogen standard, of a cerium(III)-cerium(IV) electrode containing cerium(III) ions at a concentration of 0.015 mol dm^{-3} is +1.50V at 25°C. Calculate the concentration of cerium (IV) ions in solution, given that the standard reduction potential of the electrode is +1.57 V.

The general expression for the potential (E) of an electrode reversible with respect to oxidized and reduced states is

$$E = E^{\ominus} + \frac{RT}{nF} \ln \frac{[\text{Oxidized State}]}{[\text{Reduced State}]}$$

where the brackets indicate the activities of the substances concerned, $E^{\ominus}$ is the standard potential for the electrode when the substances concerned are in their standard states of unit activity; the remaining symbols have their usual significance. In this case, $E^{\ominus}$ is the standard potential of the process

$$Ce^{4+} + e \rightarrow Ce^{3+}$$

and the [Oxidized State] is taken as $[Ce^{4+}]$ and the [Reduced State] as $[Ce^{3+}]$. Assuming the activity coefficients to be unity, the terms in brackets indicate concentrations.
Therefore

$$E = E^{\ominus} + \frac{RT}{F} \ln \frac{[Ce^{4+}]}{[Ce^{3+}]}$$

From the data given

$$1.50 = 1.57 + \frac{2.303 \times 8.31 \times 298}{96\,500} \log \frac{[Ce^{4+}]}{0.015}$$

And $\log [Ce^{4+}] = -3.0079$
$= \bar{4}.9921$
Therefore $[Ce^{4+}] = 9.819 \times 10^{-4}$ mol dm^{-3}

The concentration of cerium(IV) ions in solution is 9.8×10^{-4} mol dm^{-3}.

Example 7.10 Diffusion controlled electrolysis

In the electrolysis of an unstirred 0.02 mol dm^{-3} dicyanoargentate(I) solution at 15°C, 100% current efficiency for deposition of silver was obtained at current densities up to 5.00×10^{-4} A cm^{-2}. Given that the conductance of the dicyanoargentate(I) ion is 49.5 ohm^{-1} cm^{2} mol^{-1} at 15°C, calculate the thickness of the diffusion layer.

Ions migrate from a region of higher chemical potential to one of lower chemical potential. The diffusive force will be the decrease in chemical potential, μ, per unit distance. Hence, in a given direction x, the driving force on a mole of a given species, i, of ions will be

$$-\left(\frac{\partial \mu_i}{\partial x}\right)_T \text{ at the absolute temperature } T.$$

The mean ionic velocity under the action of unit diffusive force will be equal to the ionic mobility, u_i, (the ionic velocity in an electric field of unit strength), divided by the charge, nF coulombs, on one mole of ions.

$$\text{Units of } \frac{\mathrm{u}_i}{nF} = \frac{\text{distance} \times \text{time}^{-1}}{\text{potential} \times \text{distance}^{-1}} \cdot \frac{1}{\text{charge}} = \frac{\text{distance}^2 \times \text{time}^{-1}}{\text{energy}}$$

$$= \frac{\text{distance} \times \text{time}^{-1}}{\text{force}}$$

The actual ionic velocity for the given force $-\left(\frac{\partial \mu_i}{\partial x}\right)_T$ is given, therefore, by

$$-\frac{\mathrm{u}_i}{nF}\left(\frac{\partial \mu_i}{\partial x}\right)_T.$$

Hence the net flow, S_i, of ions in moles per unit area per unit time $= -\frac{\mathrm{u}_i}{nF}\left(\frac{\partial \mu_i}{\partial x}\right)_T c_i$ where c_i is the number of moles per unit volume.

For a dilute solution it may be written that

$$\mu_i = \mu^{\ominus} + RT \ln c_i$$

from which $$\left(\frac{\partial \mu_i}{\partial x}\right)_T = \frac{RT}{c_i}\left(\frac{\partial c_i}{\partial x}\right)_T$$

Hence $$S_i = -\frac{\mathrm{u}_i RT}{nF}\left(\frac{\partial c_i}{\partial x}\right)_T \quad \text{(i)}$$

Fick's first law of diffusion states that the net flow, S_i, is proportional to the concentration gradient, that is,

$$S_i = -D\left(\frac{\partial c_i}{\partial x}\right)_T \quad \text{(ii)}$$

in which D is the diffusion coefficient.

Comparison of (i) and (ii) gives

$$D = u_i \frac{RT}{nF}$$

But the molar ionic conductivity $\lambda = nFu_i$ and hence

$$D = \frac{RT\lambda}{n^2F^2}$$

Thus, the diffusion coefficient of an ionic species in units of $cm^2\ s^{-1}$ may be expressed in terms of the conductance in units of $ohm^{-1}\ cm^2\ mol^{-1}$.

When diffusion of ions is the rate-controlling process in ionic discharge, the activity, a', of the ions at the electrode surface differs from that, a, in the bulk of the solution, that is, there is a concentration gradient extending from the electrode surface through a thickness, δ, of solution, called the diffusion layer.

By Fick's first law, the rate of diffusion, S, of ions across the diffusion layer to the electrode surface of area θ is given by

$$S = \frac{\theta D}{\delta}(a - a')$$

where D is the diffusion coefficient of the ionic species being discharged.

If I is the current density, in amperes per unit area of electrode surface, the rate of discharge of the ions at the electrode will be given by $\theta I/nF$, where n is the number of electrons involved in the discharge process and F is the Faraday. In addition to the diffusion already considered some of these ions will be brought to the electrode surface by the normal process of ionic transport at a rate equal to $\theta I t_i/nF$, where t_i is the transport number of the ionic species being discharged.

When a steady-state is attained, the rate of discharge will be equal to the sum of the rates of diffusion and transport. Hence

$$\frac{\theta I}{nF} = \frac{\theta D}{\delta}(a - a') + \frac{\theta I t_i}{nF}.$$

With t written for $(l - t_i)$, the sum of the transport numbers of all other ionic species in the diffusion layer, other than the species being discharged, I is given by

$$I = \frac{DnF}{t\delta}(a - a')$$

from which, on writing k for $\dfrac{DnF}{t\delta}$,

$$a' = a - \frac{I}{k}$$

If the electrode processes, excepting diffusion, are rapid, the electrode will exhibit a potential, E', which will be virtually that for the reversible condition with an ionic activity equal to a'. E' will differ *in magnitude* from the reversible potential, E, for an ionic activity equal to a, that is, when no current is flowing, by an amount, ΔE, given by

$$\Delta E = E' - E = \frac{RT}{nF} \ln \frac{a}{a'}$$

which gives, on substitution of $\left(a - \dfrac{I}{k}\right)$ for a',

$$\Delta E = \frac{RT}{nF} \ln \frac{ka}{ka - I}.$$

ΔE is called the concentration polarization.

This last equation shows that when I is small by comparison with ka, ΔE is small and approximately proportional to I.

As I becomes closer in magnitude to ka, ΔE will increase very rapidly, the current density at which this rapid increase is observed being called *the limiting current density*, I_d. This current density represents the maximum rate at which the particular ionic species can be discharged in these given conditions.

Hence, the magnitude of the limiting current density, I_d, is given by

$$I_d = ka = \frac{DnFa}{t\delta}.$$

I_d can be determined experimentally by gradually increasing the current density until the electrode potential is observed to increase rapidly. The thickness, δ, of the diffusion layer may be determined using the equation for I_d. For this determination an excess of an indifferent electrolyte is used so that t is virtually unity.

The diffusion coefficient for the dicyanoargentate(I) ion may be calculated from the equation

$$D = \frac{RT\lambda}{n^2F^2}$$

For the dicyanoargentate (*I*) ion $n = 1$ and $\lambda = 49.5$ ohm^{-1} cm^2 mol^{-1} and from the above equation

$$D = \frac{8.31 \times 288 \times 49.5}{96\,500^2} \text{ cm}^2 \text{ s}^{-1}$$

$$= 1.273 \times 10^{-5} \text{ cm}^2 \text{ s}^{-1}$$

The value of the maximum current density for 100% current efficiency is effectively the limiting diffusion current density given by

$$I_d = \frac{DnFa}{\delta}$$

Using the value of the diffusion coefficient determined above and approximating activity to concentration in mol cm^{-3}, the thickness of the diffusion layer is given by

$$\delta = \frac{DnFa}{I_d} = \frac{1.273 \times 10^{-5} \times 96\,500 \times 0.02 \times 10^{-3}}{5.00 \times 10^{-4}} \text{ cm}$$

$$= 4.91 \times 10^{-2} \text{ cm}$$

The thickness of the diffusion layer is 4.9×10^{-2} cm.

Example 7.11 Polarography

The following data were obtained in the reduction at 18°C of M^+ at the dropping mercury electrode. (Applied voltages have been corrected for the iR drop and the currents have been corrected for residual current.)

Current/μA	5	15	25	35	45	50	50
Applied voltage/V	0.465	0.499	0.520	0.541	0.575	0.700	1.000

Calculate the molar free energy change for the process

$$M^+ + e + Hg \rightarrow M(Hg).$$

At 18°C $(RT/F)\ln x = 0.058 \log x$. $F = 96\,500$ coulombs. Potential of reference electrode $= +0.247$ V. (*B.Pharm., London*)

The equation of the polarographic wave at 18°C is

$$E = E_{0.5} + \frac{0.058}{n} \log \frac{(I_d - I)}{I}$$

where E is the applied voltage, I is the current at any point on the polarographic wave (minus the residual current), I_d is the diffusion current, $E_{0.5}$ is the half-wave potential and n is the number of electrons involved in the reaction.

It follows from this equation that when log $(I_d - I)/I$ is plotted against the corresponding potential (E) a straight line should be obtained of slope $0.058/n$, the intercept on the applied voltage axis giving the half-wave potential ($E_{0.5}$) of the system. Fig. 17 shows such a plot of the following applied voltage and log $(I_d - I)/I$ values. ($I_d = 50\mu A$)

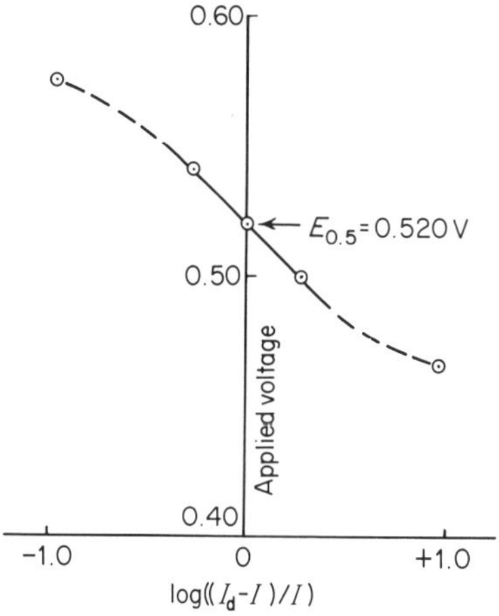

Fig. 17 Plot of log $\dfrac{(I_d - I)}{I}$ versus applied voltage

Applied voltage $(E)/V$	0.465	0.499	0.520	0.541	0.575
$\log \dfrac{(I_d - I)}{I}$	0.9542	0.3680	0.000	−0.3679	−0.9543

Inspection of the curve shows that the half-wave potential ($E_{0.5}$) is at +0.520V, that is, the half-wave potential is −0.520V versus the reference electrode, or (−0.520 + 0.247) = −0.273V versus the standard hydrogen electrode.

Thus, for the process

$$M^+ + e + Hg \rightarrow M(Hg);\ E^\ominus = -0.273V.$$

But the standard molar free energy change ($\Delta G^\ominus$) for the process is given by

$$\Delta G^\ominus = -nFE^\ominus$$
$$= +96\,500 \times 0.273 \text{ joules}$$
$$= 26.34 \text{ kJ}$$

The molar free energy change for the reduction is 26.3 kJ.

Additional Examples

1 Given that the electromotive force of the Clark cell is 1.429V at 18°C, and that the heat evolution in the reaction corresponding with one Faraday is 170.8 kJ, calculate the change of electromotive force per degree rise of temperature. (B Sc., Wales)

2 Discuss the significance of the terms in the equation $G = H - TS$ which may be used to define the Gibbs free energy function G. Derive an expression for the dependence of G upon temperature at constant pressure.

For the reaction

$$Ag + \tfrac{1}{2}Hg_2Cl_2(\text{solid}) = AgCl(\text{solid}) + Hg$$

ΔH is 5380 J; for a cell in which this reaction occurs the e.m.f. is 0.0455V (at 25°C). Find the free energy change and the temperature coefficient of the cell e.m.f. (B.Sc. (Special), London)

3 A solid state electrochemical cell in which the cell reaction is

$$Fe(s) + Mn_3O_4(s) = 3MnO(s) + FeO(s)$$

has an e.m.f. between 973 and 1400 K of

$$E = 0.197 + 2.51 \times 10^{-4} T \text{ V}.$$

Calculate $\Delta G^\ominus$, $\Delta H^\ominus$ and $\Delta S^\ominus$ for this reaction at 1000 K.

Given that the standard free energy of formation of Fe(s) in the same temperature range is

$$\Delta G^\ominus = -265\,000 + 65T \text{ J mol}^{-1},$$

derive an expression for the pressure of oxygen as a function of temperature in equilibrium with a mixture of Mn_3O_4(s) and MnO(s).

Estimate the approximate temperature at which Mn_3O_4 will completely dissociate into MnO and O_2 when the pressure of O_2 is maintained at 10^{-5} atm. (B.Sc., Bristol)

4 Assuming there is no liquid junction potential, calculate the electromotive force of a cell consisting of two silver plates dipping in a 0.1 mol dm^{-3} solution and a 0.01 mol dm^{-3} solution of silver nitrate respectively at 25°C. (B.Pharm., Wales)

5 A concentration cell consisting of two electrodes of a metal X, one dipping into a $0.5\,mol\,dm^{-3}$ solution of one of its salts and the other into a $0.05\,mol\,dm^{-3}$ solution of the same salt, has an e.m.f. of 0.028V at 18°C. Assuming there is no liquid junction potential, calculate the valency of X.

(B.Pharm., Wales)

6 A cell consisting of saturated aqueous zinc sulphate solution connecting two zinc amalgam electrodes of different concentrations was found to have an electromotive force of 0.01815V at 17.3°C. Calculate the ratio of the activities of the zinc in the two amalgams. (B.Sc., Wales)

7 The e.m.f. of the following concentration cell is 0.0284 volt at 25°C:

$$Cu \mid 0.001\,mol\,dm^{-3}\,CuSO_4 \parallel 0.01\,mol\,dm^{-3}\,CuSO_4 \mid Cu$$

The activity of the Cu^{2+} ion in the $0.01\,mol\,dm^{-3}$ solution is 0.00404 and in the $0.001\,mol\,dm^{-3}$ solution 0.00069. Calculate the transport number of the Cu^{2+} ion.

8 The standard potentials at 25°C for the electrodes Hg/Hg_2^{2+} and Hg/Hg^{2+} are 0.799 and 0.855V respectively. Calculate the equilibrium constant for the reaction

$$Hg + Hg^{2+} \rightleftharpoons Hg_2^{2+}$$

(B.Sc., Birmingham)

9 Use the data given below to determine the stability constant of the complex ion $[Cd(NH_3)_4]^{2+}$ at 25°C

$E^{\ominus}_{Cd^{2+}/Cd} = -0.400V$; $[Cd(NH_3)_4]^{2+} + 2e^- = Cd + 4NH_3$; $E^{\ominus} = -0.610V$

10 Given the following standard electrode potentials

$M^{2+} + 2e^- = M$ $\qquad E^{\ominus} = +0.50V$
$M^{3+} + e^- = M^{2+}$ $\qquad E^{\ominus} = -0.10V$

calculate $E^{\ominus}$ for the half reaction

$M^{3+} + 3e^- = M$

(Adapted from ACS Cooperative Examination: Physical Chemistry (Graduate Level).)

11 Given the following

$Tl^{+} + e^- = Tl$ $\qquad E^{\ominus} = -0.34V$
$Tl^{3+} + 3e^- = Tl$ $\qquad E^{\ominus} = +0.72V$

calculate the standard electrode potential, $E^{\ominus}$, for

$Tl^{3+} + 2e^- = Tl^{+}$

(Adapted from ACS Cooperative Examination: Physical Chemistry (Graduate Level).)

12 Explain what is meant by standard electrode potentials, $E^{\ominus}$, and derive a general expression relating electrode potential with concentration.
The following are $E^{\ominus}/V$ values for the electrode systems shown:

(*a*) $Ag(s)/Ag^{+}$ +0.799; (*b*) Normal calomel +0.280;

(*c*) $Pt/Sn^{4+}/Sn^{2+}$ +0.150; (*d*) $\frac{Pt}{H_2}/H^{+}$ 0.000.

Describe the cell reactions for the combinations (*a*) and (*c*), (*b*) and (*d*), (*c*) and (*d*), and calculate the change of free energy in each case.

(B.Sc. (Applied Science—Metallurgy and Chemical Engineering), Durham)

13 What is meant by the solubility product of a sparingly soluble salt? The following cell was set up

$$\text{Saturated calomel electrode} \,||\, AgNO_3 \,|\, Ag$$

Sufficient potassium chloride was added to the right-hand electrode to convert all the silver nitrate to silver chloride; the e.m.f. of the cell was found to be 0.2689V at 25°C. What is the solubility of silver chloride at this temperature? (Potential of the saturated calomel electrode = 0.2415V at 25°C; standard potential of Ag/Ag^{+} electrode = 0.7978V).

(B.Pharm., London)

14 A series of e.m.f. (E) measurements for the cell

$$H_2(1\text{ atm})\ Pt \mid HCl\ aq\ (m) \mid AgCl \mid Ag$$

at 25°C gave the following results:

Molalities (m)/mol kg^{-1}	0.003215	0.005619	0.05391	0.1238
E/V	0.52053	0.49257	0.38222	0.34199

Use the first two results to obtain the standard electrode potential of the silver chloride electrode, and hence find the experimental mean activity coefficient of hydrochloric acid in the last two solutions.

$$\left(2.3026\,\frac{RT}{F} = 0.05916\text{V at }25°\text{C}\right)$$

15 At 25°C, the standard e.m.f. for the cell

$$Zn(Hg) \mid ZnSO_4,\ PbSO_4(s) \mid Pb(Hg)$$

has the value 0.4085V. When the cell contains 0.0005 mol dm^{-3} zinc sulphate its e.m.f. is 0.6114V. Calculate the mean activity coefficient of zinc sulphate at 0.0005 mol dm^{-3}. Compare this with the value given by the Debye-Hückel equation

$$\log \gamma = -0.509\, z_1 z_2 \sqrt{\mu}.$$

$$\left(2.3026\,\frac{RT}{F} = 0.05916\text{V at }25°\text{C}\right)$$

(R.S.C.)

16 If the standard electrode potentials of Zn^{2+}/Zn and Cu^{2+}/Cu at 25°C are −0.761V and +0.340V, calculate the equilibrium ratio of the activities of zinc and copper(II) ions in solution when metallic zinc is shaken with dilute copper sulphate solution. Explain the principles of your calculation.

$$\left(2.303\,\frac{RT}{F} = 0.0592\text{V at } 25°\text{C}\right)$$

(R.S.C.)

17 The limiting silver ion diffusion current of an aqueous solution of 0.001 mol dm^{-3} in silver nitrate and 1 mol dm^{-3} in potassium nitrate at 25°C, at a silver cathode of area 0.03 cm^2 is 44.6 μA. Given that the thickness of the Nernst diffusion layer is 0.001 cm, calculate the diffusion coefficient of the silver ion in the solution and describe *briefly* one other method by which it could have been obtained. (B.Sc. (Special), London)

18 In an electrolysis at 15°C of 0.02 mol dm^{-3} dicyanoargentate(I) solution, agitated by a stirrer rotating at 500 times per minute, 100% curent efficiency was obtained for silver deposition at a current density of 20×10^{-4} A cm^{-2}. Taking the diffusion coefficient of the dicyanoargentate(I) ion as 1.3×10^{-5} cm^2 s^{-1} at 15°C, calculate the thickness of the diffusion layer.

19. Show that $\dfrac{\lambda RT}{n^2F^2}$ can be expressed in the same units as the diffusion coefficient, that is, as cm^2 s^{-1}, where λ is the molar conductance of the ionic species, the other symbols having their usual significance.

The conductance of the iron (II) ion in 1.4 mol dm^{-3} hydrochloric acid solution is 82.4 ohm^{-1} cm^2 mol^{-1} at 25°C. For iron (II) chloride at concentrations of 2.5×10^{-4} and 6.3×10^{-5} mol cm^{-3} in solution in 1.4 mol dm^{-3} hydrochloric acid the limiting currents are 0.552 A and 0.124 A respectively when the electrode area is 100 cm^2. Calculate the thickness of the diffusion layer at each concentration and comment on the magnitude of the percentage change in this thickness by comparison with that of the percentage change in concentration.

20 Why does the diffusion current of a particular polarographic step vary with the applied voltage?

A solution contains equimolecular concentrations of two reducible ions, M^+ and N^+, whose half wave potentials differ sufficiently for the formation of two clearly defined polarographic waves. The relevant experimental details are given in the following table, at the lower voltage only M^+ ions are being reduced.

Applied voltage/V	*Residual current/μA*	*Total cell current/μA*	*Drop time/s*
0.4	0.2	5.4	4.0
1.0	0.4	10.8	3.5

Calculate the ratio of the diffusion coefficients of M^+ and N^+, assuming the Ilkŏvic equation to be exactly obeyed. (B.Pharm., London)

21 Show how diffusion coefficients as well as the number of electrons involved in a reduction process may be derived from polarographic data.

Calculate the number of electrons concerned in the reduction process which gives rise to the following wave. (Applied voltages have been corrected for the *iR* drop.)

Current/μA	10	30	50	70	90	100	100
Applied volts/V	0.972	0.989	1.000	1.011	1.028	1.200	1.500

(B.Pharm., London)

8

Phase Equilibria

Example 8.1 Change of state—vaporization

The vapour pressure of a pure liquid of relative molecular mass 46 is 350.2 mmHg at 60°C, and 541.4 mmHg at 70°C. The latent heat of vaporization between 60°C and the boiling point is 865 J g^{-1}. Calculate

(a) the boiling point of the liquid,
(b) the entropy of vaporization,
(c) an approximate value for the critical temperature, and
(d) the molal elevation of the boiling point (ebullioscopic constant) of the liquid. (*R.S.C.*)

(a) The boiling point of the liquid

The boiling point at 760 mmHg pressure, can be calculated by application of the Clausius-Clapeyron equation:

$$\log p = C - \frac{\Delta H_v}{2.303\ RT}$$

where p is the vapour pressure at the temperature T, ΔH_v is the molar latent heat of vaporization and R is the gas constant. The constant, C, can be determined by substitution of the data for either 60°C or 70°C.

Thus, at 70°C, $$\log 541.4 = C - \frac{46 \times 865}{2.303 \times 8.31 \times 343}$$

And $$C = 8.795$$

At 760 mmHg pressure, where T is the boiling point, and substituting the value of 8.795 for C

$$\log 760 = 8.795 - \frac{46 \times 865}{2.303 \times 8.31 \times T}.$$

Hence $$T = 351.6\ \text{K}$$

(b) The entropy of vaporization

The vaporization takes place reversibly at constant temperature, 351.6 K, and pressure, 760 mmHg, and is accompanied by the absorption of 46 × 865 J mol^{-1} of heat. Therefore,

$$\Delta S = \frac{46 \times 865}{351.6} \text{ J K}^{-1}\text{ mol}^{-1}$$

$$= 113.2 \text{ J K}^{-1}\text{ mol}^{-1}$$

Note This ratio is also known as the Trouton coefficient, which for normal nonassociated liquids has the approximate value of 88. For certain liquids, such as water, alcohols, etc., the value of the coefficient is greater than 88.

(c) An approximate value for the critical temperature

It has been found empirically that, for different liquids at atmospheric pressure, the boiling point in K (T_b) is about two thirds of the critical temperature (T_c), also measured on the absolute scale:

$$T_b = \frac{2}{3} T_c.$$

For the liquid in this question

$$T_c = \frac{3}{2} \times 351.6 = 527 \text{ K}$$

(d) The ebullioscopic constant

The molal elevation of the boiling point (K_b) signifies the rise in boiling point of a one molal solution of a solute in a solvent, provided the laws of dilute solutions are applicable to such a concentration, that is,

$$K_b = \frac{RT_b^2 M_r}{\Delta H_v 1000} \text{ K mol}^{-1}\text{ kg}$$

where T_b is the boiling point of the solvent, M_r is the relative molecular mass, and ΔH_v is the molar heat of vaporization. For the liquid in this question

$$K_b = \frac{8.31 \times (351.6)^2 \times 46}{46 \times 865 \times 1000} = 1.188 \text{ K mol}^{-1}\text{ kg}$$

Summary (*a*) 352 K, (*b*) 113 J K^{-1} mol^{-1}, (*c*) 527 K, (*d*) 1.19 K mol^{-1} kg.

Example 8.2 Hydrate equilibria

For the reaction: $ZnSO_4.7H_2O = ZnSO_4.6H_2O + H_2O(liquid)$, $\Delta G = 1483\,J$ *at 18°C. The vapour pressure of water is 15.48 mmHg at the same temperature. What is the vapour pressure of zinc sulphate heptahydrate in equilibrium with the hexahydrate at 18°C?*

(*R.S.C.*)

To evaluate the equilibrium vapour pressure of the hydrate mixture it is first of all necessary to determine the free energy change for the process:

$$H_2O(\text{liquid}) = H_2O(\text{vapour})$$

The molar free energy of liquid water is equal to that of the vapour in equilibrium with it at the equilibrium temperature and pressure. Thus there is no free energy change involved in the transfer of one mole from the liquid state to the vapour state. The free energy for the process quoted above will therefore be the difference between the molar free energy of the water at its vapour pressure at the given temperature and the molar free energy in the standard state of unit fugacity.

This difference is given by

$$\Delta G = RT\ln\frac{f_1}{f_e}$$

where f_1 is unit fugacity and f_e the fugacity corresponding to the vapour pressure. At the relatively low pressures involved, the fugacities may be replaced by the pressures without causing a significant error.

Therefore $$\Delta G = RT\ln\frac{p_1}{p_e}$$

p_e is given as 15.48 mmHg and p_1 as 1 atm = 760 mmHg.

Therefore $$\Delta G = 8.31\times 291\times 2.303\log\frac{760}{15.48}\text{ J mol}^{-1}$$
$$= 9421\text{ J mol}^{-1}$$

That is, for the reaction:

$$H_2O(\text{liquid}) = H_2O(\text{vapour}),\quad \Delta G = 9421\text{ J mol}^{-1}.$$

The free energy change for the process

$$ZnSO_4.7H_2O = ZnSO_4.6H_2O + H_2O(\text{vapour, 1 atm})$$

may now be calculated from the data available, as follows:

(i) $ZnSO_4.7H_2O = ZnSO_4.6H_2O + H_2O(\text{liquid})$; $\Delta G = 1483$ J.
(ii) $H_2O(\text{liquid}) = H_2O(\text{vapour})$; $\Delta G = 9421$ J.

Addition of equations (i) and (ii) yields:

(iii) $ZnSO_4.7H_2O = ZnSO_4.6H_2O + H_2O(\text{vapour})$; $\Delta G_v = 10\,904$ J.

ΔG_v is the standard free energy change for the formation of $ZnSO_4.6H_2O$ at unit activity and H_2O(vapour) at 1 atm, from $ZnSO_4.7H_2O$, also at unit activity.

Therefore
$$-\Delta G_v = RT \ln K_p$$

where K_p is the equilibrium constant for the process described by equation (iii) and is given by $K_p = p_{H_2O}$, the vapour pressure of the hydrate system.

Therefore

$$-10\,904 = 8.31 \times 291 \times 2.303 \log p_{H_2O}$$

And
$$\log p_{H_2O} = -1.957$$
$$= \bar{2}.043.$$

Hence
$$p_{H_2O} = 0.01104 \text{ atm}$$
$$= 0.01104 \times 760 \text{ mmHg}$$
$$= 8.390 \text{ mmHg}$$

The vapour pressure of zinc sulphate heptahydrate in equilibrium with the hexahydrate at 18°C is 8.39 mmHg.

Example 8.3 Partition coefficient and solvent extraction

The partition coefficient of a substance Y between ethoxyethane and water is 3, Y being more soluble in the ethoxyethane. 100 cm^3 of an aqueous solution containing 10 g of Y is shaken with

(i) 100 cm^3 ethoxyethane,
(ii) four successive quantities of 25 cm^3 of ethoxyethane.

Calculate the weight of Y left in the aqueous phase in the two experiments. (*B. Agriculture and Subsidiary B.Sc., Q.U.B.*)

The partition law (or distribution law) states that if to a system of two liquid layers is added a third substance soluble in both layers, the substance is found to distribute itself between the two layers in a definite manner, that is,

$$\frac{\text{Concentration in liquid layer 1}}{\text{Concentration in liquid layer 2}} = K$$

where K is a constant referred to as the partition (or distribution) coefficient.

From the information given:

$$\frac{\text{Concentration of } Y \text{ in the ethoxyethane layer}}{\text{Concentration of } Y \text{ in the water layer}} = 3$$

(*i*) When $100\,\text{cm}^3$ of an aqueous solution containing 10 g of Y is shaken with $100\,\text{cm}^3$ of ethoxyethane, let x g be extracted from the aqueous layer to attain equilibrium.

Therefore, at equilibrium

$$\frac{\text{Concentration of } Y \text{ in ethoxyethane layer}}{\text{Concentration of } Y \text{ in aqueous layer}} = \frac{x}{10 - x} = 3$$

and $$x = 7.5\text{ g}$$

Therefore, the weight of Y left in the aqueous layer is $10 - 7.5 = \underline{2.5\text{ g}}$.

(*ii*) When $100\,\text{cm}^3$ of an aqueous solution containing Y is shaken with $25\,\text{cm}^3$ of ethoxyethane let a fraction z be extracted from the aqueous layer to attain equilibrium. At equilibrium

$$\frac{\text{Concentration of } Y \text{ in ethoxyethane layer}}{\text{Concentration of } Y \text{ in water layer}} = \frac{4z}{1 - z} = 3$$

and $$z = \frac{3}{7}.$$

For each of the four extractions 3/7 of the amount of Y remaining in the aqueous layer after the previous extraction is removed by the ethoxyethane. Therefore, the total fraction of Y extracted by four successive quantities of $25\,\text{cm}^3$ of ethoxyethane is

$$\frac{3}{7} + \frac{3}{7} \text{ of } \frac{4}{7} + \frac{3}{7} \text{ of } \left(\frac{4}{7}\right)^2 + \frac{3}{7} \text{ of } \left(\frac{4}{7}\right)^3 = \frac{2145}{2401}$$

Therefore, in the four successive extractions, a total of

$\frac{2145}{2401}$ of $10 = 8.933$ g of Y is extracted, and the weight of Y left in the aqueous phase is 1.067 g.

The weight of Y remaining in the aqueous phase in case <u>(i) is 2.5 g,</u> and in case <u>(ii) 1.07 g.</u>

Note The result shows that the larger number of extractions and the smaller the portions of the extracting liquid, the more complete is the extraction for a definite volume of extracting liquid.

Example 8.4 Partition and association

The following data for the distribution of benzoic acid between water and benzene at 20°C are in mol dm^{-3}:

Concentration in water	*0.0150*	*0.0195*	*0.0289*
Concentration in benzene	*0.242*	*0.412*	*0.907*

Show that benzoic acid is associated into double molecules in benzene (The ionization of benzoic acid can be neglected.) (*B.Sc., Wales*)

The equation of the type quoted in Example 8.3 applies to all cases of distribution, except when the substance being partitioned is in a different molecular state in the two phases. The required modification to the equation is illustrated by this example.

Ignoring the small amount of ionization, benzoic acid is present in the aqueous layer as single molecules (C_6H_5COOH), but when benzoic acid is dissolved in a solvent, such as benzene, it is present mainly as the dimer ($(C_6H_5COOH)_2$).

The distribution is controlled by the distribution of the single molecule form between the aqueous layer and the benzene layer and the following relationship will hold if the benzoic acid molecules in the benzene layer are almost completely in the dimeric form:

$$\frac{\text{Concentration of benzoic acid in water layer}}{\sqrt{\text{Concentration of benzoic acid in benzene layer}}} = \frac{C_W}{\sqrt{C_B}} = \text{constant}$$

The table summarizes the values for the ratio $C_W/\sqrt{C_B}$ and of C_W/C_B, as determined from the data given in the question:

C_W/mol dm^{-3}	0.0150	0.0195	0.0289
C_B/mol dm^{-3}	0.242	0.412	0.907
C_W/C_B	6.21×10^{-2}	4.733×10^{-2}	3.186×10^{-2}
$C_W/\sqrt{C_B}$	3.049×10^{-2}	3.038×10^{-2}	3.035×10^{-2}

Inspection of the results in the table shows that the ratio C_W/C_B varies considerably, whereas the ratio $C_W/\sqrt{C_B}$ is constant, showing that in benzene solution, benzoic acid is almost completely associated into double molecules.

Example 8.5 Partition and the nature of molecules in solution

A solution of iodine in aqueous potassium iodide at 14°C is shaken with carbon disulphide until equilibrium is attained. The following table shows the concentrations of the potassium iodide solutions (a), and of the iodine solutions in the carbon disulphide (b) and the potassium iodide solutions (c) at equilibrium:

(a)/mol dm^{-3}	*(b)/mol dm^{-3}*	*(c)/mol dm^{-3}*
0.125	*0.02618*	*0.004960*
0.125	*0.04995*	*0.009135*
0.125	*0.1008*	*0.01744*

From the above data, determine the equilibrium constant for the reaction: $KI+I_2 \rightleftharpoons KI_3$.

(The partition coefficient of iodine between carbon disulphide and water is 625, the iodine being more soluble in carbon disulphide.)

The equilibrium constant (K) of the reaction $\mathrm{KI+I_2 \rightleftharpoons KI_3}$ is given by

$$K=\frac{[\mathrm{KI_3}]}{[\mathrm{KI}][\mathrm{I_2}]} \qquad \text{(i)}$$

where the square brackets indicate concentrations.

The actual concentration of free iodine in the aqueous layer, $[\mathrm{I_2}]$, can be obtained from a knowledge of the partition coefficient of iodine between the carbon disulphide layer and the aqueous layer. Since the concentration of iodine in the aqueous layer, (c), includes free iodine of concentration $[\mathrm{I_2}]$ and $\mathrm{KI_3}$ of concentration $[\mathrm{KI_3}]$, the $[\mathrm{KI_3}]$ is given by (c) minus $[\mathrm{I_2}]$. Finally, the concentration of unassociated potassium iodide can be obtained by subtracting $[\mathrm{KI_3}]$ from (a), giving $[\mathrm{KI}]$. Thus all the concentration terms in equation (i) can be determined from the data given in the question and the equilibrium constant for the association between potassium iodide and iodine (in the aqueous layer) can then be calculated. Of the three constituents of the aqueous layer, it is only the iodine ($\mathrm{I_2}$) that partitions with the carbon disulphide.

The various concentration terms, calculated in the manner indicated, and the values of the equilibrium constant (K) are summarized in the table.

(All concentrations are expressed in mol dm^{-3})

(a)	(b)	(c)	$[I_2]$ $(b)/625$	$[KI_3]$ $(c)-[I_2]$	$[KI]$ $(a)-[KI_3]$	$K = \frac{[KI_3]}{[KI][I_2]}$
0.125	0.02618	0.004960	0.00004189	0.004918	0.1201	977.7
0.125	0.04995	0.009135	0.00007992	0.009055	0.1159	977.4
0.125	0.1008	0.01744	0.0001614	0.01728	0.1077	993.8

The equilibrium constant of the reaction $KI+I_2 \rightleftharpoons KI_3$ is 983.

Note The constancy of the equilibrium constant (K) supports the assumption that the KI_3 complex is present in the aqueous layer.

Example 8.6 Raoult's law and relative volatility

The saturated vapour pressure of phenylmethanol may be represented by the equation

$$\log p = 8.697 - \frac{2774.3}{T}$$

and that of phenol by the equation

$$\log p = 8.587 - \frac{2592.9}{T}$$

where p is the vapour pressure in mmHg and T is the absolute temperature.

Obtain an expression for the relative volatility of phenol with respect to phenylmethanol, assuming ideal behaviour (Raoult's Law). Evaluate this relative volatility for 140°C.

(*B.Pharm., London*)

For a binary mixture of completely miscible liquids A and B, in equilibrium with its vapour, let the mole fractions of A and B in the liquid phase be x_A and x_B, respectively, and the mole fractions in the vapour be x_A^* and x_B^* respectively.

The concentration ratios are x_A/x_B for the liquid phase and x_A^*/x_B^* for the vapour phase. The greater the amount by which x_A^*/x_B^* exceeds x_A/x_B then the richer will be the vapour phase in component A and the more readily can A be separated from B by distillation.

A measure of this ease of separation is the relative volatility (α)

which is the ratio of the concentration ratio of A and B in the vapour phase to that in the liquid phase:

$$\alpha = \frac{(x_A^*/x_B^*)}{(x_A/x_B)} = \frac{[x_A^*/(1-x_A^*)]}{[x_A/(1-x_A)]} = \frac{x_A^*(1-x_A)}{x_A(1-x_A^*)} \quad \text{(i)}$$

For non-ideal systems α changes as x_A changes. If $x_A = x_A^*$, $\alpha = 1$ and separation is not possible.

For an ideal solution at a given temperature the equilibrium partial pressure, p_A, of component A is given by Raoult's law as $p_A = P_A x_A$ where P_A is the vapour pressure of pure A at the given temperature and x_A is the mole fraction of A in the liquid phase. For the vapour phase the total pressure $P_T = p_A + p_B = P_A x_A + P_B x_B = P_A x_A + P_B(1-x_A)$.

Thus, both the partial pressures and the total pressure are linear functions of x_A at a given temperature.

For the vapour phase the mole fraction, x_A^*, is given by the ratio of the partial pressure, p_A, to the total pressure, P_T. Hence

$$x_A^* = p_A/P_T = P_A x_A/P_T \text{ and } 1-x_A^* = p_B/P_T = P_B(1-x_A)/P_T$$

Substitution of these values for x_A^* and $1-x_A^*$ in equation (i) yields

$$\alpha = P_A/P_B.$$

Thus, for ideal solutions the relative volatility is the ratio of the vapour pressures of the pure substances.

From the given data the relative volatility of phenol (Ph) with respect to phenylmethanol (B) will be given by

$$\log P_{Ph} - \log P_B = \log (P_{Ph}/P_B) = \log \alpha$$

$$= 8.587 - 8.697 + \frac{2774.3 - 2592.9}{T}$$

$$= -0.11 + \frac{181.4}{T}$$

Hence $\log \alpha = \dfrac{181.4 - 0.11T}{T}$

For 140°C, $T = 413$ K and $\log \alpha = \dfrac{181.4 - 0.11 \times 413}{413} = \dfrac{136}{413}$

$$= 0.3293$$

Hence, $\alpha = 2.134$

The relative volatility of phenol with respect to phenylmethanol $= 2.13$.

Example 8.7 Immiscible liquids—steam distillation

Methylbenzene and water are distilled together under a barometric pressure of 765 mmHg. Calculate (a) the boiling-point of the mixture, and (b) the composition of the distillate.

The vapour pressures of the two pure liquids are:

Temperature/°C	*83*	*84*	*85*	*86*
Vapour pressure of water/mmHg	*400*	*415*	*433*	*450*
Vapour pressure of methylbenzene/mmHg	*322*	*333*	*345*	*356*

(H = 1; C = 12; 0 = 16) *(B.Pharm., Wales)*

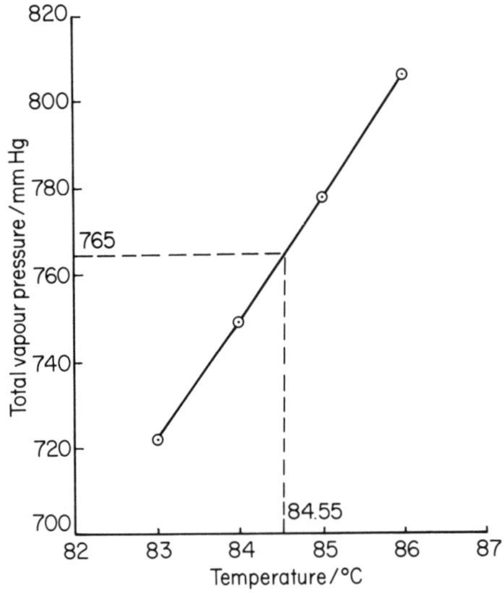

Fig. 18 Plot of total vapour pressure versus temperature for mixtures of methylbenzene and water

(*a*) Methylbenzene and water are immiscible liquids. Hence, if one is mixed with the other, the vapour pressure exerted by each is that of the pure liquid at the given temperature. The total vapour pressure (P) above the mixture is thus the sum of the vapour pressures (p^0) of the two pure constituents:

$$P = p^0_{\text{methylbenzene}} + p^0_{\text{water}}$$

The boiling point of a system is the temperature at which the total vapour pressure becomes equal to the prevailing pressure. Thus the boiling point of the given mixture at 765 mmHg may be read from a graph of total vapour pressure against temperature.

From the given data the total vapour pressures are as tabulated below:

Temperature/°C	83	84	85	86
Total vapour pressure/mmHg	722	749	778	806

The graph of total vapour pressure against temperature is shown in Fig. 18. From the graph it is seen that the vapour pressure of the mixture equals the prevailing pressure of 765 mmHg at 84.55°C.

The boiling point of the mixture is 84.6°C.

(*b*) At the boiling point the partial vapour pressure (p^0) of each component is given by:

$$p^0_{\text{methylbenzene}} = x_{\text{methylbenzene}}\, P; \qquad p^0_{\text{water}} = x_{\text{water}}\, P$$

where the symbol x denotes the mole fraction of a particular constituent in the vapour phase, and P is the total pressure. Therefore

$$\frac{p^0_{\text{methylbenzene}}}{p^0_{\text{water}}} = \frac{x_{\text{methylbenzene}}}{x_{\text{water}}} = \frac{n_{\text{methylbenzene}}}{n_{\text{water}}}$$

where n denotes the number of moles of each constituent in the mixture.

The ratio of the partial pressures is constant, so that the composition of the vapour, that is, $n_{\text{methylbenzene}}/n_{\text{water}}$ is also constant, provided both liquids are present.

But

$n = \dfrac{W}{M_r}$ where W is the mass of the constituent in a given volume of vapour

M_r is the relative molecular mass of the constituent

Therefore $$\frac{p^0_{\text{methylbenzene}}}{p^0_{\text{water}}} = \frac{W_{\text{methylbenzene}}\, M_{\text{r(water)}}}{W_{\text{water}}\, M_{\text{r(methylbenzene)}}}$$

From the given data, the following p^0 values are obtained by drawing a graph of vapour pressure against temperature for each of the constituents of the mixture, and reading off the vapour pressure at 84.55°C (Fig. 19).

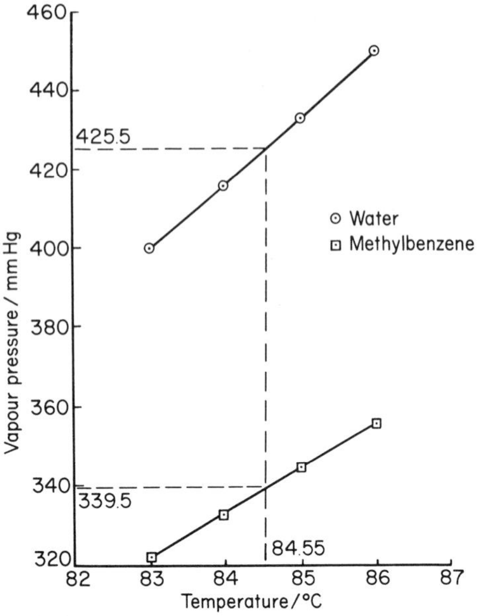

Fig. 19 Plot of vapour pressure versus temperature for methylbenzene and water

From Fig. 19 it is seen that $p^0_{\text{methylbenzene}} = 339.5\,\text{mmHg}$ and $p^0_{\text{water}} = 425.5\,\text{mmHg}$. Therefore

$$\frac{W_{\text{methylbenzene}}}{W_{\text{water}}} = \frac{339.5 \times 92}{425.5 \times 18} = 4.08$$

Thus, the distillate contains methylbenzene and water in the ratio 4.08:1.

The ratio of methylbenzene to water by mass in the distillate is 4.08:1.

Example 8.8 Binary alloy system

The following information has been given for the system FeO–MnO: the pure components melt at 1370°C (FeO) and 1785°C (MnO); at 1430°C a peritectic transformation occurs between two solid solutions containing 30 and 60 mass per cent of MnO, which exist in equilibrium with a melt containing 15 mass per cent of MnO. At 1200°C the two solid solutions contain 26 and 64 mass per cent of MnO.

Draw the binary phase diagram for the system, and label it to indicate the significance of its different areas. Briefly describe what happens when a melt containing 28 mass per cent of MnO is cooled from above the liquidus to 1200°C. (*B.Sc.(Eng.) in Metallurgy, London*)

The binary phase diagram for the system described is shown in Fig. 20.

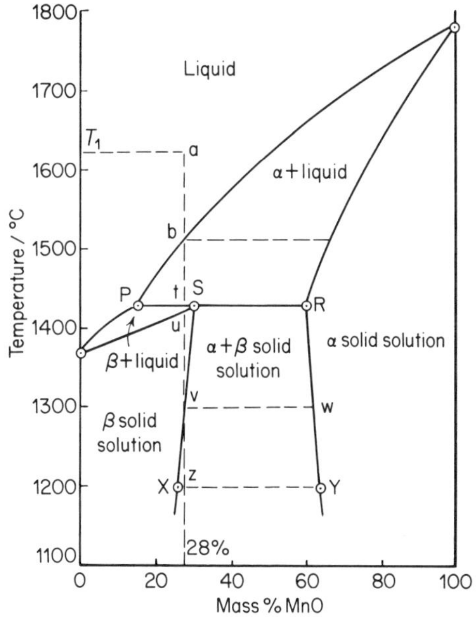

Fig. 20 The FeO–MnO peritectic system

Assume that the melt containing 28 mass per cent of MnO is cooled from some temperature, T_1, above the liquidus. On reaching the temperature corresponding to point b on the liquidus, solid solution α begins to separate. Selective crystallization of the α solid solution continues down to 1430°C, the peritectic temperature. The composition of the liquid changes along the liquidus towards P and that of the solid along the solidus towards R.

When the temperature has fallen to 1430°C the alloy is composed of solid α-crystals of composition 60 mass per cent of MnO and liquid of composition 15 mass per cent MnO, in the proportions α:liquid = Pt:tR = 13:32.

At the peritectic temperature, the α-crystals and the liquid undergo peritectic reaction to produce the β solid solution. The system however contains more FeO than is required to transform the α-phase to the β-phase, so that some liquid will remain after the peritectic reaction is complete. The composition of the β-phase formed is 30 mass per cent MnO and the proportion of β-phase to the remaining liquid is tP:tS = 13:2.

After completion of the peritectic reaction the temperature falls to u and the rest of the liquid solidifies as β-phase. The composition of the β-phase formed by the peritectic reaction, and that afterwards between the temperatures represented by t and u, changes along Su by diffusion of FeO from the liquid.

Under the equilibrium condition at temperature u the structure is homogeneous β-phase of composition u. On cooling further to the temperature v the FeO cannot hold all the MnO in solution. Accordingly MnO diffuses out of solid solution and concentrates at grain boundaries of the β-phase and undergoes rearrangement with FeO to form the α-phase of composition w. Thus at v a change from a single to a two phase system occurs. As the temperature is lowered further to 1200°C the composition of the α-phase changes along wY, and that of the β-phase along vX. At 1200°C the composition of the β-phase is 26 mass per cent MnO and that of the α-phase is 64 mass per cent MnO. The relative proportions are $\alpha:\beta$ = zX:zY = 2:36.

Example 8.9 Ternary systems—two salts and water

The following analyses of saturated solutions and the moist solids in equilibrium with them, were obtained for a system of two salts, S_1 and S_2, with an ion in common, and water at constant temperature. The analyses are in grams per 100 grams of solution or moist solid.

Solution		*Moist Solid*	
%S_1	*%S_2*	*%S_1*	*%S_2*
35.0	0.0	—	—
32.5	5.0	45.0	1.5
31.0	10.0	45.0	3.0
30.0	15.0	55.0	3.0
30.0	15.0	75.0	2.0
26.0	20.0	90.0	3.0
22.5	25.0	92.5	2.5
20.0	30.0	50.0	45.0
14.0	32.0	2.5	87.0
8.0	35.0	1.5	88.5
4.0	37.0	1.0	85.0
0.0	40.0	—	—

Relative molecular mass of S_1 = 187.

Plot the data and (i) state what compounds are formed, (ii) determine the ratio of the masses of S_1 and S_2 in the solution which deposits the greatest yield of pure anhydrous S_1 on isothermal evaporation.

Fig. 21 shows a plot of the data.

(i) An inspection of Fig. 21 shows that the only compound formed is a hydrate of S_1, represented by H and of composition 49% H_2O and 51% S_1. Since the relative molecular mass of S_1 is given as 187, this composition corresponds to a formula of $S_1.10H_2O$ for the hydrate.

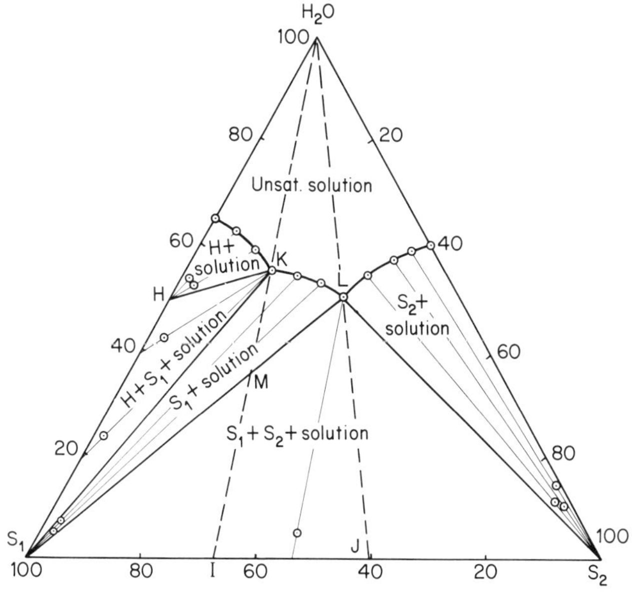

Fig. 21 Plot of S_1–S_2–H_2O ternary system

(ii) For pure anhydrous S_1 to be deposited from aqueous solution of S_1 and S_2 by isothermal evaporation, the ratio of the masses of S_1 and S_2 in the solution must be between the limits represented by I and J in Fig. 21. Little or no pure anhydrous S_1 is deposited on the isothermal evaporation of a solution containing S_1 and S_2 in the proportions represented by J. As the proportion of S_1 to S_2 increases towards I, the amount of pure S_1 deposited on isothermal evaporation of a solution increases because the intercept of the line from the apex (H_2O) to the base (S_1–S_2) passes further along the line S_1–L. Isothermal evaporation of solutions containing a greater proportion of S_1 to S_2 than that represented by I results in an impure product.

Therefore, the greatest yield of pure anhydrous S_1 is obtained by isothermally evaporating a solution of composition along the line K–H_2O to point M; such solutions contain S_1 and S_2 in the ratio 66.7 to 33.3 parts by mass, respectively.

Additional Examples

1 ΔS of vaporization at the normal boiling point of a liquid at 1 atm pressure is 85 J K^{-1} mol^{-1} and ΔH of vaporization is 21 kJ mol^{-1}. Calculate the boiling point of the liquid at 1 atm pressure.

(Adapted from ACS Cooperative Examination: Physical Chemistry (Thermodynamics).)

2 At 25°C the dissociation pressure of $CuSO_4.5H_2O$ to $CuSO_4.3H_2O$ is 7.92 mmHg, and at 35°C is 17.01 mmHg. Calculate the heat of dissociation per mole of water vapour. (B.Sc., Wales)

3 At 470°C and 1 atm pressure, caesium chloride undergoes a phase transformation in which the crystal structure changes. At 100 atm the transition occurs at 490°C. If the volume change in going from the low to the high temperature form is 7 cm^3 mol^{-1} at 1 atm, estimate the heat of transition. (B.Sc., Bristol)

4 Hydrogen containing 0.04 g dm^{-3} (corrected to s.t.p.) of ethoxyethane vapour is passed slowly through a cold trap at −78°C and 1 atm pressure. Estimate approximately the maximum percentage recovery of ethoxyethane in the trap. The normal boiling point of ethoxyethane is 35°C, and Trouton's Rule may be assumed with a constant of 92 J K^{-1} mol^{-1}.

(R.S.C.)

5 The following data refer to the saturated vapour pressure of ethanoic acid.

T/°C	90	110	130
p/mmHg	293	583	1040

The latent heat of evaporation of ethanoic acid at its normal boiling point (117.4°C) is 407 J g^{-1}. What conclusion can be reached from these data?

(B.Sc., Liverpool)

6 The aqueous vapour pressure of the hydrate system:

$$CuSO_4.5H_2O = CuSO_4.3H_2O + 2H_2O(g)$$

is 7.80 mmHg at 25°C. Calculate the free energy change (ΔG) for the process:

$$CuSO_4.5H_2O = CuSO_4.3H_2O + 2H_2O(l)$$

at 25°C, given that the vapour pressure of pure water at the same temperature is 23.8 mmHg.

7 The partition coefficient of an alkaloid between trichloromethane and water is 20, the alkaloid being more soluble in trichloromethane. Compare the masses of the alkaloid remaining in the aqueous solution after 100 cm^3 containing 1 g has been shaken (*a*) with 100 cm^3 of trichloromethane, and (*b*) with two successive quantities of 50 cm^3 of trichloromethane.

(B.Pharm., Wales)

8 An organic compound in aqueous solution is extracted with successive quantities of 25 cm^3 of trichloromethane. If the original volume of solution was 500 cm^3 and the distribution ratio of the compound is 20/1 trichloromethane/water, calculate the number of extractions required to obtain a minimum of 95% extraction of the compound. (Ph.C.)

9 Nernst, studying the distribution of benzoic acid between benzene and water, obtained the following results for the concentrations in the two solvents (in g per 100 cm^3):

Concentrations in water layer	0.0976	0.1952
Concentrations in benzene layer	1.050	4.12

In a separate experiment, a solution of 0.20 g of benzoic acid in 100 cm^3 of water froze at −0.030°C. Calculate the approximate relative atomic mass of benzoic acid in both aqueous and benzene solutions. (The molal cryoscopic constant for water is 1.86 K mol^{-1} kg.) What would have been the effect on Nernst's experiment if benzoic acid had been a much stronger acid?

(B.Pharm., Nottingham)

10 A solution of iodine in water was equilibrated through the vapour phase with a solution of iodine in aqueous potassium iodide at 25°C. The following table shows the concentration (mol dm^{-3}) of the potassium iodide solutions used (*A*), and the concentrations (mol dm^{-3}) of iodine, as determined by titration, in the water (*B*) and the potassium iodide solution (*C*) at equilibrium.

A	*B*	*C*
0.3333	0.00001471	0.003491
0.1000	0.00007086	0.004866
0.04994	0.0004410	0.01250

Assuming the activity coefficient of the iodine molecule is unity in each solution, what conclusions can be drawn from these experiments?

(R.S.C.)

11 The saturated vapour pressures of benzene and methylbenzene are both given by the equation

$$\log_{10} P = \frac{-0.05223A}{T} + B$$

where P is the pressure in mmHg, T is the temperature in degrees K and the constants A and B have the following values:

	A	B
Benzene	32 295	7.6546
Methylbenzene	39 198	8.2300

Assuming that mixtures of benzene and methylbenzene form ideal solutions, calculate the molar percentage of benzene in (*a*) a mixture which boils at 97°C, and (*b*) the initial condensate formed on distilling this mixture. (R.S.C.)

12 A mixture of bromobenzene and water at one atm pressure boils at a temperature of 95.7°C. Using the following data calculate the theoretical ratio, by mass, in which the two liquids will distil.

Temperature/°C	92	94	96	98	100
V.P. of water/mmHg	567	611	658	707	760

(H = 1; C = 12; 0 = 16; Br = 80)

(Ph.C.)

13 Tin and lead form a eutectic system of two solid solutions (α and β). Tin melts at 232°C and lead at 327°C. The eutectic temperature and composition are, respectively, 183°C and 62% by mass of tin.

The compositions of the solid solutions at certain temperatures are as follows:

Temperature/°C	Mass per cent of tin α	β
183	19	97
150	12	99
100	4	99.9

Assuming the liquidus and solidus lines to be straight, supply the following information concerning the alloy containing 37% by mass of tin:

(*i*) the temperature at which solid first separates from the melt,
(*ii*) the composition of the solid which first separates,
(*iii*) the proportion of solid in the alloy at 200°C,
(*iv*) the proportion of eutectic in the alloy at the eutectic temperature,
(*v*) the proportion of α solid solution in the alloy at 150°C.

14 Bismuth and cadmium are used to form an alloy containing 70 mass % of cadmium. The melting points of bismuth and cadmium are 270°C and 320°C respectively. The metals form no compounds or solid solutions with each other, but form a eutectic of composition 40 mass % of cadmium which solidifies at 140°C. Assuming that the liquidus lines are straight, find:

(*i*) the temperature at which the alloy begins to crystallize from the melt,
(*ii*) the proportion of solid in the alloy at 175°C,

(*iii*) the proportion of eutectic in the alloy at 20°C,
(*iv*) the density of the alloy at 20°C, given that the densities of bismuth and cadmium are respectively, 9.80 g cm^{-3} and 8.60 g cm^{-3} at 20°C.

15 Equilibrium data obtained at 30°C for the system $FeSO_4$—$(NH_4)_2SO_4$—H_2O are tabulated below, the composition of solutions and of the moist solids in equilibrium with them being expressed in mass per cent.

Saturated solution		*Moist solid*	
$FeSO_4$	*$(NH_4)_2SO_4$*	*$FeSO_4$*	*$(NH_4)_2SO_4$*
24.0	—	—	—
24.0	2.0	41.0	1.0
25.0	5.0	43.0	2.0
25.5	6.5	40.0	10.0
18.0	9.0	30.0	23.0
10.0	14.0	28.0	26.0
6.0	21.0	30.0	30.0
3.5	28.5	25.0	31.5
2.0	35.0	23.0	34.0
0.8	44.0	14.0	55.0
0.5	44.0	0.1	81.0

(Fe = 56; N = 14; S = 32; H = 1; O = 16)

Plot the given data and deduce which compounds are indicated as being formed.

16 Construct the phase diagram for the system Na_2CO_3—K_2CO_3—H_2O, using the following analyses of saturated solutions and moist solids in equilibrium with them at 36°C:

Saturated solution /mass %		*Moist solid /mass %*	
H_2O	*Na_2CO_3*	*H_2O*	*Na_2CO_3*
46.4	0.0	—	—
45.6	2.5	22.0	0.5
45.6	3.5	26.0	1.0
45.6	4.0	10.0	20.0
46.4	4.9	6.0	39.0
47.8	5.7	20.0	28.0
47.4	7.2	22.2	35.3
50.9	9.6	27.5	58.5
58.4	18.2	30.0	62.0
65.0	29.0	22.0	67.0
66.8	33.2	—	—

(Na = 23; K = 39; H = 1; C = 12; O = 16)

State which compounds are indicated as being formed, and determine the solid phase which is first deposited, on isothermal evaporation of a solution containing 64 mass % of H_2O and 4 mass % of Na_2CO_3.

17 For the following phase diagram of the ZrO_2—CoO system, sketch the cooling curves for the compositions A and B. Also, give the phases present at equilibrium and the variance of the regions labelled C, D, E, F, G, H and I. Finally, name or describe the points labelled J and K.

(University of Arizona, Tucson, USA)

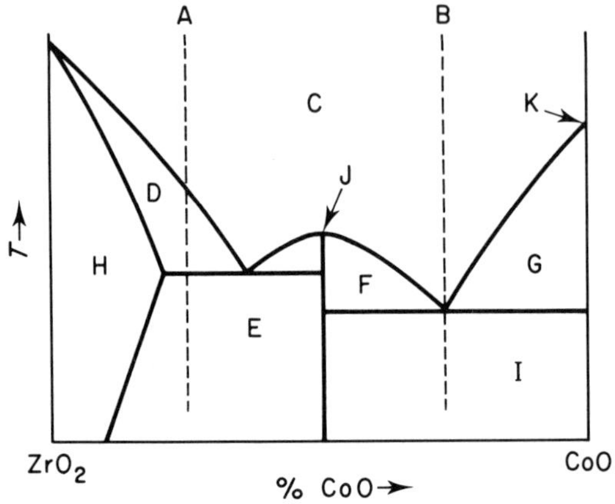

9

Reaction Kinetics

Example 9.1 First order reaction

When a solution of 2,3-dibromobutanedioic acid is heated, the acid decomposes according to the equation:

$$\begin{array}{lcll} CHBrCOOH & & CHCOOH & \\ | & = & \| & + HBr \\ CHBrCOOH & & CHCOOH & \end{array}$$

At 50°C the initial titre of a definite volume of the solution was $T_0 = 10.1$ cm³ of standard alkali. After t seconds the titre of the same volume of solution was T_t cm³ of standard alkali.

t (s)	*0*	*12 840*	*22 800*
T_t (cm³)	*10.10*	*10.37*	*10.57*

Calculate (a) the velocity constant of the equation and (b) after what time is one third of the 2,3-dibromobutanedioic acid decomposed? *(B.Pharm., London)*

The conversion of 2,3-dibromobutanedioic acid to *cis*-bromobutenedioic acid and hydrogen bromide is a first order reaction, the specific rate (k_1) of which is given by

$$k_1 = \frac{1}{t} \ln \frac{C_0}{C} \qquad \text{(i)}$$

where t represents the time from the commencement and C_0 and C the concentrations of reactant at the commencement and at time t respectively. Alternatively, this equation can be expressed in terms of the decrease in concentration $(a-x)$ of reactant, a being the initial concentration:

$$k_1 = \frac{1}{t} \ln \frac{a}{(a-x)} \qquad \text{(ii)}$$

The above reaction is conveniently followed by determining the change in total acid concentration, because one mole of 2,3-dibromobutanedioic acid on decomposition gives two moles of product acid. Hence, at time t, when $C_0 - C$ moles of 2,3-dibromobutanedioic acid have decomposed, giving rise to $2(C_0 - C)$ moles of product acid, the total acid concentration (C_{TA}) is given by $2(C_0 - C) + C$.
But C_0 is proportional to the initial titre (T_0). Therefore, C is proportional to the initial titre, less twice the increase in titre $[T_0 - 2(T_t - T_0)]$.
Substituting in equation (i), we have for $t = 0$ and $t = 12\,840$ s

$$k_1 = \frac{2.303}{12\,840}\log\frac{10.10}{10.10-2(10.37-10.10)}\ \text{s}^{-1}$$

$$= 4.27 \times 10^{-6}\ \text{s}^{-1}$$

For $t = 0$ and $t = 22\,800$ s

$$k_1 = \frac{2.303}{22\,800}\log\frac{10.10}{10.10-2(10.57-10.10)}\ \text{s}^{-1}$$

$$= 4.28 \times 10^{-6}\ \text{s}^{-1}$$

Therefore, mean value of k_1 is $4.275 \times 10^{-6}\ \text{s}^{-1}$.
To determine the time required for one third of the 2,3-dibromobutanedioic acid to decompose, it is only necessary to substitute 4.275×10^{-6} for k_1, 3 for C_0 and 2 for C in equation (i):

$$4.275 \times 10^{-6} = \frac{1}{t}\ln\frac{3}{2}$$

Therefore
$$t = \frac{2.303}{4.275 \times 10^{-6}}\log 1.5\ \text{s}$$

$$= 94\,860\ \text{s}.$$

(*a*) The velocity constant (k_1) for the decomposition of 2,3-dibromobutanedioic acid is $4.28 \times 10^{-6}\ \text{s}^{-1}$.

(*b*) One third of the 2,3-dibromobutanedioic acid is decomposed after a time of 94.9 ks.

Example 9.2 Pseudo-first order reaction

The following data were obtained in an experiment on the inversion of cane sugar:

Time/s	*0*	*432*	*1080*	*1620*	∞
Angle of rotation (α)	*+24.09°*	*+21.40°*	*+17.73°*	*+15.00°*	*−10.74°*

Show that the reaction is of the first order. (*B.Pharm., Wales*)

Cane sugar is dextro-rotatory, whereas the mixture of glucose and fructose resulting from inversion is laevo-rotatory. Thus a particular decrease in the concentration of the cane sugar, due to inversion, will be accompanied by a proportional decrease in the optical rotation. The total change in rotation $(\alpha_0-\alpha_\infty)$, therefore, will be proportional to the initial concentration of cane sugar. Also, the change in rotation $(\alpha_0-\alpha_t)$ by the time t after commencement of the inversion, is proportional to the decrease in concentration of cane sugar by that time. Thus the concentration of cane sugar remaining at time t will be proportional to

$$(\alpha_0-\alpha_\infty)-(\alpha_0-\alpha_t) = (\alpha_t-\alpha_\infty).$$

If the reaction is first order, the rate constant (k_1) is given by

$$k_1 = \frac{2.303}{t}\log\frac{a}{(a-x)} \qquad \text{(i)}$$

where a is the initial concentration of reactant, and $(a-x)$ is the concentration of reactant at time t after commencement of the reaction. Therefore, substitution of the above quantities, which are proportional to a and $(a-x)$, gives

$$k_1 = \frac{2.303}{t}\log\frac{(\alpha_0-\alpha_\infty)}{(\alpha_t-\alpha_\infty)} \qquad \text{(ii)}$$

From the given data $(\alpha_0-\alpha_\infty) = 34.83°$ and at the given times t, $(\alpha_t-\alpha_\infty)$ are as follows:

t/s	432	1 080	1 620	∞
$(\alpha_t-\alpha_\infty)$	32.14°	28.47°	25.74°	0°

Substitution of the relevant data into equation (ii), gives for $t = 432$ s

$$k_1 = \frac{2.303}{432}\log\frac{34.83}{32.14}\ \mathrm{s^{-1}}$$

$$= \frac{2.303}{432}\times 0.0350\ \mathrm{s^{-1}}$$

$$= 1.87\times 10^{-4}\ \mathrm{s^{-1}}$$

For $t = 1080$ s

$$k_1 = \frac{2.303}{1080} \log \frac{34.83}{28.47} \text{ s}^{-1}$$

$$= 1.87 \times 10^{-4} \text{ s}^{-1}$$

For $t = 1620$ s

$$k_1 = \frac{2.303}{1620} \log \frac{34.83}{25.74} \text{ s}^{-1}$$

$$= 1.87 \times 10^{-4} \text{ s}^{-1}$$

The constancy of the rate constant, at 1.87×10^{-4} s^{-1}, shows that the reaction is of the first order.

Example 9.3 Second order reaction

At 326°C the dimerization of buta-1,3-diene proceeds homogeneously in the gas phase. The following table gives values at time t of the total pressure (P).

t/min	*P/mmHg*
0	632.0
20.78	556.9
49.50	498.1
77.57	464.8
103.58	442.6

Determine the order of the reaction and the rate constant.

(*B.Sc., Wales*)

The stoichiometric equation for the dimerization is

$$\text{Buta-1,3-diene} \longrightarrow \tfrac{1}{2}\,\text{Dimer}$$

Let the total pressure at time t be P and let the partial pressures of the buta-1,3-diene and the dimer be P_B and P_D respectively. Hence

$$P = P_B + P_D$$

If P_i is the initial pressure of buta-1,3-diene and y the decrease in its pressure at time t, then

$$P_B = P_i - y \quad \text{and} \quad P_D = \tfrac{1}{2}y$$

Therefore $$P = P_i - \tfrac{1}{2}y$$

and $$y = 2P_i - 2P$$

Therefore $$P_B = 2P - P_i$$

The equation for a first order reaction is

$$k_1 = \frac{1}{t} \ln \frac{a}{a-x}$$

where a is the initial concentration of the reactant and $(a-x)$ is the concentration at time t from the commencement.

a is proportional to P_i and $(a-x)$ is proportional to $P_B = (2P-P_i)$. Therefore

$$k_1 = \frac{2.303}{t} \log \frac{P_i}{2P-P_i}$$

If the dimerization of buta-1,3-diene is first order, a plot of the following t and $\log \dfrac{P_i}{2P - P_i}$ values will give a straight line.

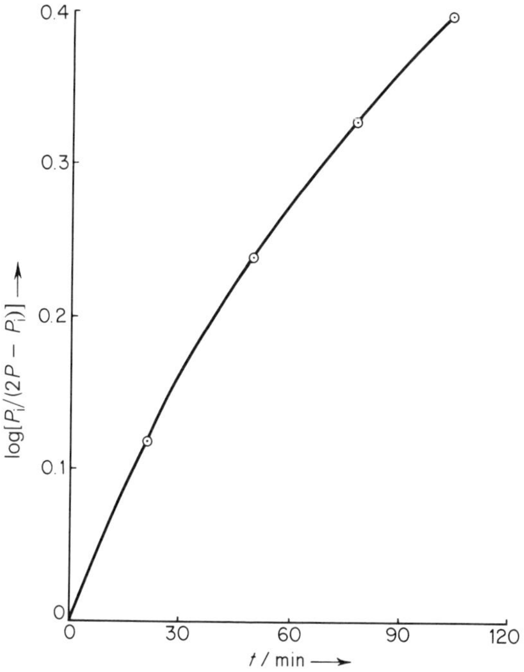

Fig. 22 Plot of time against $\log \dfrac{P_i}{2P - P_i}$

t/min	0	20.78	49.50	77.57	103.58
$2P-P_i$/mmHg	632.0	481.8	364.2	297.6	253.2
$\log \frac{P_i}{2P-P_i}$	0	0.1179	0.2394	0.3270	0.3973

As seen from Fig. 22, this plot does not give a straight line, therefore the reaction is not first order.

If the reaction is second order, the rate equation is

$$k_2 = \frac{1}{at}\left(\frac{x}{a-x}\right)$$

Since a is proportional to P_i, x is proportional to $2P_i-2P$ and $(a-x)$ is proportional to $(2P-P_i)$,

$$k_2 = \frac{1}{P_i t}\left(\frac{2P_i-2P}{2P-P_i}\right)$$

or

$$P_i k_2 t = \frac{2P_i-2P}{2P-P_i}$$

If the dimerization is second order, a plot of the following t and $(2P_i-2P)/(2P-P_i)$ values will give a straight line.

t/min	0	20.78	49.50	77.57	103.58
$2P_i-2P$/mmHg	0	150.2	267.8	334.4	378.8
$2P-P_i$/mmHg	632.0	481.8	364.2	297.6	253.2
$\frac{2P_i-2P}{2P-P_i}$	0	0.3118	0.7353	1.123	1.496

The graph shown in Fig. 23 is a straight line, indicating that the dimerization is a second order reaction. The slope of the line is given by

$$P_i k_2 = \frac{1.25}{86}\ \text{min}^{-1}$$

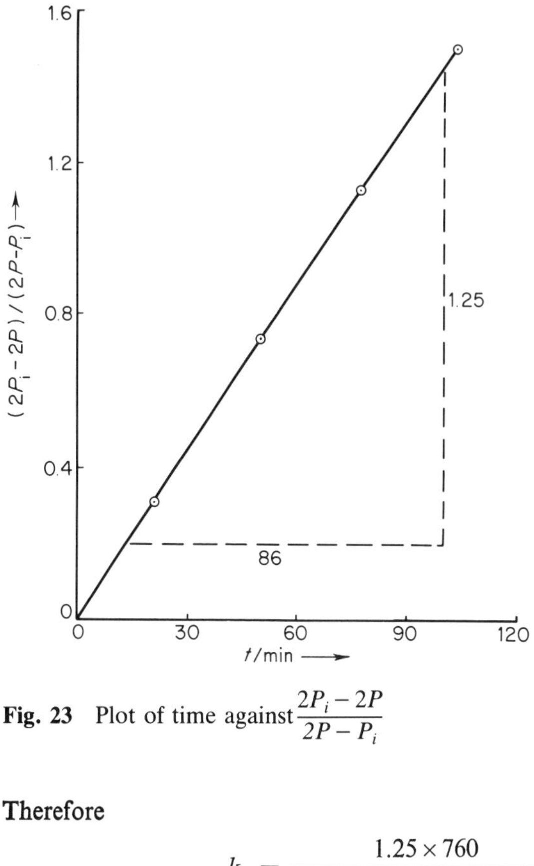

Fig. 23 Plot of time against $\dfrac{2P_i - 2P}{2P - P_i}$

Therefore

$$k_2 = \frac{1.25 \times 760}{86 \times 632 \times 1.013 \times 10^5 \times 60} \, (\text{N m}^{-2})^{-1} \, \text{s}^{-1}$$
$$= 2.88 \times 10^{-9} \, (\text{N m}^{-2})^{-1} \, \text{s}^{-1}$$

The dimerization of buta-1,3-diene is a second order reaction, the rate constant being 2.88×10^{-9} $(\text{N m}^{-2})^{-1} \text{s}^{-1}$ at 326°C.

Example 9.4 Second order reaction—initial concentration of reactants not equal

In a study of the reaction between propyl bromide and sodium thiosulphate: $C_3H_7Br + S_2O_3^{2-} = C_3H_7S_2O_3^- + Br^-$, *the reaction was followed by withdrawing samples from time to time, adding ice water to stop the reaction, and titrating the residual thiosulphate with* *standard iodine solution (Crowell, T. I., and Hammett, L. P., J.A.C.S., **70** (1948), 3444). The following data were obtained at 37.5°C:*

t/s	0	1110	2010	3192	5052	7380
Iodine titre /cm^{-3}*	37.63	35.20	33.63	31.90	29.86	28.04
t/s (contd.)		11 232		78 840		
Iodine titre/cm^3 (contd.)*		26.01		22.24		

**In cm^3 of 0.01286 mol dm^{-3} iodine solution per 10.02 cm^3 sample.*

Initial concentration of sodium thiosulphate = 0.0966 mol dm^{-3}.
From the given data, show that the reaction is second order and calculate the rate constant at 37.5°C.

The thiosulphate concentration is proportional to the iodine titre at any time. At time $t = 78\,840$ s the reaction is complete, and the iodine titre is proportional to the excess of thiosulphate. The difference between the initial and final titre is thus proportional to the amount of propyl bromide initially present in the sample volume, and hence to its concentration. The difference between the titre at any particular time and the final titre will be proportional to the concentration of propyl bromide remaining at that time. The expression for the rate constant (k_2) of a second order process ($A + B \rightarrow$ products) is

$$k_2 = \frac{2.303}{t([B]_0 - [A]_0)} \log \frac{[A]_0[B]}{[B]_0[A]} \qquad \text{(i)}$$

where the $[]_0$ terms represent the initial concentrations, and the $[]$ terms represent the concentrations at time t.
Equation (i) may be rewritten:

$$t = \frac{2.303}{k_2([B]_0 - [A]_0)} \log \frac{[A]_0}{[B]_0} + \frac{2.303}{k_2([B]_0 - [A]_0)} \log \frac{[B]}{[A]} \qquad \text{(ii)}$$

Equation (ii) is of the form $y = c + mx$ and a plot of t against $\log \frac{[B]}{[A]}$ should be a straight line, if the reaction is second order.

The data necessary for a plot of t against $\log \frac{[S_2O_3^{2-}]}{[C_3H_7Br]}$, that is, $\log \frac{[B]}{[A]}$, may be derived from the information given in the question and is tabulated below, the plot being shown in Fig. 24.

t/s	$[S_2O_3^{2-}]/(cm^3 \text{ of } I_2)$	$[C_3H_7Br]/(cm^3 \text{ of } I_2)$	$\frac{[S_2O_3^{2-}]}{[C_3H_7Br]}$
0	37.63	15.39	0.3882
1 110	35.20	12.96	0.4339
2 010	33.63	11.39	0.4701
3 192	31.90	9.66	0.5188
5 052	29.86	7.62	0.5931
7 380	28.04	5.80	0.6844
11 232	26.01	3.77	0.8388
78 840	22.24	0	

Inspection of Fig. 24 shows that a good straight line graph is obtained, proving that the reaction is second order.

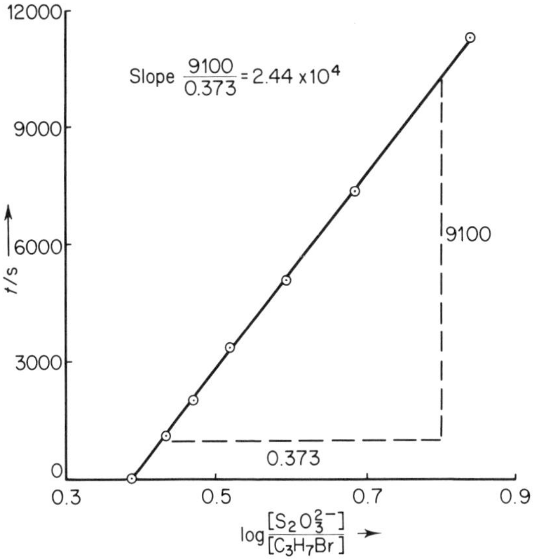

Fig. 24 Plot of time against $\log \dfrac{[S_2O_3^{2-}]}{[C_3H_7Br]}$

From the graph, the slope

$$\frac{2.303}{k_2([S_2O_3^{2-}]_0 - [C_3H_7Br]_0)} = 2.44 \times 10^4$$

But $[S_2O_3^{2-}]_0 = 0.0966M$ and $[C_3H_7Br]_0 = \dfrac{15.39}{10.02} \times 2 \times 0.01286$

$$= 0.0395 \text{ mol dm}^{-3}$$

Therefore

$$k_2 = \frac{2.303}{(0.0966-0.0395)\times 2.44\times 10^4} (\text{mol dm}^{-3})^{-1}\,\text{s}^{-1}$$

$$= 1.65\times 10^{-3}\,\text{mol}^{-1}\,\text{dm}^3\,\text{s}^{-1}.$$

The reaction $C_3H_7Br + S_2O_3^{2-} = C_3H_7S_2O_3^- + Br^-$ is second order, the rate constant being 1.65×10^{-3} mol^{-1} dm^3 s^{-1}.

Example 9.5 First order reaction—half-life period

At 858 K the decomposition of dinitrogen oxide into nitrogen and oxygen follows a first order law. The pressure (P) exerted during the decomposition of nitrous oxide in a fixed volume, was measured at times t with the following results:

t/hours	*0*	*26.5*	*62.6*
P/kg cm^{-2}	*37.43*	*41.54*	*45.59*

Calculate the 'half-life' of the reaction. (*B.Sc., Bristol*)

Dinitrogen oxide decomposes as follows:

$$N_2O \longrightarrow N_2 + \tfrac{1}{2}O_2$$

Therefore, the total pressure, $P = P_{N_2O} + P_{N_2} + P_{O_2}$. If P_i is the initial pressure of N_2O and y the decrease in its pressure at time, t, then

$$P_{N_2O} = P_i - y$$

and $$P_{N_2} = y \quad \text{and} \quad P_{O_2} = \tfrac{1}{2}y$$

Therefore $$P = P_i + \tfrac{1}{2}y$$

and $$y = 2(P - P_i)$$

Therefore $$P_{N_2O} = (3P_i - 2P)$$

The equation for a first order reaction is

$$k_1 = \frac{1}{t}\ln\frac{a}{(a-x)} \tag{i}$$

The initial concentration, a, is proportional to P_i, and the concentration at time t, $(a-x)$, is proportional to $P_{N_2O} = (3P_i - 2P)$.

Therefore, equation (i) can be written as follows:

$$k_1 = \frac{2.303}{t} \log \frac{P_i}{3P_i - 2P} \qquad \text{(ii)}$$

Fig. 25 is a plot of t against the $\log \frac{P_i}{3P_i - 2P}$ values shown in the following table:

t/hours	0	26.5	62.6
$3P_i - 2P$/kg cm^{-2}	37.43	29.21	21.11
$\log \frac{P_i}{3P_i - 2P}$	0	0.1077	0.2487

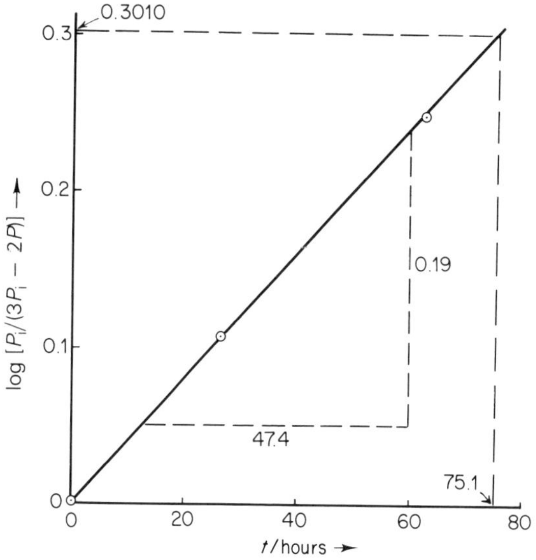

Fig. 25 Plot of time against $\log \frac{P_i}{3P_i - 2P}$

The slope of the line is given by

$$\frac{k_1}{2.303} = \frac{0.19}{47.4}$$

Therefore $\qquad k_1 = 9.232 \times 10^{-3}$ hour^{-1}

For 'half reaction' $\quad x = \frac{1}{2}P_i$.

Substitution of the data in equation (i) gives the value for the 'half-life' ($t_{1/2}$):

$$t_{1/2} = \frac{2.303}{k_1} \log \frac{P_i}{P_i - \frac{1}{2}P}$$

$$= \frac{2.303}{9.232 \times 10^{-3}} \log 2 \text{ hours}$$

$$= 75.09 \text{ hours}$$

The 'half-life' of the decomposition of dinitrogen oxide at 858K is 75.1 hours.

Note Alternatively, $t_{1/2}$ can be read directly from the graph by reading off the value of t corresponding to the value of log 2 (= 0.3010) for $\log P_i/(3P_i - 2P)$. This also gives 75.1 hours.

Example 9.6 Reversible first order reaction

The acid catalyzed conversion of 3-hydroxy-butanoic acid into its lactone was studied in 0.2 mol dm^{-3} HCl solution at 25°C. The initial concentration of the hydroxy acid (measured in arbitrary units) was 18.23. The concentration of lactone (expressed in the same units) is shown as a function of time in the following table:

Time/min	0	21	36	50	65	80	100	∞
Lactone concentration	0	2.41	3.73	4.96	6.10	7.08	8.11	13.28

Calculate the equilibrium constant and the first order velocity coefficients for the forward and reverse processes.

(*B.Sc., Southampton*)

The reaction scheme may be represented

$$\text{Acid} \underset{k}{\overset{k}{\rightleftharpoons}} \text{Lactone}$$

where k and k' are the first order velocity coefficients for the forward and reverse processes respectively.

Let the initial acid concentration be a units of concentration and that at time t be $(a-x)$ units of concentration. The concentration of lactone at time t is thus x units of concentration.

The net rate of reaction at time t is given by

$$\frac{dx}{dt} = k(a-x)-k'x \qquad \text{(i)}$$

At equilibrium $dx/dt = 0$, and

$$k(a-x_e) = k'x_e \qquad \text{(ii)}$$

where x_e is the equilibrium value of x.
Thus

$$\frac{k}{k'} = K = \frac{x_e}{a-x_e} \qquad \text{(iii)}$$

where K is the equilibrium constant for the reaction. From the given data $x_e = 13.28$ and $a = 18.23$. Therefore, the equilibrium constant for the process is given by

$$K = \frac{13.28}{4.95} = 2.68$$

Substitution of the value of k' given by equation (ii) into equation (i) yields

$$\frac{dx}{dt} = k(a-x)-\frac{kx}{x_e}(a-x_e)$$

$$= \frac{ka}{x_e}(x_e-x) \qquad \text{(iv)}$$

Integration of equation (iv) between the limits of $t = 0$ and $t = t$, and $x = 0$ and $x = x$ yields

$$\frac{kat}{x_e} = \ln\left(\frac{x_e}{x_e-x}\right) \qquad \text{(v)}$$

From equation (ii), it is seen that $ka/x_e = k+k'$, and substitution of this value in equation (v) yields

$$(k+k')t = \ln\left(\frac{x_e}{x_e-x}\right)$$

and

$$t = \frac{2.303}{(k+k')}\log\left(\frac{x_e}{x_e-x}\right)$$

or
$$t = \frac{2.303}{(k+k')} \log x_e - \frac{2.303}{(k+k')} \log (x_e - x)$$

Thus a graph of t against $\log (x_e - x)$ should give a straight line of slope $-2.303/(k+k')$. Fig. 26 shows such a plot made from the data in the following table:

Time/min	0	21	36	50	65	80	100
$(x_e - x)$	13.28	10.87	9.55	8.32	7.18	6.20	5.17
$\log (x_e - x)$	1.123	1.036	0.980	0.920	0.856	0.792	0.714

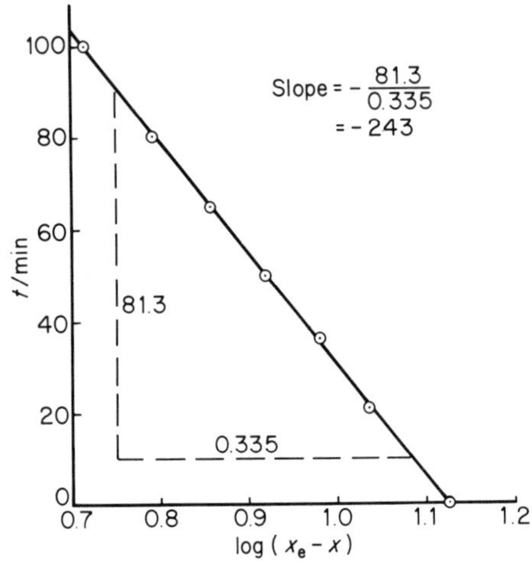

Fig. 26 Plot of time versus $\log (x_e - x)$

Examination of Fig. 26 shows that the slope

$$-\frac{2.303}{(k+k')} = -243.$$

Therefore

$$k+k' = 9.48 \times 10^{-3} \text{ min}^{-1} \qquad \text{(vi)}$$

Since $\frac{k}{k'} = K = 2.68$, substitution for k in equation (vi) yields

$$3.68k' = 9.48 \times 10^{-3} \text{ min}^{-1}$$

Therefore $k' = 2.58 \times 10^{-3} \text{ min}^{-1}$

and hence $k = 6.90 \times 10^{-3} \text{ min}^{-1}$

The equilibrium constant for the conversion of 3-hydroxy-butanoic acid into its lactone is 2.68. The first order velocity coefficient for the forward reaction is $6.90 \times 10^{-3}\ \text{min}^{-1}$ and that for the reverse reaction is $2.58 \times 10^{-3}\ \text{min}^{-1}$.

Example 9.7 Order of reaction and half-life period

The decomposition of a compound in solution gave the following data at 57.4°C:

Initial conc. /mol dm^{-3}	*0.50*	*1.10*	*2.48*
Time for half decomposition / s	*4280*	*885*	*174*

Deduce the order and rate coefficient for the reaction.

(B.Sc., Wales)

Since the time for half decomposition is not independent of the initial concentration of reactant, the reaction is not a first order process.

For a reaction of the nth order, the rate equation is

$$-\frac{d[A]}{dt} = k_n[A]^n \tag{i}$$

where $[A]$ is the concentration of the reactant and k_n is the reaction rate coefficient.

Integration of equation (i) when $n \geqslant 2$ yields

$$t = \text{constant} + \frac{1}{k_n(n-1)} \cdot \frac{1}{[A]^{n-1}} \tag{ii}$$

When $t = 0$, equation (ii) reads

$$\text{constant} = -\frac{1}{k_n(n-1)} \cdot \frac{1}{[A]_0^{n-1}} \tag{iii}$$

$[A]$ and $[A]_0$ in equations (ii) and (iii) are the concentrations of the reactant at time $t = t$ and the time $t = 0$ respectively. Therefore, the time for half decomposition, $t_{1/2}$, is given by

$$t_{1/2} = \frac{1}{k_n(n-1)} \left(\frac{2^{(n-1)} - 1}{[A]_0^{(n-1)}} \right)$$

On taking logarithms

$$\log t_{1/2} = \log\left(\frac{2^{(n-1)}-1}{k_n(n-1)}\right) - (n-1)\log [A]_0 \qquad \text{(iv)}$$

Equation (iv) is of the form $y = c+mx$, therefore a graph of $\log t_{1/2}$ against $\log [A]_0$ should be a straight line of slope $-(n-1)$.

From the information given in the question, the following data may be calculated and used to plot the graph shown in Fig. 27.

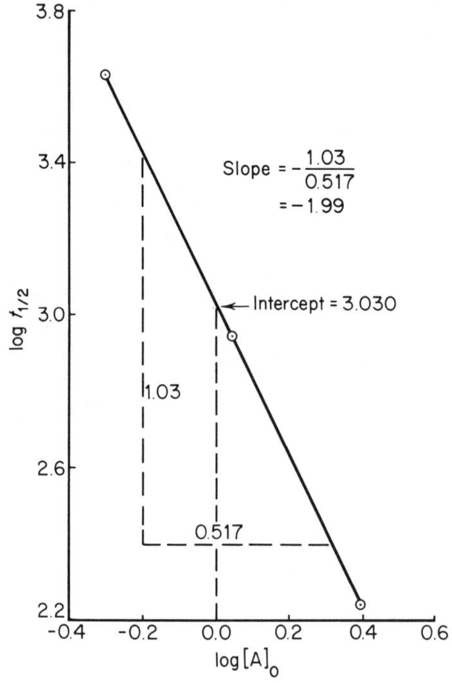

Fig. 27 Plot of $\log t_{1/2}$ against $\log [A]_0$

$\log [A]_0$	−0.3010	0.0414	0.3945
$\log t_{1/2}$	3.6314	2.9469	2.2405

The graph is a straight line of slope −1.99, hence

$$-(n-1) = -1.99$$

and

$$n = 2.99$$

The reaction is therefore, third order.

For a third order reaction, the constant term in equation (iv) becomes $\log \frac{3}{2k_3}$, where k_3 is the third order rate coefficient. From the intercept of the graph in Fig. 27.

$$\log \frac{3}{2k_3} = 3.030.$$

Therefore

$$\frac{3}{2k_3} = 1072$$

and $$k_3 = 1.399 \times 10^{-3}\ (\text{mol dm}^{-3})^{-2}\ \text{s}^{-1}$$

The reaction is third order and the rate coefficient is 1.4×10^{-3} $\text{mol}^{-2}\,\text{dm}^6\,\text{s}^{-1}$.

Note k_3 can also be calculated directly from equation (iv):

$$t_{1/2} = \frac{1}{2k_3} \cdot \frac{3}{[A]_0^2}$$

or $$k_3 = \frac{3}{2} \cdot \frac{1}{t_{1/2}[A]_0^2}$$

Substituting 4280 for $t_{1/2}$ and 0.50 for $[A]_0$

$$k_3 = \frac{3}{2 \times 4280 \times 0.25}\ \text{mol}^{-2}\,\text{dm}^6\,\text{s}^{-1}$$

$$= 1.4 \times 10^{-3}\ \text{mol}^{-2}\,\text{dm}^6\,\text{s}^{-1}$$

Example 9.8 Energy and entropy of activation

The following values have been obtained for the velocity constant in the decomposition of N_2O_5:

$t/°C$	0	25	45	65
k/min^{-1}	4.7×10^{-5}	2.0×10^{-3}	3.0×10^{-2}	3.0×10^{-1}

What information can you derive from these data?

(B.Sc. (Subsid. Subject), Bristol)

The velocity constant (k) is given by the Arrhenius equation

$$k = Ae^{-E/RT} \tag{i}$$

where E is the energy of activation, R the gas constant, T the absolute temperature and A the frequency factor. Sometimes A is replaced by the product PZ, where Z is the collision rate between reactant molecules and P is the probability factor which is inserted to allow for the disparity between calculated and observed values of k.

The logarithmic form of equation (i) is

$$\log k = \log A - \frac{E}{2.303RT} \tag{ii}$$

Equation (ii) shows a linear relationship between $\log k$ and $1/T$, the slope being $-E/2.303R$ and the intercept on the $\log k$ axis is $\log A$.

From the data given in the question, the energy of activation, E, and the frequency factor, A, may be determined directly. Additionally, the enthalpy of activation, $\Delta H^{\ominus\ddagger}$, and the entropy of activation, $\Delta S^{\ominus\ddagger}$, may be calculated from the values of E and A.

The values of $\log k$ and $1/T$, shown in the table, are plotted in Fig. 28.

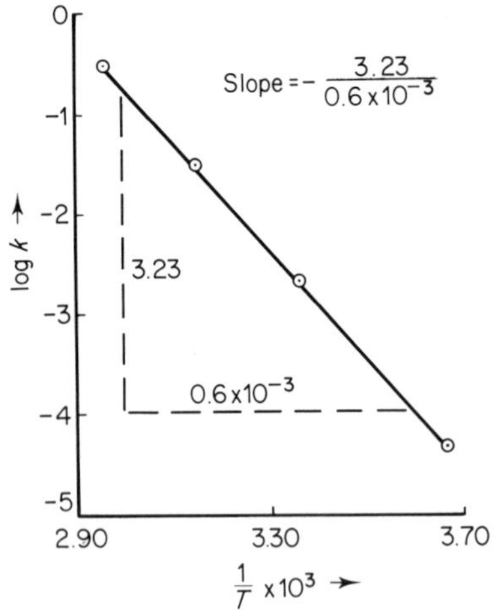

Fig. 28 Plot of $\log k$ versus $1/T$

$\log k$	-4.328	-2.699	-1.523	-0.523
T/K	273	298	318	338
$1/T$/K^{-1}	3.66×10^{-3}	3.36×10^{-3}	3.15×10^{-3}	2.96×10^{-3}

Inspection of Fig. 28 shows that the slope

$$-\frac{E}{2.303R} = -\frac{3.23}{0.6\times10^{-3}}$$

Therefore

$$E = \frac{2.303\times8.31\times3.23}{0.6\times10^{-3}}\ \text{J mol}^{-1}$$

$$= \underline{103\ \text{kJ mol}^{-1}}$$

From the transition-state theory, the rate constant, k, is given by

$$k = \frac{RT}{Lh}\,e^{\Delta S^{\ominus\ddagger}/R}\,e^{-\Delta H^{\ominus\ddagger}/RT} \tag{iii}$$

where L is the Avogadro number, h is Planck's constant, $\Delta S^{\ominus\ddagger}$ is the entropy of activation and $\Delta H^{\ominus\ddagger}$ is the enthalpy of activation.

Equation (iii) is of the same form as equation (i) if $\Delta H^{\ominus\ddagger}$ is approximated to the activation energy, E. Hence, the frequency factor, A, is equal to $\frac{RT}{Lh}e^{\Delta S^{\ominus\ddagger}/R}$. For liquid and solid systems and for unimolecular gas reactions

$$E = \Delta H^{\ominus\ddagger} + RT$$

Hence, for the decomposition of N_2O_5 at 0°C

$$\Delta H^{\ominus\ddagger} = 103\,000 - 8.31\times273\ \text{J mol}^{-1}$$

$$= 103\,000 - 2269\ \text{J mol}^{-1}$$

$$= \underline{100.7\ \text{kJ mol}^{-1}}$$

Taking the data for 0°C and substituting in equation (ii)

$$-4.328 = \log A - \frac{103\,000}{2.303\times8.31\times273}$$

Therefore

$$\log A = \frac{103\,000}{2.303\times8.31\times273} - 4.328$$

$$= 15.382$$

and $\underline{A = 2.41\times10^{15}\ \text{min}^{-1} = 4.17\times10^{13}\ \text{s}^{-1}}$

Since
$$A = \frac{RT}{Lh} e^{\Delta S^{\ominus\ddagger}/R}$$

$$\log A = \log \frac{RT}{Lh} + \frac{\Delta S^{\ominus\ddagger}}{2.303R}$$

A must be expressed in units of s^{-1} to be consistent with the units for h. Hence, at 0°C

$$13.620 = \log \frac{8.31 \times 273}{6.02 \times 10^{23} \times 6.624 \times 10^{-34}} + \frac{\Delta S^{\ominus\ddagger}}{2.303 \times 8.31}$$

$$= 12.755 + \frac{\Delta S^{\ominus\ddagger}}{2.303 \times 8.31}$$

Therefore
$$\Delta S^{\ominus\ddagger} = 0.8650 \times 2.303 \times 8.31 \text{ J K}^{-1} \text{ mol}^{-1}$$

$$= 16.57 \text{ J K}^{-1} \text{ mol}^{-1}.$$

Summary From the data given in the question, it is possible to derive
(*a*) the Arrhenius energy of activation, $E = 103$ kJ mol^{-1}
(*b*) the enthalpy of activation, $\Delta H^{\ominus\ddagger} = 100.7$ kJ mol^{-1}
(*c*) the Arrhenius frequency factor, $A = 4.17 \times 10^{13}$ s^{-1}
and (*d*) the entropy of activation, $\Delta S^{\ominus\ddagger} = 16.6$ J K^{-1} mol^{-1}.

Example 9.9 The collision theory of bimolecular reactions

At 283°C at a concentration of one mole per dm^3, the number of molecules of hydrogen iodine colliding per second is 6×10^{31} per cm^3. The activation energy of the reaction is 187 kJ. Calculate the number of molecules reacting per cm^3. (*R.S.C.*)

The reaction is $2HI = H_2 + I_2$.

If Z is the number of molecules colliding per cm^3 per second in a system containing one mole of reactant per dm^3, and x the fraction of these that are activated, then the specific rate (k) of the bimolecular reaction in molecules per cm^3 per second is given by

$$k = Zx \quad \text{(i)}$$

Z is given in the question, x can be calculated from the following equation:

$$x = e^{-E/RT} \quad \text{(ii)}$$

where E is the energy of activation, R = the gas constant and T = the absolute temperature.
Combining equations (i) and (ii)

$$k = Ze^{-E/RT} \qquad \text{(iii)}$$

Substitution of the data given in the question in equation (iii) gives

$$k = 6 \times 10^{31}\, e^{-187\,000/(8.31 \times 556)}$$

Taking logarithms

$$\log k = \log (6 \times 10^{31}) - \frac{187\,000}{8.31 \times 2.303 \times 556}$$

$$= 31.778 - 17.57$$

$$= 14.208$$

Therefore $\qquad k = 1.614 \times 10^{14}$ molecules reacting $cm^{-3}\,s^{-1}$.

The number of molecules reacting is $\underline{1.6 \times 10^{14}\ cm^{-3}\,s^{-1}}$.

Example 9.10 Heterogeneous gas reaction

The following results were obtained for the decomposition of ammonia on a tungsten wire at 856°C:

Total pressure/mmHg	*228*	*250*	*273*	*318*
Time/s	*200*	*400*	*600*	*1000*

Find the order of the reaction and comment on the mechanism of the decomposition. How would you expect this to be affected by working at much lower pressures?

Calculate the rate constant of the reaction, expressing concentration in moles per dm^3 *and time in seconds.* (*R.S.C.*)

Gas reactions catalysed by solids proceed at the surface of the catalyst. The catalytic reaction depends, among other factors, on the adsorption of the reacting gases on the catalyst surface.

The concentration on the catalyst surface of a single reactant gas is proportional to the fraction (θ) of surface covered by the gas and the rate of reaction ($-\mathrm{d}P/\mathrm{d}t$) is proportional to this fraction:

$$-\frac{\mathrm{d}P}{\mathrm{d}t} = k\theta \qquad \text{(i)}$$

where P is the partial pressure of the gas. For a strongly adsorbed gas, $\theta = 1$ and the rate of reaction is given by

$$-\frac{\mathrm{d}P}{\mathrm{d}t} = k \qquad \text{(ii)}$$

Equation (ii) shows that the reaction velocity is independent of pressure and the reaction is therefore zero order. Ammonia decomposes:

$$NH_3 = \tfrac{1}{2}N_2 + \tfrac{3}{2}H_2$$

that is, one mole of ammonia gives two moles of products, so that the rate of increase in total pressure (P_T) is equal to the rate of decrease in ammonia pressure. The particular form of equation (ii) applicable to this decomposition is, therefore

$$\frac{\mathrm{d}P_T}{\mathrm{d}t} = k \qquad \text{(iii)}$$

If the ammonia decomposition shows zero order kinetics, the pressure/time data given in the question, when plotted against one another should give a straight line of slope $\mathrm{d}P_T/\mathrm{d}t = k$. Fig. 29 shows this to be the case and the slope $\mathrm{d}P_T/\mathrm{d}t = \dfrac{86}{760}$ mm s^{-1}. Therefore

$$\begin{aligned}
k &= \frac{86}{760}\ \text{mm s}^{-1} \\
&= \frac{86}{760 \times 760}\ \text{atm s}^{-1} \\
&= \frac{86 \times 1.013 \times 10^5}{(760)^2 RT \times 10^3}\ \text{mol dm}^{-3}\ \text{s}^{-1} \\
&= \frac{86 \times 1.013 \times 10^2}{(760)^2 \times 8.31 \times 1129}\ \text{mol dm}^{-3}\ \text{s}^{-1} \\
&= 1.609 \times 10^{-6}\ \text{mol dm}^{-3}\ \text{s}^{-1}
\end{aligned}$$

The rate constant of the reaction is $\underline{1.61 \times 10^{-6}\ \text{mol dm}^{-3}\ \text{s}^{-1}}$.

Since the reaction is zero order it can be concluded that the adsorption of ammonia is such as to cover all the available sites on the catalyst

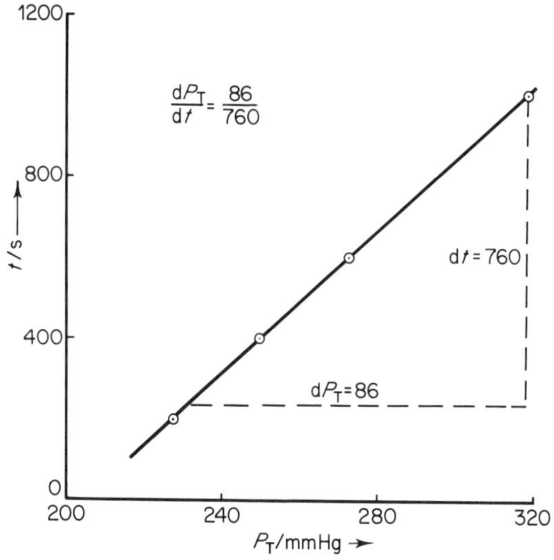

Fig. 29 Plot of pressure versus time

surface. When the system acquires its activation energy molecular hydrogen and nitrogen are formed on the surface. Since the product gases are not strongly adsorbed they diffuse away from the surface leaving adsorption sites available for more ammonia molecules.

The zero order constant prevails for the ammonia decomposition, down to very low pressures. Working at much lower pressures, however, will cause the fraction of the surface covered to show a proportionality to the pressure, so that equation (i) takes the form

$$-\frac{dP}{dt} = kP$$

Hence, at much lower pressures the ammonia decomposition would be expected to show a departure from zero order kinetics and approach the characteristics of a first order reaction.

Example 9.11 Ionic reaction

The reaction $BrCH_2COO^- + S_2O_3^{2-} = S_2O_3CH_2COO^{2-} + Br^-$ in which the sodium salts were used, was followed by taking 50 cm^3 portions of the reaction mixture at definite times, adding 25 cm^3 of iodine solution, and back titrating the excess with standard thiosulphate solution.

In a particular run at 25°C the initial concentrations of the reactants were each 0.0005 mol dm^{-3}. The excess iodine at the times t after starting the run were as follows:

t/min	*0*	*2112*	*3356*	*3559*
Excess iodine/cm^3	*0.2*	*6.15*	*8.49*	*8.80*

The rate constants obtained for runs at the same temperature but for different values of the initial concentrations are listed below:

Concentration/mol dm^{-3}	*0.0007*	*0.0010*	*0.0014*	*0.0020*
Rate constant/dm^3 mol^{-1} min^{-1}	*0.309*	*0.324*	*0.343*	*0.366*

Evaluate (a) the second order rate constant for the initial concentration of 0.0005 mol dm^{-3}; (b) the rate constant when the ionic activity coefficients are unity. (The Debye-Hückel constant at 25°C = 0.509.)

From the given data, the amount (x cm^3) of iodine equivalent to the thiosulphate remaining in the 50 cm^3 portions of reaction mixture at times t are as follows:

t/min	*x/cm^3*
0	$25.0 - 0.2 = 24.8$
2112	$25.0 - 6.15 = 18.85$
3356	$25.0 - 8.49 = 16.51$
3559	$25.0 - 8.80 = 16.20$

These quantities of iodine solution are directly proportional to the concentrations of thiosulphate remaining at times t. Furthermore, since the reaction is a second order process, and the initial concentrations of reactants are equal, the quantities (x) will also be proportional to the concentrations of bromoethanoate ion at times t. The concentrations of reactants at times t are as listed:

t/min	*Concentration/mol dm^{-3}*
0	0.0005
2112	$0.0005 \times \frac{18.85}{24.8} = 0.000380$
3356	$0.0005 \times \frac{16.51}{24.8} = 0.000333$
3559	$0.0005 \times \frac{16.2}{24.8} = 0.000327$

Using the second order rate equation in the form

$$k = \frac{1}{t}\left(\frac{1}{[A]} - \frac{1}{[A]_0}\right) \quad \text{(i)}$$

where k = the second order rate constant, t = time, $[A]$ and $[A]_0$ are the concentrations at time t and at the commencement respectively. Therefore

$$k = \frac{1}{2112}\left(\frac{1}{0.00038} - \frac{1}{0.0005}\right) \text{ dm}^3 \text{ mol}^{-1} \text{ min}^{-1}$$
$$= 0.298 \text{ dm}^3 \text{ mol}^{-1} \text{ min}^{-1}$$

The data for the other times yield values of 0.299 and 0.297 $\text{dm}^3 \text{ mol}^{-1} \text{ min}^{-1}$. Mean value of k = 0.298 $\text{dm}^3 \text{ mol}^{-1} \text{ min}^{-1}$.

The ionic activity coefficients of the reactants will be unity in a solution of zero ionic strength, and the rate constant in such a solution may be deduced using the Brönsted-Bjerrum equation:

$$\log k_{obs} = \log k_0 + 2Az_Az_B\sqrt{\mu} \quad \text{(ii)}$$

where k_{obs} is the experimentally determined rate constant, k_0 is the rate constant in a solution of zero ionic strength, A is the Debye-Hückel constant, z_A and z_B are the valencies of the reacting ionic species, and μ is the total ionic strength of the solution (see Example 6.16).

Equation (ii) is a linear relationship between $\log k_{obs}$ and $\sqrt{\mu}$ of slope $2Az_Az_B$ and intercept $\log k_0$. z_A and z_B are the valencies of the thiosulphate ion and bromoethanoate ion respectively.

The initial ionic strengths of the solutions are quoted in the following table:

Concentration /mol dm^{-3}	μ	$\sqrt{\mu}$	k_{obs}	$\log k_{obs}$
0.0005	0.0020	0.0447	0.298	$\bar{1}.4742$
0.0007	0.0028	0.0529	0.309	$\bar{1}.4900$
0.0010	0.0040	0.0633	0.324	$\bar{1}.5105$
0.0014	0.0056	0.0748	0.343	$\bar{1}.5353$
0.0020	0.0080	0.0894	0.366	$\bar{1}.5635$

The graph of $\log k_{obs}$ against $\sqrt{\mu}$ is shown in Fig. 30 and the intercept on the ordinate is $\bar{1}.385$.

Therefore $\log k_0 = \bar{1}.385$

And $k_0 = 0.243 \text{ dm}^3 \text{ mol}^{-1} \text{ min}^{-1}$

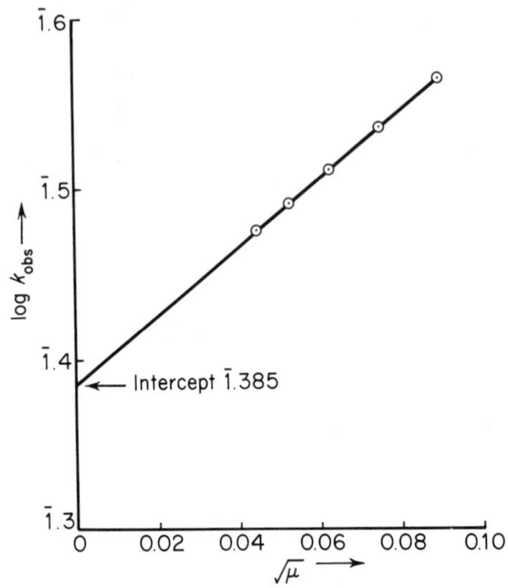

Fig. 30 Plot of log k_{obs} versus $\sqrt{\mu}$

(*a*) The second order rate constant for the initial concentration of 0.0005 mol dm^{-3} is 0.298 dm^3 mol^{-1} min^{-1} = 4.97 × 10^{-3} dm^3 mol^{-1} s^{-1}.

(*b*) The rate constant when the ionic activity coefficients are unity is 0.243 dm^3 mol^{-1} min^{-1} = 4.05 × 10^{-3} dm^3 mol^{-1} s^{-1}.

Note Since the reaction is in aqueous solution at 25°C, the slope of the graph (Fig. 30) should be

$$2Az_Az_B = 2 \times 0.509 \times 1 \times 2$$
$$= 2.036$$

The actual slope is 2.0, showing good agreement between the observed and theoretical values.

Example 9.12 Enzyme reactions—the Michaelis constant

Progress curves were obtained for an enzyme for a series of substrate concentrations, the results were as follows (temperature 37°C; pH 6.5):

Substrate concentration $/\mathrm{mol\,dm^{-3}}$	$\frac{1}{5}$	$\frac{1}{10}$	$\frac{1}{20}$	$\frac{1}{40}$	$\frac{1}{60}$	$\frac{1}{80}$	$\frac{1}{100}$
Initial velocity $\times 10^6$ $/\mathrm{dm^3\,O_2\,min^{-1}}$	19.2	18.2	16.7	14.3	12.5	11.2	10.0

Substrate concentration (contd.) $/\mathrm{mol\,dm^{-3}}$	$\frac{1}{200}$	$\frac{1}{500}$	$\frac{1}{1000}$
Initial velocity $\times 10^6$ *(contd.)* $/\mathrm{dm^3\,O_2\,min^{-1}}$	6.7	3.3	1.8

Obtain the Michaelis constant. *(B.Sc., Wales)*

Theoretical background

Enzyme reactions proceed in two stages:

(*a*) Formation of a complex between the enzyme and the substrate:

$$E + S \underset{k'}{\overset{k}{\rightleftharpoons}} ES \qquad \text{(i)}$$

(*b*) Decomposition of the complex into reaction products, with regeneration of the enzyme

$$ES \xrightarrow{k_t} \text{Products} + E \qquad \text{(ii)}$$

The rate equation governing such reactions is the Michaelis-Menten equation which may be derived as follows:

Assume that a fraction θ of enzyme molecules are involved in complex formation. The rate of formation of the complex (equation (i) from left to right) will be proportional to the concentration of the free enzyme, that is, to $(1-\theta)\,[E]_0$ (where $[E]_0$ is the total enzyme concentration), and also to the substrate concentration.
Therefore

$$v = k(1-\theta)\,[E]_0[S] \qquad \text{(iii)}$$

The rate of the reverse reaction in process (i) is proportional to the concentration of complex, that is, to θ.
Therefore

$$v' = k'\theta[E]_0$$

At equilibrium $v = v'$, and

$$k(1-\theta)[E]_0[S] = k'\theta[E]_0$$

Therefore
$$\frac{\theta}{(1-\theta)} = \frac{k}{k'}[S] \qquad \text{(iv)}$$

But $k/k' = K$, the equilibrium constant for process (i).
Therefore, from equation (iv)

$$\theta = \frac{K[S]}{1+K[S]} \qquad \text{(v)}$$

If it is assumed that process (ii) is sufficiently slow for the equilibrium represented by process (i) to be effectively undisturbed, then the rate of reaction, v_t, which is proportional to the concentration of complex will be

$$v_t = k_t\theta[E]_0$$
$$= \frac{k_tK[S][E]_0}{1+K[S]}$$

which may be written as

$$v_t = \frac{k_t[S][E]_0}{K_m+[S]} \qquad \text{(vi)}$$

where $K_m = 1/K$ is the *Michaelis constant*, and is the dissociation constant of the enzyme-substrate complex.

Equation (vi) may be rearranged as follows:

$$v_t(K_m+[S]) = k_t[S][E]_0$$

Therefore

$$\frac{v_t}{[S]} = \frac{k_t[E]_0}{K_m} - \frac{v_t}{K_m} \qquad \text{(vii)}$$

Thus a plot of v_t/S against v_t should be a straight line of slope $-1/K_m$. This treatment of the experimental data was suggested by G. S. Eadie (*J. Biol. Chem.*, **146** (1942), 85). The intercept on the v_t axis is $k_t[E]_0$ which is the rate for which $\theta = 1$, that is, the maximum rate obtained when the substrate concentration is so high that the enzyme is practically completely in the form of the complex. In this condition, further increase in substrate concentration can produce no further increase in complex concentration, so that the reaction rate, which is proportional to the complex concentration, becomes independent of substrate concentration and attains a limiting value.

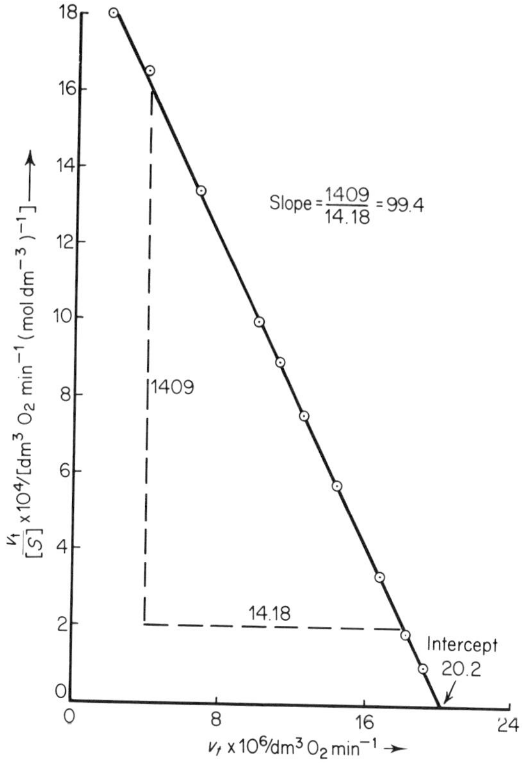

Fig. 31 Eadie plot for determining the Michaelis constant

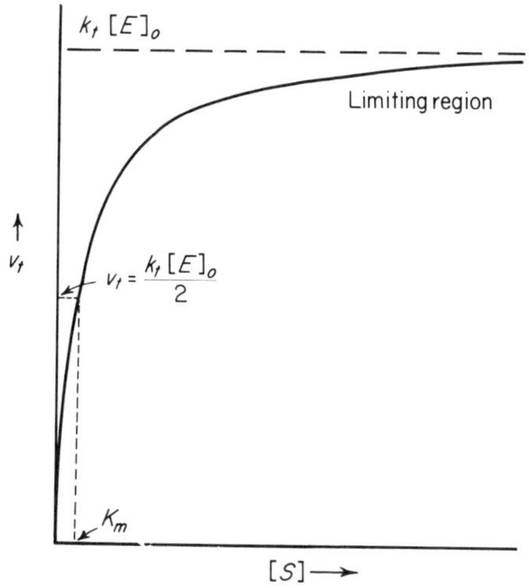

Fig. 32 Illustration of type of plot obtained when initial rate (v_t) is plotted against substrate concentration

Solution

From the given data the following table may be made:

$(v_t/[S]) \times 10^6/\text{dm}^3\,O_2\,\text{min}^{-1}\,(\text{mol dm}^{-3})^{-1}$	96	182	334	572	748.4	896
$v_t \times 10^6\,\text{dm}^3\,O_2\,\text{min}^{-1}$	19.2	18.2	16.7	14.3	12.5	11.2
$v_t/[S] \times 10^6$ (contd.)	1000	1340	1650	1800		
$v_t \times 10^6$ (contd.)	10.0	6.7	3.8	1.8		

The Eadie plot obtained from these data is shown in Fig. 31. The slope of the graph is found to be 99.4 $(\text{mol dm}^{-3})^{-1}$. Therefore, the Michaelis constant

$$K_m = 1/99.4 = 0.0101\ \text{mol dm}^{-3}.$$

The Michaelis constant is 0.0101 mol dm^{-3}.

Note From the intercept of the graph (Fig. 31) on the v_t axis, the limiting reaction rate is found to be 20.2×10^{-6} dm^3 O_2 min^{-1}.

From equation (vi) it is seen that when $[S] = K_m$, $v_t = k_t[E]_0/2$. Thus the Michaelis constant K_m is equal to the substrate concentration at which the observed rate is one half of the limiting value. Thus the initial rate can be plotted against substrate concentration, and if the substrate concentration is taken to sufficiently high values, a plot of the type shown in Fig. 32 is obtained.

The limiting value may be estimated from the limiting region. It is clear that this method of obtaining K_m is not so accurate as the Eadie method, since the limiting rate can only be estimated approximately.

Additional Examples

1 The hydrolysis of bromomethane is a first order reaction whose progress may be followed chemically by titrating samples of the reaction mixture with silver nitrate. The volume required for 10 cm^3 samples at 330 K in a typical experiment are:

t/s	0	528	18 000	24 720	∞
$AgNO_3$/cm^3	0	5.9	17.3	22.1	49.5

Calculate the velocity constant for this reaction. (B.Sc., Durham)

2 The muta-rotation of glucose is a proton catalysed reaction. The following polarimeter readings were observed for the reaction at 25°C when the concentration of hydrochloric acid in the reaction mixture was 0.01 mol dm^{-3}.

Time/s	0	300	1500	∞
Reading/arbitrary units	33.2	31.2	25.5	18.0

Calculate the first order velocity constant under these conditions.

(B.Sc., Wales)

3 The following data refer to the decomposition of *N*-(phenylazo) chloride

$$C_6H_5N_2Cl = C_6H_5Cl + N_2$$

at a starting concentration of 10 g dm^{-3}, in solution at 50°C.

Time/s	360	540	720	840	1080	1320	1440	1560	1800	∞
N_2 evolved/cm^3	19.3	26.0	32.6	36.0	41.3	45.0	46.5	48.4	50.4	58.3

Find the order, the rate constant and the half-life of the reaction.

(R.S.C.)

4 In a spectrophotometric study of the first order solvolysis reaction of cinnamal chloride in ethanolic sodium hydroxide at 22.6°C, Andrews (*J.A.C.S.*, **69** (1947), 3062) followed the reaction by noting the rate of disappearance of the absorption maximum at 260 nm. The following observations were made:

Time/hours	0	0.167	0.516	1.23	2.21
Absorbance (at 260 nm)	0.406	0.382	0.338	0.255	0.184

Calculate the rate constant of the reaction.

5 An acid solution of sucrose was hydrolysed to the extent of 57% after 66 minutes. Assuming the reaction to be unimolecular calculate (*a*) the time taken for 75% hydrolysis, (*b*) the extent of hydrolysis after 2 hours.

(B.Pharm., Wales)

6 A substance *A* decomposes homogeneously in the gas phase according to the equation

$$A = 2B + C$$

The following table gives the value of the total pressures, *p*, at time, *t*, for a given temperature

t/s	0	180	360	540	720	1260
p/mmHg	169.3	189.2	207.1	224.1	240.2	282.6

Calculate the first order rate constant. (B.Sc., Wales)

7 Why does the inversion of sucrose

$$C_{12}H_{22}O_{11} + H_2O = C_6H_{12}O_6 + C_6H_{12}O_6$$

follow a first order law despite the fact that water enters into the stoichiometric equation? The following results were obtained in a study of the reaction at 25°C:

Time/s	0	1800	3600	5400	7800	10 800
Sucrose inverted/mol dm^{-3}	0	0.1350	0.2626	0.3737	0.5028	0.6312

The initial concentration of sucrose was 1.352 mol dm^{-3}. Calculate the first order rate constant, and state how long it would take to invert 50% of a kilogram of sucrose. (B.Sc., Southampton)

8 In a study of the alkaline hydrolysis of ethyl 2-methylpropenoate in 84.7% ethanol at 40°C Thomas and Watson (*J.A.C.S.*, **771** (1956), 3962) made the following observations:

The initial concentration of both ester and alkali was 0.0508 mol dm^{-3}. 10 cm^3 of the reaction mixture were removed from the reaction vessel at the times stated, pipetted into 10 cm^3 of 0.0668 mol dm^{-3} hydrochloric acid and the excess acid titrated with 0.0511 mol dm^{-3} sodium hydroxide:

Time/s	600	1500	2400	3600	4800	6600
NaOH titre/cm^3	4.03	5.11	5.98	6.86	7.57	8.36

Calculate the mean value of the second order rate constant.

9 (*a*) The process of breathing maintains the concentration of oxygen in human blood in the lungs at 1.6×10^{-6} moles of oxygen per dm^3 of blood. The oxygen reacts in the blood with a compound, haemoglobin (represented below by Hb), to yield oxyhaemoglobin (HbO_2).

$$Hb + O_2 \longrightarrow HbO_2$$

The lung processes keep the haemoglobin concentration constant in the lungs at 8.0×10^{-6} moles of haemoglobin per dm^3 of blood. The velocity constant for the reaction is $k = 2.1 \times 10^6$ dm^3 mol^{-1} s^{-1} at body temperature.

Calculate (*i*) the rate of formation of oxyhaemoglobin per dm^3 of blood, and (*ii*) the rate of consumption of oxygen per dm^3 of blood.

(*b*) In certain illnesses it is necessary that the rate of formation of oxyhaemoglobin should be increased to 1.1×10^{-4} mol dm^{-3} s^{-1}. Since the haemoglobin concentration remains constant, to what value must the oxygen concentration be changed in order to achieve this raised rate of oxyhaemoglobin formation? (G.C.E. 'A' Level (Nuffield), London)

10 A quantity of ethyl ethanoate is mixed with an excess of sodium hydroxide and allowed to react at 25°C. 100 cm^3 of the reaction mixture required 68.2 cm^3 of 0.05 mol dm^{-3} hydrochloric acid for neutralization at the commencement of the reaction. After 30 minutes, 100 cm^3 of the mixture similarly required 49.7 cm^3 of the acid and when the reaction was complete, 100 cm^3 of the mixture required 15.6 cm^3 of the acid. Calculate the reaction velocity coefficient in dm^3 mol^{-1} min^{-1}.

11 The following observations were recorded for the alkaline hydrolysis of methyl ethanoate at 25°C for an experiment in which the initial concentration of the ester was the same as that of the hydroxyl ion, 0.0100 mol dm^{-3}.

Time/s	*[OH⁻]/mol dm⁻³*	*Time/s*	*[OH⁻]/mol dm⁻³*
0	0.0100	600	0.00464
180	0.00740	720	0.00416
240	0.00683	900	0.00363
300	0.00634	1080	0.00319
360	0.00589	1260	0.00288
420	0.00550	1500	0.00254
480	0.00519		

Determine the order of reaction, and calculate the rate constant. If the energy of activation is 51.7 ± 1.3 kJ mol^{-1} how long will the reaction take to go to half-completion at 40°C? (B.Sc., Southampton)

12 A solution was found to have the following concentrations at the times stated after making up:

t/s	0	600	3000	6000	9000
Concentration/mol dm^{-3}	1.0000	0.9616	0.8235	0.6776	0.5572

Find the order of the reaction, and the time required for 50% decomposition. (B.Sc., Wales)

13 Show how two opposing bimolecular reactions must inevitably result in an equilibrium of all four molecular species and derive an expression for the equilibrium constant.

One mole of a certain carboxylic acid was reacted with one mole of ethanol, and after reaching equilibrium 50% of the acid was converted to ester. The reaction was repeated using one mole of acid, one mole of ethanol and one mole of water. How much ester was formed? (B.Pharm., London)

14 The cis-trans isomerization of 1,2-dimethylcyclopropane at 453°C is a reversible first order reaction. The percentage composition of the mixture is shown as a function of time in the following table:

Time/s	0	45	90	225	270	360	495	585	675	∞
Cis form/%	100	89.2	81.1	62.3	58.2	50.7	43.5	39.9	37.2	30.0

Calculate the equilibrium constant, and the rate constants for the forward and reverse processes. (B.Sc., Southampton)

15 The conversion of *para*-hydrogen to the *ortho*-form was studied at 650°C by Farkas, who obtained the following values for the times of half-life:

Initial pressure/mmHg	50	100	200	400
Half-life/s	648	450	318	222

Determine graphically the order of this reaction. (B.Sc., Wales)

16 The conversion of *para*-hydrogen to *ortho*-hydrogen at 923 K has a half-life ($t_{1/2}$) which depends on the total pressure of hydrogen in the following manner:

P/mmHg	50	100	200	400
$t_{1/2}$/s	640	450	318	222

At 1023 K and at a hydrogen pressure of 100 mmHg the half-life is 20.0 s. Calculate the order of the reaction and its activation energy. Comment on the results you obtain. (The dissociation energy of hydrogen is 431 kJ mol^{-1}.) (University of Oxford)

17 It is often stated as an approximate rule that for room temperature (20°C) the rate of a reaction will double for a 10°C rise in temperature to 30°C. What activation energy is implied by this statement?
(Adapted from ACS Cooperative Examination: Physical Chemistry (Graduate Level).)

18 The thermal isomerization of cyclopropane to give propene obeys a first order law and the following table gives the velocity constant k at three temperatures:

Temperature/°C	470	500	519
k/s^{-1}	1.13×10^{-4}	5.95×10^{-4}	16.7×10^{-4}

Show graphically that these data conform to the Arrhenius equation and derive the activation energy E. (B.Sc., Bristol)

19 The thermal decomposition of gaseous methoxymethane follows the equation

$$(CH_3)_2O \longrightarrow CH_4 + H_2 + CO$$

In the following tables a = initial pressure of ether in mmHg and x the increase in pressure after t s.

$T = 504$°C t/s	$a = 312$ x/mmHg	$T = 552$°C t/s	$a = 420$ x/mmHg
320	96	114	323
771	176	219	534
1195	250	299	634
2030	368	543	778
3155	467	∞	838
∞	619		

Show that this reaction follows a first order law, and determine the mean velocity constants at these temperatures. Calculate the mean energy of activation over the range 504°C–552°C. (B.Sc., Durham)

20 Ethylamine decomposes according to the following equation:

$$C_2H_5.NH_2 = C_2H_4 + NH_3$$

The reaction rate was followed by observing the pressure changes accompanying the decomposition, with the following results:

At 500°C		*At 520°C*		*At 540°C*	
t/s	$p/mmHg$	t/s	$p/mmHg$	t/s	$p/mmHg$
0	55	0	55	0	55
120	64	120	72.5	120	84
360	79	360	92.5	360	104
600	89	600	102	—	—

What can be deduced from these observations? (R.S.C.)

21 The following values were obtained for the second-order rate constant of the reaction of *N*,*N*-dimethylphenylamine and iodomethane in solution:

$T/°C$	24.8	40.1	60.0	80.1
$10^5\,k/\text{dm}^3\,\text{mol}^{-1}\,\text{s}^{-1}$	8.39	21.0	77.2	238

Determine values for the enthalpy and entropy of activation. Would either of these values be affected by the choice of concentration units used to record the measurements, e.g., mol cm^{-3} rather than mol dm^{-3}.

(R.S.C.)

22 In the homogeneous decomposition of dinitrogen oxide it is found that at a constant temperature the time needed for half the reaction to be completed ($t_{1/2}$) is inversely proportional to the initial pressure (p_0). On varying the temperature the following results are obtained:

Temperature/°C	694	757	812
p_0/mmHg	294	360	345
$t_{1/2}$/s	1520	212	53

Deduce the order of the reaction, and calculate

(*a*) the rate constant ($\text{dm}^3\,\text{mol}^{-1}\,\text{s}^{-1}$) at 694°C,
(*b*) the molar fraction of nitrogen in the mixture at time $t_{1/2}$, and
(*c*) the activation energy of the reaction. (R.S.C.)

23 In the decomposition of ammonia on a tungsten wire at 1100°C, the following values of the half-time (τ) of reaction were obtained as a function of the initial ammonia pressure

p/mmHg	265	130	58	16
τ/s	456	222	102	60

Use these data to deduce the order of this heterogeneous reaction. What conclusions may be drawn regarding the mechanism of the reaction?

(B.Sc., Bristol)

24 The following two series of results refer to the reaction between the

2,3-dichlorobutanedioate ion, $C_2H_2Cl_2(COO)_2^{2-}$, and the hydroxide ion at 25°C:

$a = 0.0214$		$a = 0.03990$	
t	x	t	x
965	0.00530	600	0.01284
3900	0.01222	2280	0.02565

a is the initial concentration of both reactants in moles per dm^3, and x is the amount that has reacted, in the same units, after t minutes.

Determine the order of the reaction, and discuss the influence of the ionic strength on the velocity of this reaction. (R.S.C.)

25 The reaction between peroxodisulphate(VI) and iodide ions:

$$S_2O_8^{2-} + 2I^- = 2SO_4^{2-} + I_2$$

is a second order process. In a study of this reaction in solutions of different ionic strengths, the following data were obtained by King and Jacobs (*J.A.C.S.*, **53** (1931), 1704) at 25°C, using potassium peroxodisulphate (VI) at an initial concentration of 0.00015 mol dm^{-3}, and varying initial concentrations of potassium iodide:

Initial KI concentration /mol dm^{-3}	0.0020	0.0032	0.0080	0.0100	0.0120	0.0180
k_{obs}/dm^3 mol^{-1} min^{-1}	1.05	1.12	1.26	1.33	1.40	1.58

Use the given data to test the predictions of the Brönsted-Bjerrum equation and evaluate the rate constant when the ionic activity coefficients are unity. [The Debye-Hückel constant at 25°C = 0.509.]

26 The hydrolysis of methyl 3-phenylpropanoate is catalysed by the enzyme chymotrypsin. The data (for 25°C, pH 7.6 and a constant enzyme concentration) tabulated below show initial reaction rates for the corresponding initial substrate concentrations.

[Methyl 3-phenylpropanoate] $\times 10^3$/mol dm^{-3}	30.8	14.6	8.57	4.6	2.24	1.28	0.32
Initial rate $\times 10^8$ /mol dm^{-3} s^{-1}	20	17.5	15.0	11.5	7.5	5.0	1.5

Evaluate the limiting rate of reaction and the Michaelis constant.

27 The following data were obtained for the decomposition of 0.056 mol dm^{-3} glucose at 140°C at various concentrations of hydrochloric acid catalyst:

k/$hour^{-1}$	0.00366	0.00580	0.00818	0.01076
H_3O^+/mol dm^{-3}	0.0108	0.0197	0.0295	0.0394

Determine, by a graphical method, the value of the catalytic coefficient of the hydrogen ion expressed in units of dm^3 mol^{-1} $hour^{-1}$. What is the value of the catalytic coefficient in units of dm^3 mol^{-1} s^{-1}?

10

Spectra and Statistical Thermodynamics

Example 10.1 Line spectrum of hydrogen

If the electron of the hydrogen atom has been excited to a level corresponding to 10.2 eV, what is the wavelength of the line emitted when the atom returns to its ground state? (1 eV = 1.6 × 10⁻¹⁹ J)

(B.Sc., Wales)

According to Bohr's quantum theory, spectral lines result when an electron jumps from one energy level to another. When an electron jumps from a higher energy level (E_2) to a lower energy level (E_1) the atom emits a quantum of energy whose frequency (ν) is given by

$$\Delta E = E_2 - E_1 = h\nu = h\frac{c}{\lambda} \qquad \text{(i)}$$

where h is Planck's constant, c the velocity of light and λ the wavelength of the radiation.

But

$$\Delta E = 10.2 \text{ eV}$$

$$= 10.2 \times 1.6 \times 10^{-19} \text{ J.}$$

Therefore

$$\lambda = \frac{6.624 \times 10^{-34} \times 3 \times 10^8}{10.2 \times 1.6 \times 10^{-19}} \text{ m}$$

$$= \frac{6.624 \times 10^{-34} \times 3 \times 10^8 \times 10^9}{10.2 \times 1.6 \times 10^{-19}} \text{ nm}$$

$$= 121.8 \text{ nm.}$$

The wavelength of the line emitted when the atom returns to its ground state is 122 nm.

Note ΔE in equation (i) above is expressed in joules when h is

expressed in J s, c in m s^{-1} and λ in m.
1 nanometre (nm) $= 10^{-9}$ m.

Example 10.2 Spectral series of atomic hydrogen

The line of greatest wavelength of a particular series in the atomic spectrum of hydrogen is at 656.3 nm. What is this series?
($R_H = 1.09678 \times 10^7\ m^{-1}$.) *(B.Sc., B.Met., Sheffield)*

The general form of the Balmer formula for hydrogen is

$$\tilde{\nu} = \frac{1}{\lambda} = R_H\left(\frac{1}{n_1^2} - \frac{1}{n_2^2}\right) \tag{i}$$

where λ is the wavelength of the line in the spectrum, $\tilde{\nu}$ the wave number, R_H the Rydberg constant and n_1 and n_2 are integers.

The value of n_1 is fixed for a given series. Thus it is 1 for the Lyman series, 2 for the Balmer series, 3 for the Paschen series, and so on, whilst n_2 takes on a series of consecutive values beginning with $n_2 = (n_1 + 1)$. Thus the line of longest wavelength is given by

$$\frac{1}{\lambda} = R_H\left(\frac{1}{n_1^2} - \frac{1}{(n_1+1)^2}\right) \tag{ii}$$

Substitution of the data given in the question in equation (ii) gives

$$\frac{1}{656.3 \times 10^{-9}} = 1.09678 \times 10^7\left(\frac{1}{n_1^2} - \frac{1}{(n_1+1)^2}\right) \tag{iii}$$

For the Lyman series $n_1 = 1$ and if on substituting this value of n_1 in equation (iii) the L.H.S. = R.H.S. then the line is of the Lyman series:

$$\frac{1}{656.3 \times 10^{-9}} = 1.09678 \times 10^7\left(\frac{1}{1} - \frac{1}{4}\right)$$

$$1.524 \times 10^6 \neq 8.226 \times 10^6$$

Therefore the line is *not* of the Lyman series.

For the Balmer series $n_1 = 2$ and substitution of this value in equation (iii) gives

$$1.524 \times 10^6 = 1.09678 \times 10^7\left(\frac{1}{4} - \frac{1}{9}\right)$$

$$\simeq 1.523 \times 10^6$$

The agreement between the L.H.S. and R.H.S. is sufficiently close for the line to belong to the Balmer series.

Example 10.3 Particle in a box

Consider an electron in a cubic box of 1 cm edge. Calculate the energy required to raise the electron from its lowest level to the state where $n_x = 1$, $n_y = 2$, $n_z = 1$.
(Electron rest mass = 9.109×10^{-28} g.)

The total energy, E, of a particle constrained in a box of sides a, b and c is given by

$$E = \frac{h^2}{8m}\left(\frac{n_x^2}{a^2} + \frac{n_y^2}{b^2} + \frac{n_z^2}{c^2}\right)$$

Therefore, the energy, ΔE required to raise an electron from its lowest level, where $n_x = 1$, $n_y = 1$ and $n_z = 1$, to the level where $n_x = 1$, $n_y = 2$, and $n_z = 1$, in a cubic box of 1 cm edge is given by

$$\Delta E = \frac{h^2}{8m}\left[\frac{1+4+1}{(0.01)^2} - \frac{1+1+1}{(0.01)^2}\right]$$

$$= \frac{(6.624 \times 10^{-34})^2}{8 \times 9.109 \times 10^{-31}}\left(\frac{3}{10^{-4}}\right)\frac{\text{J}^2\ \text{s}^2}{\text{kg m}^2}$$

$$= 1.807 \times 10^{-33}\ \text{J}^2\ \text{J}^{-1}$$

$$= 1.81 \times 10^{-33}\ \text{J}.$$

Example 10.4 Rotational spectra

Hydrogen bromide gives a series of lines in the far infra-red having a separation of 16.94 cm^{-1}. Calculate the moment of inertia of the molecule and the internuclear distance. (H = 1.008; Br = 79.92.)

(*R.S.C.*)

The rotational spectrum of a diatomic molecule can be accounted for by considering the molecule as a rigid rotator. Wave mechanics show that the energy (E_J) of a rigid rotator in any given rotational quantum level (J) is given by

$$E_J = \left(\frac{h^2}{8\pi^2 I}\right) J(J+1) \qquad \text{(i)}$$

where h is Planck's constant and I the moment of inertia.

The selection rule for rotational levels is found to be $\Delta J = 0$ or ± 1, hence the expression for ΔE in this case is

$$\Delta E = h \,.\, B[J(J+1) - J'(J'+1)]$$
$$= 2hBJ \qquad \text{(ii)}$$

where $B = h/8\pi^2 I$.

But $\Delta E = h\nu$, where ν is in Hz (waves s^{-1}).

Therefore

$$\nu = 2BJ \qquad \text{(iii)}$$

On substitution of the relevant data in equation (iii) for the transition to be from $J = 1$ to $J = 0$, and converting cm^{-1} to m^{-1} we have

$$1694 \times 3.00 \times 10^8 = \frac{2 \times 6.624 \times 10^{-34}}{8(3.142)^2 I}$$

Therefore

$$I = \frac{2 \times 6.624 \times 10^{-34}}{8(3.142)^2 \times 1694 \times 3.00 \times 10^8} \text{ kg m}^2$$
$$= 3.302 \times 10^{-47} \text{ kg m}^2.$$

But $I = \mu r^2$, where μ is the reduced mass in kg and r the internuclear distance in metres. Hence

$$3.302 \times 10^{-47} = \left(\frac{m_1 m_2}{m_1 + m_2}\right) r^2$$

where m_1 is the mass in kg of the hydrogen atom and m_2 is the mass in kg of the bromine atom.

Therefore

$$3.302 \times 10^{-47} = \left(\frac{1.008 \times 79.92 \times 10^{-3}}{1.008 + 79.92}\right) \times \frac{r^2}{6.02 \times 10^{23}}$$

And $$r = \sqrt{\frac{3.302\times10^{-47}\times6.02\times10^{23}\times80.93}{1.008\times79.92\times10^{-3}}}\ \text{m}$$
$$= 1.413\times10^{-10}\ \text{m}$$
$$= 1.413\ \text{Å}$$

The moment of inertia of the hydrogen bromide molecule is $\underline{3.30\times10^{-47}\ \text{kg m}^2}$ and the internuclear distance $\underline{1.41\ \text{Å}}$.

Example 10.5 Vibration-rotation spectra

Some rotational lines at the centre of the $H^{35}Cl$ fundamental absorption band have wave numbers 2927, 2906, 2866, 2847 cm^{-1}. An overtone is centred at 5679 cm^{-1}. Calculate (a) the bond length, (b) the force constant, (c) the anharmonicity constant.

(Mass of $^{12}C = 1.969\times10^{-26}$ kg.) *(B.Sc., Wales)*

The total vibrational energy (E_v) of a molecule of vibrational quantum number, v, is

$$E_v = (v+\tfrac{1}{2})hc\bar{\nu}_0-(v+\tfrac{1}{2})^2hcx\bar{\nu}_0 \quad \text{(i)}$$

where h is Planck's constant, c the velocity of the radiation, $c\bar{\nu}_0$ the fundamental vibration frequency and x an empirical factor termed the 'anharmonicity constant'.

If the anharmonicity of the oscillations is neglected and the assumption made that rotational and vibrational energies (E_{rot} and E_v) of a diatomic molecule are additive, then

$$E = E_v+E_{rot} = (v+\tfrac{1}{2})hc\bar{\nu}_0+\frac{h^2}{8\pi^2 I}J(J+1) \quad \text{(ii)}$$

where I is the moment of inertia and J the rotational quantum number.

For a simultaneous vibrational and rotational transition from v to v' and J to J' (±1), remembering that for the fundamental band $v-v'$ is unity, it can be shown that

$$\Delta E = \Delta E_v+\Delta E_{rot} = hc\bar{\nu}_0+\frac{2h^2}{8\pi^2 I}m \quad \text{(iii)}$$

where m can be ±1, ±2, ±3, etc.

The wave number of the spectral line corresponding to the energy change is obtained by dividing ΔE by hc. Therefore, since $\Delta E = h\nu$,

$$\bar{\nu} = \bar{\nu}_0+\frac{h}{4\pi^2 Ic}m \quad \text{(iv)}$$

The first term on the right-hand side of equation (iv) gives the origin (centre) of the fundamental band, and the second term gives the rotational fine structure. If m is positive we have the R-branch lines, that is, the short wave side of the origin (2927 and 2906 cm^{-1} for $H^{35}Cl$), and if m is negative we have the P-branch lines, that is, the long wave side of the origin (2866 and 2847 cm^{-1} for $H^{35}Cl$).

(a) Calculation of bond length

If a pair of the rotational lines are taken (say the 2906 and 2927 cm^{-1} lines) and their wave numbers in m^{-1} substituted in equation (iv) along with the other relevant data, we have

$$2.906\times10^{5} = \bar{\nu}_0 + \frac{6.624\times10^{-34}}{4\times(3.142)^2\times I\times3.00\times10^{8}}\cdot(+1) \qquad \text{(v)}$$

$$2.927\times10^{5} = \bar{\nu}_0 + \frac{6.624\times10^{-34}}{4\times(3.142)^2\times I\times3.00\times10^{8}}\cdot(+2) \qquad \text{(vi)}$$

From equations (v) and (vi)

$$\bar{\nu}_0 = 2.885\times10^{5}\ \text{m}^{-1}$$

and

$$I = 2.665\times10^{-47}\ \text{kg m}^2.$$

$$I = \mu r^2 \qquad \text{(vii)}$$

where r is the bond length and μ the reduced mass.
Therefore

$$2.665\times10^{-47} = \left(\frac{1\times35}{36}\right)\left(\frac{1.969\times10^{-26}}{12}\right) r^2\ \text{kg m}^2$$

And

$$r = \sqrt{\frac{2.665\times10^{-47}\times12\times36}{35\times1.969\times10^{-26}}}\ \text{m}$$

$$= 1.292\times10^{-10}\ \text{m}$$

$$= \underline{1.29\ \text{Å}}$$

Note The same value of r is obtained by using the data for the P-branch lines. Somewhat higher values are obtained for other pairs of lines, the variation being due to the fact that the frequency separation is not constant.

(c) Calculation of the anharmonicity constant

Returning now to equation (i), when the vibrational energy of the molecule changes from that in which $v = 0$ to that in which $v = 1$, in absorption, the band produced is the fundamental and the energy change is

$$E_1 - E_0 = (1-2x)hc\bar{\nu}_0 \qquad \text{(viii)}$$

Therefore the frequency of the corresponding spectral line, $\bar{\nu}_1$, which is the origin of the fundamental band, is

$$\bar{\nu}_1 = (1-2x)\bar{\nu}_0 \qquad \text{(ix)}$$

when the initial value of v is 0 and the final value 2, the energy change is

$$E_2 - E_0 = (1-3x)2hc\bar{\nu}_0 \qquad \text{(x)}$$

and the corresponding spectral line, $\bar{\nu}_2$, which is the origin of the overtone is

$$\bar{\nu}_2 = (1-3x)2\bar{\nu}_0 \qquad \text{(xi)}$$

Thus, knowing the origins of the fundamental and overtone bands, it is possible to evaluate the fundamental vibration frequency ($\bar{\nu}_0$) and the anharmonicity constant from equations (ix) and (xi):

$$2.885 \times 10^5 = (1-2x)\bar{\nu}_0 \qquad \text{(xii)}$$

$$5.679 \times 10^5 = (1-3x)2\bar{\nu}_0 \qquad \text{(xiii)}$$

From equations (xii) and (xiii), the anharmonicity constant

$$= \underline{1.527 \times 10^{-2}}$$

(b) Calculation of the force constant

From equation (xii), the fundamental vibration frequency

$$\bar{\nu}_0 = 2.977 \times 10^5 \text{ m}^{-1}$$

The force constant (the restoring force acting between the nuclei) can now be obtained by means of the relationship:

$$f = 4\pi^2\bar{\nu}_0^2c^2\mu \qquad \text{(xiv)}$$

where f is the force constant, the remaining terms having the significance defined above.

Substitution of the relevant data in equation (xiv) gives

$$f = 4\times(3.142)^2(2.977\times10^5)^2(3.00\times10^8)^2\,\frac{35}{36}\times\frac{1.969\times10^{-26}}{12}$$

$$= \underline{5.023\times10^2\ \mathrm{N\,m^{-1}}}$$

Summary

For $H^{35}Cl$ (*a*) The bond length is 1.29 Å.
(*b*) The force constant is 5.02×10^2 N m^{-1}.
(*c*) The anharmonicity constant is 1.53×10^{-2}.

Example 10.6 Spectroscopic evaluation of dissociation energy

The band progression given below is found in the absorption spectrum of the ClO radical.

v	4	5	6	7	8	9	13
$\tilde{\nu}$ (*cm*$^{-1}$)	*32 945*	*33 402*	*33 839*	*34 261*	*34 664*	*35 056 . . .*	*36 360*

v	14	15	18	19	20
$\tilde{\nu}$ (*cm*$^{-1}$)	*36 627*	*36 874 . . .*	*37 425*	*37 569*	*37 689*

Calculate the dissociation energy from the ground state to products in the upper state. Explain clearly the basis of the calculation.

(*B.Sc., Wales*)

The vibrational energy of a molecule may be written as a power series in $(v+1)$, where v is the vibrational quantum number:

$$\varepsilon_v = (v+\tfrac{1}{2})h\nu_e-(v+\tfrac{1}{2})^2xh\nu_e+(v+\tfrac{1}{2})^3yh\nu_e- \ \ldots \qquad \text{(i)}$$

where ν_e is the equilibrium frequency of vibration, h is Planck's constant, x and y are constants.

The gain in energy on passing from v to the next higher state $(v+1)$ is

$$\Delta\varepsilon_{v\to(v+1)} = h\nu_e\left[1-2(v+1)x+3\left(v^2+2v+\frac{13}{12}\right)y\right] \qquad \text{(ii)}$$

or, by the Bohr frequency condition

$$\Delta\varepsilon_{v\to(v+1)} = h\nu \qquad \text{(iii)}$$

where ν is the frequency of the light absorbed in the transition. The energy of dissociation (D) is the sum of all these increments:

$$D = \Sigma\Delta\varepsilon_{v\to(v+1)} = h\sum_{v=0}\nu \qquad \text{(iv)}$$

When the quanta of light absorbed are small and numerous, the summation may be replaced by an integration.

Differentiation of equation (i) gives

$$\frac{1}{h}\frac{\mathrm{d}\varepsilon}{\mathrm{d}v} = \nu_e[1-2(v+\tfrac{1}{2})x+3(v+\tfrac{1}{2})^2y] = \nu \qquad \text{(v)}$$

where $h\nu$ is the average value of the quantum of radiation absorbed by a molecule in the vth state when it enters into the next higher state.

That is,

$$\mathrm{d}\varepsilon = h\nu\,\mathrm{d}v \qquad \text{(vi)}$$

Integration of equation (vi) gives

$$D = \int \mathrm{d}\varepsilon = h\int_{v=0} \nu\,\mathrm{d}v \qquad \text{(vii)}$$

v	$\bar{\nu}_{0\to v} = \dfrac{\nu_{0\to v}}{c}$ /cm^{-1}	$\bar{\nu}_{(v\to(v+1))} = \dfrac{\nu_{(v\to(v+1))}}{c}$ /cm^{-1}
4	32 945	457
5	33 402	437
6	33 839	422
7	34 261	403
8	34 664	392
9	35 056	
13	36 360	267
14	36 627	247
15	36 874	
18	37 425	144
19	37 569	120
20	37 689	

The integral in equation (vii) can be evaluated by plotting the step by step increase in frequency ν, against the quantum number v from $v = 0$ to $v = v_{\text{lim}}$.

Applying the method to the data given in the question, the first column gives the vibrational state into which the ground state molecule is raised by the absorption of light, the wave numbers of which are given in the second column. The third column gives the step by step increase in wave numbers which are plotted against v in Fig. 33.

The extrapolation shown in Fig. 33 by the dotted line is necessary to obtain the step by step increase in wave number for values of v in excess of 20. Hence, when $v = 20$, 21 and 22 the corresponding $\bar{\nu}_{v\to(v+1)}$ values are 90, 60 and 28 cm^{-1}, respectively. Adding these

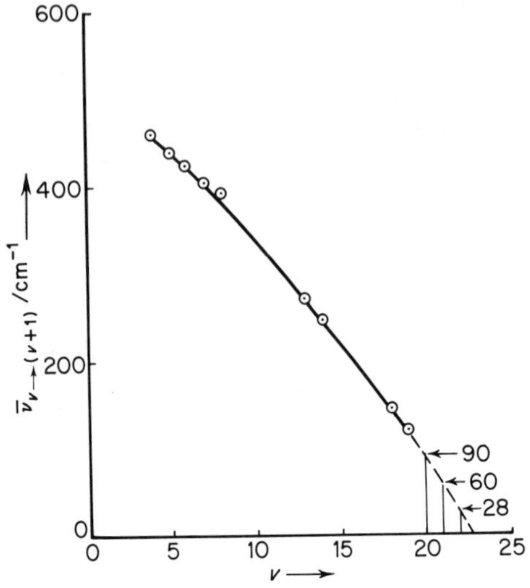

Fig. 33 Plot of vibrational state versus the step by step increase in wave number

values on to 37 689 cm^{-1} we obtain the energy required to dissociate the molecule from its ground state.
Hence

$$D = 37\,689+90+60+28 = 37\,867\ \text{cm}^{-1} = 3.7867 \times 10^6\ \text{m}^{-1}$$

$$= 3.7867 \times 10^6 \times 3.00 \times 10^8\ \text{s}^{-1}$$

$$= 3.7867 \times 10^6 \times 3.00 \times 10^8 \times 6.624 \times 10^{-34} \times 6.02 \times 10^{23}\ \text{J mol}^{-1}$$

$$= 453.2\ \text{kJ mol}^{-1}$$

The dissociation energy of the ClO radical from the ground state is 453 kJ mol^{-1}.

Example 10.7 Spectrophotometry

When excess naphthazarin (a substituted naphthaquinone) is added to solutions containing thorium, a coloration is produced due to the formation of a complex in which the thorium:naphthazarin ratio is 1:2. The following results were obtained when the absorption of light at 570 nm and 620 nm was studied for three different concentrations in a cell of thickness 1 cm (all the thorium can be present as the complex).

Concentration of thorium /mol dm^{-3}	13.9×10^{-6}	34.7×10^{-6}	55.5×10^{-6}
Percentage transmission at 570 nm	62.4	30.9	15.2
Percentage transmission at 620 nm	49.6	16.7	5.7

Show that Beer's Law is obeyed, and derive the molar absorptivity for the complex at these wavelengths. (*B.Sc., Bristol*)

Beer's Law states that when monochromatic light passes through a transparent medium of 1 cm thickness, the intensity of the light beam decreases exponentially as the concentration of the absorbing medium increases arithmetically, that is,

$$I_t = I_0 \, e^{-kc} \qquad \text{(i)}$$

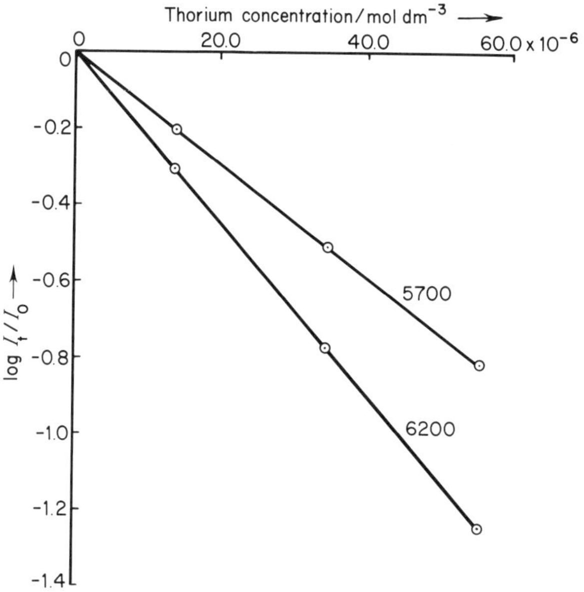

Fig. 34 Plot of log transmission versus thorium concentration

where I_0 is the intensity of the incident light and I_t the intensity of the transmitted light, c the concentration of the absorbing medium (in mol dm^{-3}) and k is a constant. Rearranging equation (i) and taking logarithms we have

$$\log \frac{I_t}{I_0} = -\frac{kc}{2.303} \qquad \text{(ii)}$$

Equation (ii) is a linear relationship between $\log I_t/I_0$ and c, the line passing through the origin.

I_t/I_0 is termed the *transmission* and $(I_t/I_0) \times 100$ is the *percentage* transmission

Fig. 34 shows a plot of the 570 nm and 620 nm log (% transmission/100) values versus the thorium concentration as detailed in the table:

Concentration of thorium /mol dm^{-3}	13.9×10^{-6}	34.7×10^{-6}	55.5×10^{-6}
$\log (I_t/I_0)$ at 570 nm	−0.2068	−0.5100	−0.8182
$\log (I_t/I_0)$ at 620 nm	−0.3045	−0.7773	−1.2441

In both cases a good straight line, passing through the origin, is obtained thus showing that Beer's law is obeyed.

The slope of each line is given by $-k/2.303$, where $k/2.303$ is the *molar absorptivity* for the complex at these wavelengths.

Thus for 570 nm

$$-\frac{k}{2.303} = -\frac{0.8182}{55.5 \times 10^{-6}}$$

and

$$\frac{k}{2.303} = 14\,740.$$

For 620 nm

$$-\frac{k}{2.303} = -\frac{1.2441}{55.5 \times 10^{-6}}$$

and

$$\frac{k}{2.303} = 22\,420.$$

Beer's Law is obeyed by the complex at both wavelengths and the molar absorptivity is 14 740 at 570 nm and 22 420 at 620 nm.

Example 10.8 Nuclear magnetic resonance

Use the given data to determine the frequency at which nuclear magnetic resonance absorption is observed for the nuclei ^{31}P and ^{35}Cl in a magnetic field of strength 1.5 T.

Nucleus	*Spin (I)*	*Magnetic moment (μ) /nuclear magnetons*
^{31}P	$\frac{1}{2}$	1.96
^{35}Cl	$\frac{3}{2}$	1.06

The nuclear magnetic moment, μ, is related to the spin quantum number, I, by the expression

$$\mu = g_N \mu_N [I(I+1)]^{1/2} \tag{i}$$

in which g_N is a quantum mechanical factor which is characteristic of the nucleus, and μ_N is the nuclear magneton which has the value $\dfrac{eh}{4\pi\, m_p}$ in which m_p is the proton mass, h is the Planck constant and e is the elementary charge. The nuclear magneton $= 5.050 \times 10^{-27}$ J T^{-1} = 5.050×10^{-31} J gauss^{-1}.
(The tesla (T) has the units kg s^{-2} A^{-1} and is equivalent to 10^4 gauss.) The potential energy, U, of a magnetic dipole in a magnetic field of strength H_0 is given by the product of the component, μ, of its moment in the direction of the field and the field strength, that is,

$$U = \mu_0 H_0$$

The component μ_0 is restricted to values given by $\mu_0 = m g_N \mu_N$ where $m = I, I-1, I-2, \ldots, -I$.
Thus, for transitions between neighbouring energy levels, where m is unity:

$$\Delta U = [g_N \mu_N I H_0 - g_N \mu_N (I-1) H_0]$$
$$= |g_N \mu_N H_0| \text{ J when } H_0 \text{ is expressed in T.}$$

According to the quantum theory, a transition will occur when

$\Delta U = h\nu$ where ν is the frequency at which resonance absorption occurs.

Hence

$$\nu = \frac{|g_N \mu_N H_0|}{h} \tag{ii}$$

The modulus sign, $|\ldots|$ indicates that magnitudes only are considered i.e. negative signs are ignored.

The nuclear *g*-factor, g_N, for each nuclear species may be calculated using equation (i), remembering that μ_N is set equal to unity since the magnetic moment μ has been quoted in nuclear magnetons.

^{31}P

$$1.96 = g_N \times 1 \times [\tfrac{1}{2}(\tfrac{1}{2}+1)]^{\frac{1}{2}} = g_N \times (0.75)^{\frac{1}{2}}$$

$$g_N = \frac{1.96}{(0.75)^{\frac{1}{2}}} = \underline{2.263}$$

^{35}Cl

$$1.06 = g_N \times 1 \times [\tfrac{3}{2}(\tfrac{3}{2}+1)]^{\frac{1}{2}} = g_N \times (3.75)^{\frac{1}{2}}$$

$$g_N = \frac{1.06}{(3.75)^{\frac{1}{2}}} = \underline{0.5474}$$

The frequency at which resonance absorption is observed in the given magnetic field strength of 1.5 T may now be calculated using equation (ii). It is important to remember that in this calculation the nuclear magneton, μ_H, must be quoted in units of J T^{-1} since the frequency is never expressed in units involving nuclear magnetons.

^{31}P

$$\nu = \frac{2.263 \times 5.050 \times 10^{-27} \times 1.5}{6.624 \times 10^{-34}} \text{ Hz}$$

$$= \underline{2.587 \times 10^{7} \text{ Hz}}$$

^{35}Cl

$$\nu = \frac{0.5474 \times 5.050 \times 10^{-27} \times 1.5}{6.624 \times 10^{-34}} \text{ Hz}$$

$$= \underline{6.259 \times 10^{6} \text{ Hz}}$$

In a magnetic field of strength 1.5 T, nuclear magnetic resonance absorption is observed for the nuclei ^{31}P and ^{35}Cl at 25.9 and 6.26 MHz respectively.

Example 10.9 Photoelectron spectroscopy

In photoelectron spectroscopy a sample is irradiated with very energetic monochromatic radiation. An electron in a molecule which absorbs a photon is ejected from the molecule and its kinetic energy is measured. The kinetic energy plus its binding energy (that is, the energy level of the orbital from which it was ejected) equals the energy of the absorbed photon.

58.4 nm radiation from He^+ falls on benzene vapour. The most energetic electrons ejected from benzene have 11.99 eV kinetic energy. What is the binding energy of the highest occupied molecular orbital in benzene? (This is also the first ionization potential of benzene) (1 eV = 1.60×10^{-19} J.)

(University of Connecticut, Storrs, USA)

The energy of the irradiating radiation is given by

$$E = h\nu$$

$$= h\frac{c}{\lambda}$$

where ν is the frequency, c the velocity of the radiation and λ is the wavelength.

Substituting the numerical data gives

$$E = 6.624 \times 10^{-34} \left(\frac{3.00 \times 10^8}{58.4 \times 10^{-9}} \right) \text{J}$$

$$= 34.03 \times 10^{-19} \text{ J}$$

This energy (in J) corresponds to

$$\frac{34.03 \times 10^{-19}}{1.60 \times 10^{-19}} \text{ eV}$$

$$= 21.27 \text{ eV}$$

Therefore, the binding energy of the highest occupied molecular orbital of benzene is

$$21.27 - 11.99 \text{ eV}$$

$$= \underline{9.28 \text{ eV}}.$$

Example 10.10 The molecular partition function

For 1 mol of gaseous nitrogen at 298 K and 1 atmosphere pressure calculate the molecular translational, rotational and vibrational partition functions given that the moment of inertia of the nitrogen molecule is 1.410×10^{-46} kg m², the relative molecular mass is 28.00 and the wave number of the fundamental vibration is 2359.6 cm^{-1}.

The molecular partition function

The energy of an individual molecule in a gas is made up of contributions from its various modes of motion—translational, rotational, vibrational and electronic. If it is assumed that the modes of motion are independent of each other the molecular partition function is simply the product of the partition functions for each mode.

$$q = q_{\text{trans}} \times q_{\text{rot}} \times q_{\text{vib}} \times q_{\text{elect}} \qquad \text{(i)}$$

Since the modes of motion are not completely independent of each other, equation (i) is an approximation which, however, is adequate for most situations. It has the signal usefulness that it permits the contributions from the different modes of motion to be assessed separately.

The translational partition function (q_{trans})

The partition function for translational motion (q_{trans}) in a gas occupying a container of volume $V\,\text{m}^3$ is

$$q_{\text{trans}} = V\left(\frac{2\pi mkT}{h^2}\right)^{\frac{3}{2}} \qquad \text{(ii)}$$

where m is the molecular mass, k is Boltzmann's constant, h is Planck's constant and T is the absolute temperature.

Assuming that the nitrogen gas at 298 K and 1 atmosphere pressure behaves ideally, the volume occupied by 1 mol is given by

$$V = \frac{RT}{P} = \frac{8.31 \times 298}{1.013 \times 10^5}\,\text{m}^3$$

$$= \underline{0.0245\ \text{m}^3}$$

For nitrogen

$$m = \frac{28.00 \times 10^{-3}}{6.02 \times 10^{23}}\,\text{kg}$$

$$= \underline{4.65 \times 10^{-26}\ \text{kg}}$$

From equation (ii)

$$q_{\text{trans}} = 0.0245\left[\frac{2\pi \times 4.65 \times 10^{-26} \times 1.381 \times 10^{-23} \times 298}{(6.624 \times 10^{-34})^2}\right]^{\frac{3}{2}}$$

$$= \underline{3.52 \times 10^{30}}$$

The rotational partition function (q_{rot})

For heteronuclear diatomic molecules the rotational partition function (q_{rot}) is

$$q_{\text{rot}} = \frac{8\pi^2 IkT}{h^2} \qquad \text{(iii)}$$

where I is the moment of inertia of the molecule, k is Boltzmann's constant, h is Planck's constant and T is the absolute temperature.

For homonuclear diatomic molecules, rotation through an angle of 180° about an axis normal to the line joining the atomic centres interchanges two identical atoms and the new orientation of the molecule is indistinguishable from the old. For such molecules it is necessary to divide the right hand side of equation (iii) by 2 so that indistinguishable orientations are not doubly counted.

Equation (iii) is generally written as

$$q_{\text{rot}} = \frac{8\pi^2 IkT}{\sigma h^2} \qquad \text{(iv)}$$

in which the symmetry number, σ, is 1 for heteronuclear diatomic molecules and 2 for homonuclear diatomic molecules.

For nitrogen at 298 K

$$q_{\text{rot}} = \frac{8\pi^2 \times 1.410 \times 10^{-46} \times 1.381 \times 10^{-23} \times 298}{2 \times (6.624 \times 10^{-34})^2}$$

$$= \underline{52.2}$$

The vibrational partition function (q_{vib})

The vibrational mode of a diatomic molecule has associated with it a set of vibrational states which may be assumed to be simple harmonic, so that the vibrational energies, E_{vib}, are given by

$$E_{\text{vib}} = (v + \tfrac{1}{2})h\nu \qquad \text{(v)}$$

in which ν is the fundamental vibration frequency and v is the vibrational quantum number.

The zero-point level ($v = 0$) has an energy of $\frac{1}{2}h\nu$ so that the vibrational energy of any quantum level measured from the zero-point level will be

$$E'_{\text{vib}} = (v + \tfrac{1}{2})h\nu - \tfrac{1}{2}h\nu$$
$$= vh\nu$$

The vibrational partition function, q_{vib}, will be given by

$$q_{\text{vib}} = \sum_{v=0}^{\infty} e^{-E'_{\text{vib}}/kt} = \sum_{v=0}^{\infty} e^{-vh\nu/kT}$$

$$= \frac{1}{1 - e^{-h\nu/kT}} = \frac{1}{1 - e^{-hc\bar{\nu}/kT}} \qquad \text{(vi)}$$

For 298 K and the wave number of the fundamental vibration for nitrogen ($\bar{\nu} = 2359.6\,\text{cm}^{-1} = 235\,960\,\text{m}^{-1}$)

$$\frac{hc\bar{\nu}}{kT} = \frac{6.624 \times 10^{-34} \times 3.00 \times 10^{8} \times 235\,960}{1.381 \times 10^{-23} \times 298}$$

$$= 11.39$$

$$q_{\text{vib}} = \frac{1}{1 - e^{-11.39}} = \underline{1.000}$$

This value for q_{vib} shows that at 298 K the nitrogen molecules are virtually all in the vibrational ground state.

Note For diatomic molecules in general

$$q_{\text{elect}} = 1.$$

Summary

The values of the partition functions are:–

$$q_{\text{trans}} = 3.52 \times 10^{30};$$
$$q_{\text{rot}} = 52.2;$$
$$q_{\text{vib}} = 1.00.$$

Example 10.11 Intrinsic energy and enthalpy

Calculate the molar intrinsic energy and molar enthalpy for carbon monoxide at 1500 K. The wave number of the fundamental vibration is 2170 cm^{-1}.

The molar intrinsic energy, $U - U_0$, of a gas relative to the zero-point energy, U_0, is given by

$$U - U_0 = RT^2 \left(\frac{\partial \ln q}{\partial T} \right) \quad \text{(i)}$$

where T is the absolute temperature and q is the molecular partition function.

$$\text{Since } q = q_{\text{trans}} \times q_{\text{rot}} \times q_{\text{vib}} \times q_{\text{elect}} \quad \text{(ii)}$$

then

$$\ln q = \ln q_{\text{trans}} + \ln q_{\text{rot}} + \ln q_{\text{vib}} + \ln q_{\text{elect}} \quad \text{(iii)}$$

For diatomic molecules in general $q_{\text{elect}} = 1$ and $\ln q_{\text{elect}} = 0$

$$\text{Hence } \left(\frac{\partial \ln q}{\partial T} \right) = \left(\frac{\partial \ln q_{\text{trans}}}{\partial T} \right) + \left(\frac{\partial \ln q_{\text{rot}}}{\partial T} \right) + \left(\frac{\partial \ln q_{\text{vib}}}{\partial T} \right)$$

The contributions to $\left(\frac{\partial \ln q}{\partial T} \right)$ arising from translational, rotational and vibrational modes of motion may, therefore, be calculated separately.

The intrinsic energy of a gas consists of a temperature independent component, U_0, and a temperature dependent component, U, which may be expressed as

$$U = U_0 + (U - U_0) \quad \text{(v)}$$

Likewise the enthalpy may be written as

$$H = H_0 + (H - H_0) \quad \text{(vi)}$$

H_0 and U_0 are the enthalpy and intrinsic energy per mole if all the molecules occupied the lowest allowed energy states.

Since $H = U + PV$ then from equations (v) and (vi)

$$H_0 + (H - H_0) = U_0 + (U - U_0) + PV$$

For an ideal gas $PV = RT$ and at 0K, $H_0 = U_0$.

Hence $$H - H_0 = U - U_0 + RT$$

Translational contribution

$$U_{\text{trans}} = RT^2 \left(\frac{\partial \ln q_{\text{trans}}}{\partial T} \right)$$

and $$q_{\text{trans}} = V \left(\frac{2\pi mkT}{h^2} \right)^{\frac{3}{2}}$$

Hence $$\left(\frac{\partial \ln q_{\text{trans}}}{\partial T} \right) = \frac{\partial}{\partial T} \left[\ln V \left(\frac{2\pi mkT}{h^2} \right)^{\frac{3}{2}} \right]$$

$$= \frac{\partial}{\partial T} \left[\ln V \left(\frac{2\pi mk}{h^2} \right)^{\frac{3}{2}} + \ln T^{\frac{3}{2}} \right]$$

$$= \frac{3}{2} \left(\frac{1}{T} \right)$$

Hence $$\underline{U_{\text{trans}} = RT^2 \times \frac{3}{2} \left(\frac{1}{T} \right) = \frac{3}{2} RT}$$

Rotational contribution

$$U_{\text{rot}} = RT^2 \left(\frac{\partial \ln q_{\text{rot}}}{\partial T} \right) \text{ and } q_{\text{rot}} = \left(\frac{8\pi^2 IkT}{\sigma h^2} \right)$$

Hence $$\left(\frac{\partial \ln q_{\text{rot}}}{\partial T} \right) = \frac{\partial}{\partial T} \left[\ln \left(\frac{8\pi^2 IkT}{\sigma h^2} \right) \right]$$

$$= \frac{\partial}{\partial T} \left[\ln \left(\frac{8\pi^2 Ik}{\sigma h^2} \right) + \ln T \right]$$

$$= \frac{1}{T}$$

Hence $$\underline{U_{\text{rot}} = RT^2 \times \frac{1}{T} = RT}$$

Vibrational contribution

This is calculated relative to the zero-point energy U_0 (see Example 10.10).

$$U_{vib} = RT^2\left(\frac{\partial \ln q_{vib}}{\partial T}\right)$$

Since
$$q_{vib} = \frac{1}{1 - e^{-h\nu/kT}}$$

$$\left(\frac{\partial \ln q_{vib}}{\partial T}\right) = -\frac{\partial}{\partial T}\ln\left(1 - e^{-h\nu/kT}\right)$$

$$= \frac{h\nu\, e^{-h\nu/kT}}{kT^2\left(1 - e^{-h\nu/kT}\right)}$$

$$= \frac{h\nu}{kT^2} \times \frac{1}{(e^{h\nu/kT} - 1)}$$

Hence
$$U_{vib} = RT \times \frac{h\nu}{kT} \times \frac{1}{(e^{h\nu/kT} - 1)}$$

For carbon monoxide at 1500 K, $\bar{\nu} = 2170\,\text{cm}^{-1} = 217\,000\,\text{m}^{-1}$

$$\frac{h\nu}{kT} = \frac{hc\bar{\nu}}{kT} = \frac{6.624 \times 10^{-34} \times 3.00 \times 10^{8} \times 217\,000}{1.381 \times 10^{-23} \times 1500}$$

$$= 2.082$$

Hence
$$U_{vib} = RT \times 2.082 \times \frac{1}{(e^{2.082} - 1)}$$

$$= RT \times \frac{2.082}{7.021}$$

$$= \underline{0.2966\, RT}$$

The total intrinsic energy, $U - U_0$, relative to the zero-point energy is thus

$$U - U_0 = \frac{3}{2}RT + RT + 0.2966\, RT$$
$$= \underline{2.797\, RT}$$

Hence, at 1500 K

$$U - U_0 = 2.797 \times 8.31 \times 1500\,\mathrm{J\,mol^{-1}}$$
$$= \underline{34\,865\,\mathrm{J\,mol^{-1}}}$$

$$H - H_0 = U - U_0 + RT$$
$$= 34\,865 + 8.31 \times 1500\,\mathrm{J\,mol^{-1}}$$
$$= \underline{47\,330\,\mathrm{J\,mol^{-1}}}$$

For carbon monoxide at 1500 K the molar intrinsic energy is 34.9 kJ $\mathrm{mol^{-1}}$ and the molar enthalpy is 47.3 kJ $\mathrm{mol^{-1}}$.

Example 10.12 Entropy from molecular parameters

From the following molecular parameters for hydrogen chloride calculate the standard entropy of the gas at 298 K

Relative molecular mass (M_r)	$= 36.45$
Moment of inertia (I)	$= 2.644 \times 10^{-47}\ kg\ m^2$
Wave number of fundamental vibration ($\bar{\nu}$)	$= 2990\ cm^{-1}$

In general there are translational, vibrational, rotational and electronic contributions to the entropy of a substance. For hydrogen chloride, as for most diatomic molecules, the electronic partition function (q_{elect}) is unity so there is no electronic contribution to the entropy.

Molar entropy and the partition function

For a gas with negligible molecular interactions and indistinguishable molecules the molar or canonical partition function (Q) is related to the molecular partition function (q) by the equation

$$Q = q^L/L! \tag{i}$$

Since $q = q_{\mathrm{trans}} \times q_{\mathrm{vib}} \times q_{\mathrm{rot}} \times q_{\mathrm{elect}}$

$$Q = (q_{\mathrm{trans}} \times q_{\mathrm{vib}} \times q_{\mathrm{rot}} \times q_{\mathrm{elect}})^L/L!$$
$$= (q^L_{\mathrm{trans}}/L!) \times q^L_{\mathrm{vib}} \times q^L_{\mathrm{rot}} \times q^L_{\mathrm{elect}} \tag{ii}$$

In terms of the canonical partition function Q the molar entropy $S^\ominus$ is given by

$$S^\ominus = \frac{(U - U_0)}{T} + k \ln Q \qquad \text{(iii)}$$

Comparison of equations (ii) and (iii) show that for hydrogen chloride, for which $q_{\text{elect}} = 1$,

$$S^\ominus = \frac{(U - U_0)}{T} + k[\ln (q^L_{\text{trans}}/L!) + \ln q^L_{\text{rot}} + \ln q^L_{\text{vib}}] \qquad \text{(iv)}$$

In Example 10.11 it was shown that $(U - U_0)$ is equal to $(U_{\text{trans}} + U_{\text{rot}} + U_{\text{vib}})$ so that we may write an equation of the same form as (iii) for each of the modes of motion,

i.e.

$$S^\ominus_{\text{trans}} = \frac{U_{\text{trans}}}{T} + k \ln (q^L_{\text{trans}}/L!) \qquad \text{(v)}$$

$$S^\ominus_{\text{rot}} = \frac{U_{\text{rot}}}{T} + k \ln q^L_{\text{rot}} \qquad \text{(vi)}$$

$$S^\ominus_{\text{vib}} = \frac{U_{\text{vib}}}{T} + k \ln q^L_{\text{vib}} \qquad \text{(vii)}$$

Addition of equations (v), (vi) and (vii) gives us the total standard molar entropy.

Translational contribution

$$S^\ominus_{\text{trans}} = \frac{U_{\text{trans}}}{T} + k \ln (q^L_{\text{trans}}/L!)$$

$$= \frac{U_{\text{trans}}}{T} + kL \ln q_{\text{trans}} - k \ln L! \qquad \text{(viii)}$$

By Stirling's formula for the factorials of large numbers ($\ln X! = X \ln X - X$) equation (viii) becomes

$$S^\ominus_{\text{trans}} = \frac{U_{\text{trans}}}{T} + kL \ln q_{\text{trans}} - kL \ln L + kL$$

$$= \frac{U_{\text{trans}}}{T} + kL \ln q_{\text{trans}} - kL \ln L + kL \ln \text{e}$$

since $1 = \ln \text{e}$.

In Example 10.11 U_{trans} was shown to be $\frac{3}{2} RT$, and $q_{trans} = V\left(\frac{2\pi mkT}{h^2}\right)^{\frac{3}{2}}$

Hence

$$S^{\ominus}_{trans} = \tfrac{3}{2}R + kL \ln\left[V\left(\frac{2\pi mkT}{h^2}\right)^{\frac{3}{2}}\right] - kL \ln L + kL \ln e$$

$$= \tfrac{3}{2}\, R \ln e + R \ln\left[\frac{Ve^{\frac{5}{2}}}{L}\left(\frac{2\pi mkT}{h^2}\right)^{\frac{3}{2}}\right]$$

$$S^{\ominus}_{trans} = R \ln\left[\frac{Ve^{\frac{5}{2}}}{L}\left(\frac{2\pi mkT}{h^2}\right)^{\frac{3}{2}}\right] \qquad \text{(ix)}$$

This is the Sackur-Tetrode equation. If the gas under consideration had been an ideal montomic gas this would be the total entropy since there would be a contribution from translational motion only.

For HC1 $\qquad m = \dfrac{36.45 \times 10^{-3}}{6.02 \times 10^{23}}$ kg

and, assuming ideal behaviour, the volume occupied by 1 mol at 298 K and 1 atmosphere pressure is 0.0245 m^3.

Thus, from equation (ix)

$$S^{\ominus}_{trans} = 8.31 \ln\left[\frac{0.0245 \times 12.18}{6.02 \times 10^{23}}\left(\frac{2\pi \times 36.45 \times 10^{-3} \times 1.381 \times 10^{-23} \times 298}{6.02 \times 10^{23} \times (6.624 \times 10^{-34})^2}\right)^{\frac{3}{2}}\right]$$

$$= 8.31 \ln (10.568 \times 10^7)\ \mathrm{J\,K^{-1}\,mol^{-1}}$$

$$= 8.31 \times 18.476\ \mathrm{J\,K^{-1}\,mol^{-1}}$$

$$S^{\ominus}_{trans} = \underline{153.5\ \mathrm{J\,K^{-1}\,mol^{-1}}}$$

Rotational contribution

$$S^{\ominus}_{rot} = \frac{U_{rot}}{T} + k \ln q^{L}_{rot} \qquad \text{(vi)}$$

In Example 10.11 U_{rot} was shown to be RT

Hence, $S^{\ominus}_{rot} = R + kL \ln q_{rot}$

$$= R \ln e + kL \ln \left(\frac{8\pi^2 IkT}{\sigma h^2} \right)$$

Since the HCl molecule is heteronuclear the symmetry number, σ, is unity and

$$S^{\ominus}_{rot} = R \ln \left(\frac{e\ 8\pi^2 IkT}{h^2} \right) \quad (x)$$

From equation (x)

$$S^{\ominus}_{rot} = 8.31 \times \ln \left(\frac{e \times 8\pi^2 \times 2.644 \times 10^{-47} \times 1.381 \times 10^{-23} \times 298}{(6.624 \times 10^{-34})^2} \right) \text{J K}^{-1} \text{mol}^{-1}$$

$$= 8.31 \times \ln 53.239 \text{ J K}^{-1} \text{mol}^{-1}$$

$$S^{\ominus}_{rot} = \underline{33.03 \text{ J K}^{-1} \text{mol}^{-1}}$$

Vibrational contribution

In Example 10.11, U_{vib} was shown to be given by

$$U_{vib} = RT \times \frac{h\nu}{kT} \times \frac{1}{(e^{h\nu/kT} - 1)} \quad (xi)$$

Also $$q_{vib} = \frac{1}{(1 - e^{-h\nu/kT})} \quad (xii)$$

Hence $$L \ln q_{vib} = -L \ln (1 - e^{-h\nu/kT}) \quad (xiii)$$

$$S^{\ominus}_{vib} = \frac{U_{vib}}{T} + k \ln q^{L}_{vib} \quad (viii)$$

Hence, from equations (xi), (xii), (xiii) and (viii)

$$S^{\ominus}_{vib} = \frac{RT}{T} \times \frac{h\nu}{kT} \times \frac{1}{(e^{h\nu/kT} - 1)} - kL \ln (1 - e^{-h\nu/kT})$$

$$S^{\ominus}_{vib} = R \left[\frac{h\nu}{kT} \times \frac{1}{(e^{h\nu/kT} - 1)} - \ln (1 - e^{-h\nu/kT}) \right] \quad (xiv)$$

For HCl the wave number of the fundamental vibration is 2990 cm^{-1} $= 299\,000 \text{ m}^{-1}$

and $$\frac{h\nu}{kT} = \frac{hc\bar{\nu}}{kT} = \frac{6.624 \times 10^{-34} \times 3.00 \times 10^{8} \times 299\,000}{1.381 \times 10^{-23} \times 298}$$

$$= 14.44$$

Hence, $S^{\ominus}_{\text{vib}}$ is virtually zero.

The total entropy is virtually $= S^{\ominus}_{\text{trans}} + S^{\ominus}_{\text{rot}}$

$$= 153.5 + 33.03\,\text{J K}^{-1}\,\text{mol}^{-1}$$

$$= 186.5\,\text{J K}^{-1}\,\text{mol}^{-1}$$

The standard entropy of HCl at 298 K = $187\,\text{J K}^{-1}\,\text{mol}^{-1}$.

Example 10.13 Chemical equilibrium

Calculate the equilibrium constant (K_p) at 1000 K for the reaction

$$H_2(g) + D_2(g) = 2HD(g)$$

using the molecular parameters tabulated below.

Parameter	H_2	D_2	*HD*
Moment of inertia $(I)/kg\ m^2$	4.60×10^{-48}	9.20×10^{-48}	6.13×10^{-48}
Relative molecular mass (M_r)	2.015	4.028	3.022
Dissociation energy $(D_m)/kJ\,mol^{-1}$	431.87	439.33	435.24
Wave number $(\bar{\nu})$ *of fundamental vibration/*cm^{-1}	4395	3119	3817

The work function

$$A - A_0 = U - U_0 - TS \quad \text{(i)}$$

and $$S = \frac{U - U_0}{T} + k \ln Q \quad \text{(ii)}$$

Hence, $$A - A_0 = -kT \ln Q \quad \text{(iii)}$$

$$G - G_0 = \text{A} - \text{A}_0 + PV = A + RT$$

for an ideal gas

so that $$G - G_0 = -kT \ln Q + RT \quad \text{(iv)}$$

By Stirling's formula

$$\ln L! = L \ln L - L = L \ln L - L \ln e$$

and
$$L! = (L/e)^L$$

Hence
$$Q = q^L/L! = (qe/L)^L \tag{v}$$

From (iv) and (v)

$$\begin{aligned} G - G_0 &= -kT \ln (qe/L)^L + RT \\ &= -LkT \ln (qe/L) + RT \\ &= -RT \ln (q/L) - RT \ln e + RT \end{aligned}$$

$\ln e = 1$ so that $G - G_0 = -RT \ln(q/L)$

To obtain $G^\ominus - G_0^\ominus$ the molecular partition function ($q^\ominus$) must be calculated at a pressure of 1 atmosphere, and V in the translational partition function is calculated from $V = RT/P$ with $P = 1\,\text{atm}$ ($1.013 \times 10^5\,\text{N m}^{-2}$).

For a component A, $G_A^\ominus - G_{A(0)}^\ominus = -RT \ln (q_A^\ominus/L)$ (vi)

Equation (vi) gives the Gibbs free energy $G_A^\ominus$ at a temperature T relative to that at $T = 0\,\text{K}$ when the lowest level for $q_A^\ominus$ is the ground state of A.

For general reaction

$$aA + bB = sS + rR$$

$$\begin{aligned} \Delta G^\ominus &= (sG_S^\ominus + rG_R^\ominus) - (aG_A^\ominus + bG_B^\ominus) \\ &= (sG_{S(0)}^\ominus + rG_{R(0)}^\ominus) - (aG_{A(0)}^\ominus + bG_{B(0)}^\ominus) \\ &\quad -sRT \ln (q_S^\ominus/L) - rRT \ln (q_R^\ominus/L) + aRT \ln (q_A^\ominus/L) \\ &\quad + bRT \ln (q_B^\ominus/L) \end{aligned}$$

$$\Delta G^\ominus = \Delta G_{(0)}^\ominus - RT \ln \left[\frac{(q_S^\ominus)^s \, (q_R^\ominus)^r}{(q_A^\ominus)^a \, (q_B^\ominus)^b} \left(\frac{1}{L} \right)^{\Delta n} \right]$$

where $\Delta n = (s + r) - (a + b)$

$$\begin{aligned} \ln K_p &= -\Delta G^\ominus/RT \\ &= -\Delta G_0^\ominus/RT + \ln \left[\frac{(q_S^\ominus)^s \, (q_R^\ominus)^r}{(q_A^\ominus)^a \, (q_B^\ominus)^b} \left(\frac{1}{L} \right)^{\Delta n} \right] \end{aligned}$$

$$\text{and } K_p = \frac{(q^{\ominus}_{S})^s\,(q^{\ominus}_{R})^r}{(q^{\ominus}_{A})^a\,(q^{\ominus}_{B})^b}\left(\frac{1}{L}\right)^{\Delta n} \exp\left(-\frac{\Delta G^{\ominus}_{(0)}}{RT}\right) \qquad \text{(vii)}$$

In equation (vii) $\Delta G^{\ominus}_{(0)}$ is the standard Gibbs free energy change for the reaction at $T = 0$ K and is the same as $\Delta U^{\ominus}_{0}$. It is the difference in energy between the ground states of reactants and products, and is generally written as ΔE_0.

It may be calculated from the dissociation energies in the usual way, i.e.

$$\Delta E_0 = D_{H_2} + D_{D_2} - 2D_{HD} \qquad \text{(viii)}$$

for the reaction specified in the equation.

By equation (viii)

$$\Delta E_0 = 431.87 + 439.33 - 870.48\,\text{J mol}^{-1}$$

$$= \underline{720\,\text{J mol}^{-1}}$$

Each molecular partition function $q^{\ominus}$ is the product of the partition functions for each mode of motion.

$$q^{\ominus} = q_{trans} \times q_{rot} \times q_{vib} \times q_{elect}$$

For diatomic molecules, in general $q_{elect} = 1$ so that in the example under consideration it is necessary only to evaluate q_{trans}, q_{rot} and q_{vib}.

$\boldsymbol{q_{vib}}$ For 1000 K and the given values of the wave number ($\bar{\nu}$) of the fundamental vibration, the following values of the vibrational partition functions have been obtained.

$\underline{H_2(\bar{\nu} = 4395\ \text{cm}^{-1} = 439\,500\ \text{m}^{-1})}$

$$\frac{hc\bar{\nu}}{kT} = \frac{6.624 \times 10^{-34} \times 3.00 \times 10^{8} \times 439\,500}{1.381 \times 10^{-23} \times 1000}$$

$$= 6.324$$

$$q_{vib(H_2)} = \frac{1}{(1 - e^{-6.324})} = \underline{1.002}$$

$D_2(\bar{\nu} = 3119\ \text{cm}^{-1} = 311\,900\ \text{m}^{-1})$

$$\frac{hc\bar{\nu}}{kT} = \frac{6.624 \times 10^{-34} \times 3.00 \times 10^{8} \times 311\,900}{1.381 \times 10^{-23} \times 1000}$$

$$= 4.488$$

$$q_{\text{vib}(D_2)} = \frac{1}{(1 - e^{-4.488})} = \underline{1.011}$$

$HD(\bar{\nu} = 3817\ \text{cm}^{-1} = 381\,700\ \text{m}^{-1})$

$$\frac{hc\bar{\nu}}{kT} = \frac{6.624 \times 10^{-34} \times 3.00 \times 10^{8} \times 381\,700}{1.381 \times 10^{-23} \times 1000}$$

$$= 5.493$$

$$q_{\text{vib(HD)}} = \frac{1}{(1 - e^{-5.493})} = \underline{1.004}$$

$\mathbf{q_{trans}}$ The translational partition function is calculated from

$$q_{\text{trans}} = V\left(\frac{2\pi mkT}{h^2}\right)^{\frac{3}{2}}$$

in which V is the volume calculated from $V = RT/P$ with $T = 1000\ \text{K}$ and $P = 1\ \text{atm}\ (1.013 \times 10^5\ \text{Nm}^{-2})$.

$\mathbf{q_{rot}}$ The rotational partition function is calculated from

$$q_{\text{rot}} = \frac{8\pi^2 IkT}{\sigma h^2}$$

$q^{\ominus}$ can now be written for each species

$$q^{\ominus}_{H_2} = V\left(\frac{2\pi m_{H_2}kT}{h^2}\right)^{\frac{3}{2}} \times \frac{8\pi^2 I_{H_2}kT}{\sigma_{H_2} h^2} \times 1.002 \times 1 \qquad \text{(ix)}$$

$$q^{\ominus}_{D_2} = V\left(\frac{2\pi m_{D_2}kT}{h^2}\right)^{\frac{3}{2}} \times \frac{8\pi^2 I_{D_2}kT}{\sigma_{D_2} h^2} \times 1.011 \times 1 \qquad \text{(x)}$$

$$q^{\ominus}_{HD} = V\left(\frac{2\pi m_{HD}kT}{h^2}\right)^{\frac{3}{2}} \times \frac{8\pi^2 I_{HD}kT}{\sigma_{HD} h^2} \times 1.004 \times 1 \qquad \text{(xi)}$$

For the given reaction

$$K_p = \frac{(q^{\ominus}_{HD})^2}{q^{\ominus}_{H_2} \times q^{\ominus}_{D_2}}\left(\frac{1}{L}\right)^{\Delta n} \exp\left(-\frac{\Delta E_0}{RT}\right) \qquad \text{(xii)}$$

For the reaction $H_2 + D_2 = 2HD$, $\Delta n = 0$ so that $\left(\dfrac{1}{L}\right)^{\Delta n} = 1$.

On substitution of the values of $q^{\ominus}_{H_2}$, $q^{\ominus}_{D_2}$ and $q^{\ominus}_{HD}$ from equations (ix), (x) and (xi) into equation (xii) the fundamental constants and the volumes cancel out leaving

$$K_p = \left(\frac{m^2_{HD}}{m_{H_2} \times m_{D_2}}\right)^{\frac{3}{2}} \left(\frac{I^2_{HD}}{I_{H_2} \times I_{D_2}}\right) \left(\frac{\sigma_{H_2} \times \sigma_{D_2}}{\sigma^2_{HD}}\right) \left(\frac{1.004^2}{1.002 \times 1.001}\right) \exp\left(\frac{-720}{8.31 \times 1000}\right)$$

Since
$$\frac{m^2_{HD}}{m_{H_2} \times m_{D_2}} = \frac{M^2_{r(HD)}}{M_{r(H_2)} \times M_{r(D_2)}}$$

$$\ln K_p = \frac{3}{2} \ln\left(\frac{3.022^2}{2.015 \times 4.028}\right) + \ln\left(\frac{6.13^2}{4.60 \times 9.20}\right) + \ln\left(\frac{2 \times 2}{1^2}\right) + \ln\left(\frac{1.004^2}{1.002 \times 1.011}\right) - \frac{720}{8.31 \times 1000}$$

$$= \frac{3}{2} \ln 1.125 + \ln 0.8879 + \ln 4 + \ln 0.9951 - 0.0866$$

$$= 0.1767 - 0.1189 + 1.3863 - 0.0049 - 0.0866$$

$$= 1.3526$$

From which $K_p = \underline{3.866}$

The equilibrium constant (K_p) for the reaction

$H_2(g) + D_2(g) = 2HD(g)$ is 3.87.

This example shows that when the number of molecules of reactants is the same as the number of molecules of products, all the constants in the $q^{\ominus}_{trans}$ and $q^{\ominus}_{rot}$ values cancel out, thereby reducing considerably the extent of calculation.

Example 10.14 Molecular dissociation

From the following molecular parameters for Na_2 *and* Na *calculate* K_p *for the dissociation process* $Na_2 = 2Na$ *at 1000 K.*

Parameter	Na_2	*Na*
Moment of inertia (I)/*kg m*^{2}	181.2×10^{-47}	–
Relative molecular mass (M_r)	45.98	22.99
Dissociation energy (D_m)/*kJ mol*$^{-1}$	70.46	–
Wave number of fundamental vibration $(\bar{\nu})$/*cm*$^{-1}$	159.23	–

Equation (vii) in Example 10.13 is the general equation for K_p. From this, the equilibrium constant for $Na_2 = 2Na$ is

$$K_p = \frac{(q^{\ominus}_{Na})^2}{q^{\ominus}_{Na_2}} \left(\frac{1}{L}\right)^{\Delta n} \exp\left(-\frac{\Delta E_0}{RT}\right) \quad \text{(i)}$$

For the given reaction ΔE_0 is the dissociation energy of Na_2, i.e. 70.46 kJ mol^{-1} and $\Delta n = 1$, so that

$$K_p = \frac{(q^{\ominus}_{Na})^2}{q^{\ominus}_{Na_2}} \left(\frac{1}{L}\right) \exp\left(-\frac{70\,460}{8.31 \times 1000}\right) \quad \text{(ii)}$$

The molecular partition function $(q^{\ominus})$ is given by

$$q^{\ominus} = q_{trans} \times q_{rot} \times q_{vib} \times q_{elect}$$

In Examples 10.10, 10.11, 10.12 and 10.13 it has been assumed, in general, for diatomic molecules that $q_{elect} = 1$. This assumption cannot be applied generally to atoms. The general expression for the molecular partition function is

$$q = \sum_i g_i \, e^{-\varepsilon_i/kT}$$

When more than one molecular or atomic states have the same energy ε'_i, the energy level is described as degenerate and is given a statistical weighting, g_i, which is equal to the number of molecular states which possess the energy, ε'_i. As an illustration, if $\varepsilon_3 = \varepsilon_4 = \varepsilon_5$, the states $i = 3, 4$ and 5 constitute a set with triple degeneracy and $g_i = 3$. In such instances, i indicates the different sets of states and not the individual states. g_i is called the degeneracy of the energy level.

In general, the electronic energy levels are so widely separated that the terms $e^{-\varepsilon_i/kT}$ are all very small, apart from that of the ground state (the only populated level) with energy ε_0 relative to some arbitrary zero. Hence,

$$q_{elect} = g_0 \, e^{-\varepsilon_0/kT} \quad \text{(iii)}$$

If the electronic energies are measured from the ground state of the molecule or atom then $\varepsilon_0 = 0$ and the electronic partition function is given by

$$q_{\text{elect}} = g_0$$

For many species, including diatomic gases, $g_o = 1$ so that $q_{\text{elect}} = 1$.

However, a number of atomic species have degenerate ground states. The alkali metals have doubly degenerate ground states, ($g_0 = 2$), so that

$$q_{\text{elect}} = 2.$$

Hence, in this problem which involves atomic sodium we must include electronic contributions, in order to evaluate $q^{\ominus}_{\text{Na}}$.

There are some diatomic gases, however, which have electronically degenerate ground states. For example, the nitrogen(II) oxide has a doubly degenerate ground state. Furthermore, the lowest excited electronic energy level for nitrogen(II) oxide is close to the ground state and is also doubly degenerate. For this excited level, $\bar{\nu} = 121\,\text{cm}^{-1}$. Thus, if the temperature is elevated this excited state will make a significant contribution to the electronic partition function.

Thus
$$q_{\text{elect}} = \sum_i g_i \mathrm{e}^{-\varepsilon_i/kT}$$
$$= 2\mathrm{e}^{-\varepsilon_0/kT} + 2\mathrm{e}^{-\varepsilon_x/kT}$$

in which ε_0 = ground state energy and is set = 0 since the electronic energy is measured from the ground state and $(\varepsilon_x - \varepsilon_0)$ is the energy of the first excited state relative to that of the ground state.

Thus
$$q_{\text{elect}} = 2(1 + \mathrm{e}^{-(\varepsilon_x - \varepsilon_0)/kT})$$
$$(\varepsilon_x - \varepsilon_0)/kT = hc\bar{\nu}/kT$$

and
$$q_{\text{elect}} = 2(1 + \mathrm{e}^{-hc\bar{\nu}/kT}) \text{ for NO}$$

There is a similar situation for the fluorine atom. The ground electronic state is quadruply degenerate and there is a doubly degenerate excited state only $404\,\text{cm}^{-1}$ above it, so that for the fluorine atom

$$q_{\text{elect}} = 4 + 2\mathrm{e}^{-hc\bar{\nu}/kT}$$
$$= 2(2 + \mathrm{e}^{-hc\bar{\nu}/kT})$$

At elevated temperatures the excited state will make a significant contribution to the partition function of the fluorine atom and must be considered in the calculation of $q^{\ominus}_{F}$ (see Additional Example 30).

$\boldsymbol{q^{\ominus}_{Na_2}}$ There are contributions to $q^{\ominus}_{Na_2}$ from translational, rotational and vibrational modes of motion only. $q_{elect} = 1$ for the diatomic molecule.

$$q^{\ominus}_{Na_2} = q_{Na_2(trans)} \times q_{Na_2(rot)} \times q_{Na_2(vib)}$$

$$q^{\ominus}_{Na_2} = V\left(\frac{2\pi m_{Na_2} kT}{h^2}\right)^{\frac{3}{2}} \left(\frac{8\pi^2 I_{Na_2} kT}{\sigma_{Na_2} h^2}\right) \left(\frac{1}{1 - e^{-h\nu/kT}}\right)$$

$$\sigma_{Na_2} = 2 \text{ since } Na_2 \text{ is homonuclear.}$$

V = volume occupied by 1 mole of gas at 1000 K and 1 atm. Assuming ideal behaviour

$$V = \frac{RT}{P} = \frac{8.31 \times 1000}{1.013 \times 10^5}\ \text{m}^3$$

$$q_{Na_2(trans)} = \frac{8.31 \times 1000}{1.013 \times 10^5} \times \left(2\pi \times \frac{45.98 \times 10^{-3}}{6.02 \times 10^{23}} \times \frac{1.381 \times 10^{-23} \times 1000}{(6.624 \times 10^{-34})^2}\right)^{\frac{3}{2}}$$

$$= \underline{1.523 \times 10^{32}}$$

$$q_{Na_2(rot)} = \frac{8\pi^2 \times 181.2 \times 10^{-47} \times 1.381 \times 10^{-23} \times 1000}{2 \times (6.624 \times 10^{-34})^2}$$

$$= \underline{2252}$$

$$q_{Na_2(vib)} = \frac{1}{(1 - e^{-hc\bar{\nu}/kT})}$$

$$\frac{hc\bar{\nu}}{kT} = \frac{6.624 \times 10^{-34} \times 3.00 \times 10^8 \times 15\,923}{1.381 \times 10^{-23} \times 1000}$$

$$= \underline{0.2291}$$

and

$$q_{Na_2(vib)} = \frac{1}{(1 - e^{-0.2291})} = 4.884$$

Therefore $$q^{\ominus}_{Na_2} = 1.523 \times 10^{32} \times 2252 \times 4.884$$
$$= \underline{16.75 \times 10^{35}}$$

$q^{\ominus}_{Na}$ There are contributions to $q^{\ominus}_{Na}$ from translational and electronic modes of motion only.

$$q_{Na(trans)} = \frac{8.31 \times 1000}{1.013 \times 10^5}\left(2\pi \times \frac{22.99 \times 10^{-3}}{6.02 \times 10^{23}} \times \frac{1.381 \times 10^{-23} \times 1000}{(6.624 \times 10^{-34})^2}\right)^{\frac{3}{2}}$$

$$= \underline{5.385 \times 10^{31}}$$

$$q_{Na(elect)} = \underline{2}$$

Therefore $$q^{\ominus}_{Na} = 5.385 \times 10^{31} \times 2$$
$$= \underline{10.77 \times 10^{31}}$$

From equation (ii)

$$K_p = \frac{(10.77 \times 10^{31})^2}{(16.75 \times 10^{35})} \times \frac{1}{6.02 \times 10^{23}} \exp\left(\frac{-70\,460}{8.31 \times 1000}\right)$$

$$= \frac{116.0 \times 10^{62}}{16.75 \times 10^{35}} \times \frac{1}{6.02 \times 10^{23}} \times 0.000\,207\,8$$

$$= \underline{2.39}$$

<u>The equilibrium constant (K_p) for the reaction, $Na_2 = 2Na$, is 2.39.</u>

Additional Examples

1 What is the energy, in joules, required to shift the electron of the hydrogen atom from the first Bohr orbit to the fifth Bohr orbit, and what is the wavelength of the line emitted when the electron returns to the ground state? ($R_H = 1.09678 \times 10^7\,m^{-1}$.)

2 What would be the total amount of energy, in joules, required to shift *all* the electrons from the first Bohr orbit to the fifth Bohr orbit in a mole of hydrogen atoms?

3 The ionization energy of the hydrogen atom is 13.6 eV. Assuming the same magnitude for the Rydberg constant, what is the expected ionization energy of the He^+ ion? ($1\,eV = 1.6 \times 10^{-19}\,J$.)

(Adapted from ACS Cooperative Examination: Physical Chemistry (Graduate Level).)

4 The wavelength of a certain line in the Balmer series is observed at 487.6 nm. To what value of n_2 does this correspond? ($R_H = 1.09678 \times 10^7\,m^{-1}$).

5 Given that the Rydberg constant for hydrogen is $1.10 \times 10^7\,m^{-1}$, compute in m^{-1} (*a*) the Rydberg constant for Be^{3+}, and (*b*) the position of the third line in the Balmer series.

(Atomic masses: H = 1.008; Be = 9.013.)

(University of New Orleans, USA)

6 Calculate (*a*) the ground state energy for an electron in a one dimensional box 1 nm long and (*b*) the wavelength of the radiation absorbed when the electron makes the transition to the state $n = 3$.

7 The diameter of a small nucleus is of the order of 100 fm. (*a*) Calculate the energies for a proton in a three-dimensional box of 100 fm edge for $n_x = n_y = n_z = 1$ and 2, respectively. (*b*) What is the lowest energy of an election held in such a box? Comment on the likelihood of an electron existing within the nucleus.

(Proton rest mass = 1.673×10^{-24} g; electron rest mass = 9.109×10^{-28} g.)

8 If two diatomic molecules absorb microwave energy at 110 GHz and 220 GHz, respectively, how do their reduced masses compare, assuming the inter-nuclear spacings are the same in each case?

(University of New Orleans, USA)

9 A certain diatomic molecule (B) has its lowest energy rotational line at a wavelength of 10 cm. At what wavelength would you expect the corresponding absorption to occur in the unlikely molecule with the same reduced mass and twice the internuclear separation?

(University of New Orleans, USA)

10 The diatomic molecule $^{12}C^{32}S$ undergoing the $J = 0 \rightarrow 1$ rotational transition absorbs microwave energy at 49 170 MHz, and the fundamental vibrational frequency is observed as an infra-red absorption band at $1285\,cm^{-1}$.

Calculate the bond length and force-constant for this molecule.

(B.Sc., Wales)

11 In the far infra-red spectrum of HBr is a series of lines having a separation of $16.94\,cm^{-1}$. Calculate the internuclear separation from this datum.

(H = 1.008; Br = 79.92.)

(University of Washington, Seattle, USA)

12 The mean internuclear distance in carbon monoxide is 1.2 Å and, assuming simple harmonic oscillation, the force constant of the bond is

$1.9 \times 10^3\,N\,m^{-1}$. Estimate, for the molecule $^{12}C^{16}O$, the wavelength of the first line in the pure rotational spectrum and of the origin of the fundamental vibrational band. (R.S.C.)

13 The following are wave numbers, $\bar{\nu}$, of radiation absorbed by the hydrogen molecule during vibrational excitation from the ground state, v being the quantum numbers:

v	1	2	3	4	5	9
$\bar{\nu}/cm^{-1}$	4162	8085	11 779	15 248	18 488 . . .	. 29 123
v (contd.)	10	11	12	13	14	
$\bar{\nu}/cm^{-1}$	31 150	32 888	34 307	35 355	35 976	

Calculate the molar dissociation energy of the hydrogen molecule.

14 In the near infra-red, the strongest vibrational absorptions of the $^1H^{35}Cl$ molecule are at the wave numbers $2886\,cm^{-1}$, and $5668\,cm^{-1}$. Deduce ν_e, $\propto$, a force constant for the bond and, assuming

$$\frac{E_{vib}}{h} = \nu_e(n+\tfrac{1}{2}) - \propto\nu_e(n+\tfrac{1}{2})^2,$$ a value for the dissociation energy.

(Mass $^{12}C = 1.969 \times 10^{-26}\,kg$; $1\,cm^{-1} = 11.96\,J\,mol^{-1}$.)

(B.Sc., Wales)

15 A certain diatomic molecule (A) has its fundamental vibration at $3000\,cm^{-1}$.

(*a*) Where (in m^{-1}) would you expect the fundamental absorption of a molecule with the same force constant as A but four times the reduced mass to occur?

(*b*) Where (in m^{-1}) would you expect the fundamental absorption of a molecule with the same reduced mass as A but twice the force constant to occur? (University of New Orleans, USA)

16 A $0.02\,mol\,dm^{-3}$ solution absorbs 25% of the incident light of a certain wavelength in a cell of 1 cm path length. What concentration of the same solution would be required to absorb 50% of the light in a cell of 5 cm path length? (R.S.C.)

17 4.046 mg of the compound K_2ReCl_6 were dissolved in $100\,cm^3$ of a solution which was $4\,mol\,dm^{-3}$ with respect to hydrochloric acid. When a few cm^3 of this solution were placed in a 1.000 cm quartz cell in a spectrophotometer, the transmission of the solution at 281.5 nm was 10% compared with 100% transmission for pure $4\,mol\,dm^{-3}$ hydrochloric acid in the same cell. Calculate the molar absorptivity of K_2ReCl_6 (Cl = 35.5; K = 39.1; Re = 186.2.) (B.Sc., Queen's University, Belfast)

18 The following readings were taken when a 0.05% solution, in cyclohexane, of a concentrated vitamin A was examined in a photoelectric spectrophotometer, a 1 cm silica cell being used:

λ/nm	312.5	327.5	337.5
Absorbance (A)	0.772	0.901	0.774

The absorbance at 327.5 nm, corrected for irrelevant absorption, is given by

$$7(A_{327.5\,\text{nm}} - 0.405\,A_{312.5\,\text{nm}} - 0.595\,A_{337.5\,\text{nm}}).$$

Calculate the potency of the vitamin A, using the relationship:

$$\text{Potency in Units g}^{-1} = 1900 \times A_{1\%}^{1\,\text{cm.}} \text{ at } 327.5\text{ nm}.$$

19 Use the following data to determine at what frequency nuclear magnetic resonance absorption is observed for the nuclei ^{2}H, ^{19}F and ^{29}Si when the magnetic field strength is 2T.

Nucleus	*Spin* (I)	*Magnetic moment* (μ) /*nuclear magnetons*
^{2}H	1	1.21
^{19}F	$\frac{1}{2}$	4.55
^{29}Si	$\frac{1}{2}$	−0.96

(Nuclear magneton $= 5.050 \times 10^{-27}$ J T^{-1}.)

20 How do simple e.s.r. spectra arise? Describe briefly how they are observed and why they are of interest in molecular studies.

Calculate the resonance frequency (Hz) for the ^{31}P nucleus ($I = \frac{1}{2}$) in a field of 1 tesla, the g factor for ^{31}P being 2.261.

(Nuclear magneton $= 5.050 \times 10^{-27}$ J tesla^{-1}.) (B.Sc., Wales)

21 For the proton the magnetic moment is 4.84 nuclear magnetons and its spin quantum I is $\frac{1}{2}$. If in a particular nuclear magnetic resonance spectrometer the resonance absorption for protons is observed at 42.6 MHz, what is the magnetic field strength at which the instrument is operating? At what field strength will resonance absorption occur at this frequency for ^{10}B of magnetic moment 2.08 nuclear magnetons and spin quantum number 3?

(Nuclear magneton $= 5.050 \times 10^{-27}$ J T^{-1}.)

22 21.19 eV radiation from a helium discharge source falls on a nitrosamine during an ultraviolet photoelectron spectroscopic (UPS) examination. The most energetic electrons ejected have 9.01 and 9.75 eV kinetic energy. What is the wavelength, in nm, of the helium radiation used and what are the binding energies of the emitted electrons? (1 eV $= 1.60 \times 10^{-19}$ J.)

23 Calculate the entropy of (a) argon and (b) xenon at the normal boiling point (T_b) from the data given below.

Gas	*Argon*	*Xenon*
Relative molecular mass (M_r)	39.95	131.3
T_b/K	87.29	165.1

24 Calculate the entropy of iodine in the gaseous state at 298 K and 1 atmosphere pressure. (Relative molecular mass = 253.8; wave number of fundamental vibration = 214.6 cm^{-1}; moment of inertia 750.5×10^{-47} kg m^2.)

25 Evaluate the molecular partition function ($q^{\ominus}$) for gaseous chlorine at 298 K. (Relative molecular mass = 70.9; wave number of fundamental vibration = 564.9 cm^{-1}; moment of inertia = 115.0 × 10^{-47} kg m^2.)

26 Calculate the molar intrinsic energy and molar enthalpy for hydrogen gas at 1000 K. (Wave number of fundamental vibration = 4395 cm^{-1}.)

27 Calculate the entropy of gaseous nitrogen at 298 K and 1 atmosphere pressure. (Relative molecular mass = 28.0; wave number of fundamental vibration = 2359.6 cm^{-1}; moment of inertia = 14.07 × 10^{-47} kg m^2.)

28 For the gaseous dissociation of iodine, $I_2(g) = 2I(g)$, calculate K_p at 1273 K using the molecular parameters listed below.

Parameter	*I_2*	*I*
Moment of inertia/kg m^2	7.50 × 10^{-45}	—
Relative molecular mass	253.8	126.9
Dissociation energy/kJ mol^{-1}	148.5	
Wave number of fundamental vibration/cm^{-1}	214.6	
Ground state degeneracy	1	4

29 For the reaction, $H_2(g) + I_2(g) = 2HI(g)$, calculate K_p at 298 K using the molecular parameters listed below.

Parameter	*H_2*	*I_2*	*HI*
Moment of inertia/kg m^2	0.472 × 10^{-47}	750.5 × 10^{-47}	4.33 × 10^{-47}
Relative molecular mass	2.015	253.8	127.9
Dissociation energy/kJ mol^{-1}	431	148.5	295.0
Wave number of fundamental vibration/cm^{-1}	4395	214.6	2310

30 Determine the heat of dissociation of fluorine, $F_2(g) = 2F(g)$ for which $K_{p(obs)} = 1.20 \times 10^{-2}$ at 1010 K using the following molecular parameters.

Parameter	*F_2*	*F*
Moment of inertia/kg m^2	31.7 × 10^{-47}	—
Relative molecular mass	38.00	19.00
Wave number of fundamental vibration/cm^{-1}	892	
Ground state degeneracy	1	4
Wave number of lowest excited electronic state/cm^{-1}		404
Degeneracy of lowest excited state		2

11

The Crystalline State

Example 11.1 Interpretation of X-ray powder photograph

An X-ray powder photograph was taken of a cubic crystalline substance using radiation of wavelength 1.790Å. Reflections were observed at the following Bragg angles:

$$10.6°, \quad 17.6°, \quad 20.8°, \quad 21.7°, \quad 25.4°, \quad 31.6°, \quad 33.8°$$

Calculate the value of a for the material, and give the crystal lattice type.

Note $1\text{Å} = 100\,\text{pm} = 10^{-10}\,\text{m}$.

For a crystal in the cubic system, the interplanar spacing (d) is given by

$$d = a/(h^2+k^2+l^2)^{1/2}$$

where h, k and l are the indices of the planes concerned.

This may be combined with the Bragg equation,

$$\lambda = 2d \sin \theta,$$

where λ is the wavelength of the radiation and θ is the angle of reflection from the plane of spacing d, to give

$$\sin^2 \theta = \frac{\lambda^2}{4a^2}(h^2+k^2+l^2) \qquad \text{(i)}$$

Equation (i) shows that $\sin^2 \theta$ values for the Bragg angles in a cubic system have the common factor $\lambda^2/4a^2$.

For the given Bragg angles the following table may be composed:

θ	10.6°	17.6°	20.8°	21.7°	25.4°	31.6°	33.8°
$\sin^2 \theta$	0.0338	0.0914	0.1261	0.1367	0.1840	0.2746	0.3095

The common factor found for the first two values of $\sin^2\theta$ is about 0.0114.

If the $\sin^2\theta$ values are divided by this quantity, a series of values of $(h^2+k^2+l^2)$ will be obtained.

For a primitive cubic lattice, the quantity $(h^2+k^2+l^2)$ can have values equal to any integer which can be expressed as the sum of three squares.

For the face-centred cubic lattice (F) h, k and l must be either all odd or all even and for the body-centred lattice (I) $(h+k+l)$ must be even. These conditions impose restrictions on the possible values of $(h^2+k^2+l^2)$ for F and I lattices. Thus certain reflections will be systematically absent from the photographs obtained from crystals with F or I cubic structures.

For the given photograph, values of $\sin^2\theta/0.0114$ are as follows:

2.97 8.02 11.07 11.99 16.12 24.10 27.12

These values approximate very closely to:

3, 8, 11, 12, 16, 24, and 27.

The values of h, k and l which give these values of $(h^2+k^2+l^2)$ are either all odd or all even, so that the lattice must be the cubic F lattice.

The larger Bragg angles can be measured more accurately than the smaller, so that a more accurate value of $\lambda^2/4a^2$ may be found by dividing $\sin^2\theta$, for $\theta = 33.8°$, by 27.

That is

$$\frac{\lambda^2}{4a^2} = \frac{0.3095}{27} = 0.01146$$

Therefore

$$a = \frac{1.790}{2\times(0.01146)^{1/2}}\ \text{Å} = 8.36\ \text{Å}$$

The lattice type is cubic face-centred and $a = 8.36$ Å.

Example 11.2 Determination of crystal structure and Avogadro number from X-ray powder data

An X-ray powder photograph of ammonium chloride at room temperature is taken using a camera of radius 10.0 cm and an X-ray wavelength of 1.537 Å. Reflections from (100), (110) and (111) planes produce arcs separated by 7.99 cm, 11.38 cm, and 14.04 cm, respectively, on the film. The intensity of the 110 arcs is very much greater than that of the 100 arcs. Determine (a) the structure of ammonium chloride at room temperature and (b) the Avogadro constant, L. (N = 14.01, Cl = 35.46, H = 1.008; density of $NH_4Cl = 1.53\ g\ cm^{-3}$.) *(B.Sc., Southampton)*

(*a*) The distance (D) between the arcs (of Bragg angle θ) on a powder photograph, taken in a cylindrical camera of radius r is given by

$$D = 4r\theta$$

and hence

$$\theta = D/4r \text{ radians.}$$

From the given data, the following table may be computed:

Reflection Planes	(100)	(110)	(111)
D	7.99	11.38	14.04
$D/4r$	0.1998	0.2845	0.3510
$\theta°$	11.45	16.30	20.12
$\sin\theta$	0.1985	0.2807	0.3440

For the cubic system the ratio of the interplanar spacings, $d_{(100)}:d_{(110)}:d_{(111)}$, depends on whether the lattice is primitive, face-centred or body-centred as shown in the table.

Lattice	*P*	*F*	*I*
$d_{(100)}:d_{(110)}:d_{(111)}$	$a:a/\sqrt{2}:a/\sqrt{3}$ that is 1:0.707:0.577	$a/2:a/2\sqrt{2}:a/\sqrt{3}$ 1:0.707:1.154	$a/2:a/\sqrt{2}:a/2\sqrt{3}$ 1:1.414:0.577

By the Bragg law

$$d_{(100)}:d_{(110)}:d_{(111)} = \frac{\lambda}{2\sin\theta_{(100)}}:\frac{\lambda}{2\sin\theta_{(110)}}:\frac{\lambda}{2\sin\theta_{(111)}}$$

$$= \frac{1}{\sin\theta_{(100)}}:\frac{1}{\sin\theta_{(110)}}:\frac{1}{\sin\theta_{(111)}}$$

For ammonium chloride:

$$d_{(100)}:d_{(110)}:d_{(111)} = \frac{1}{0.1985}:\frac{1}{0.2807}:\frac{1}{0.3440}$$

$$= 5.037:3.563:2.907$$

$$= 1:0.7073:0.5770$$

This is very close to the ratio for a primitive cubic cell.
Thus, ammonium chloride has a primitive cubic unit cell.

The diffracting power of an atom is dependent on its number of extra-nuclear electrons, and on the angle of diffraction. Thus, of the NH_4^+ and Cl^- ions, the Cl^- ion will have the greater diffracting power, since the ratio of the numbers of extra-nuclear electrons is $Cl^-:NH_4^+ = 18:10$. The dependence of the diffracting power on angle of diffraction is roughly the same for both ions, so that the ratio of diffracting power will be close to 18:10 for all low angles of diffraction.

The intensity of the 110 arcs is found to be much greater than that of the 100 arc. This would arise from a structure for ammonium chloride, in which a chlorine ion is located at each of the corners of the unit cell, with an ammonium ion located at the centre. In this way the unit cell would contain only one NH_4^+ ion and one Cl^- ion.

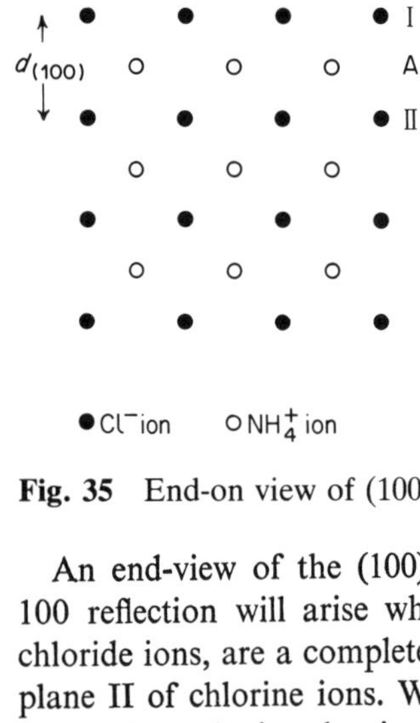

Fig. 35 End-on view of (100) lattice planes

An end-view of the (100) lattice planes is shown in Fig. 35. The 100 reflection will arise when X-rays reflected from the plane I of chloride ions, are a complete wavelength behind X-rays reflected from plane II of chlorine ions. When this condition is satisfied, X-rays reflected from the interleaving plane A (of ammonium ions) will be one half-wavelength behind X-rays reflected from plane I of chlorine ions, because the plane A is situated mid-way between planes I and II. Thus the X-rays reflected from the planes of ammonium ions are exactly out of phase with those reflected from the planes of chlorine ions. If the diffracting powers of the two ions were equal, the resulting reflection would be of zero intensity. Since, however, the diffracting power of the ammonium ion is just over half that of the chlorine ion the intensity will be reduced. If the amplitudes of the diffracted waves from the chlorine ion and ammonium ion planes are f_{Cl^-} and $f_{NH_4^+}$ respectively, the resulting amplitude will be $(f_{Cl^-} - f_{NH_4^+})$. The intensity (I) of the diffracted beam is proportional to the square of the amplitude, so that

$$I_{100} \propto (f_{Cl^-} - f_{NH_4^+})^2$$

An end-on view of the (110) lattice planes is shown in Fig. 36. The ammonium ions and chlorine ions lie in the same planes. Since the 110 reflection arises when X-rays reflected from plane Y are a

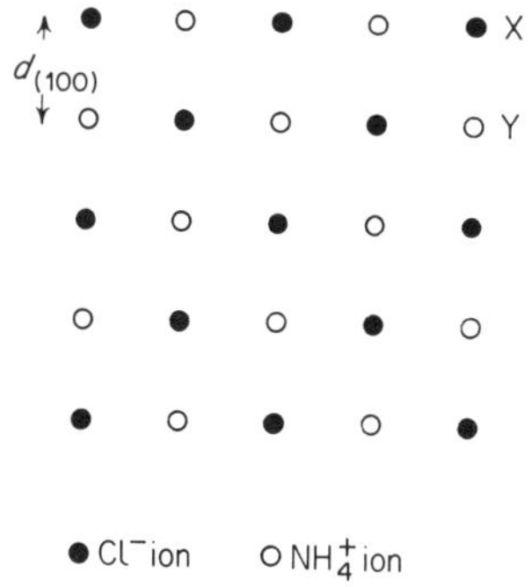

Fig. 36 End-on view of (110) lattice planes

complete wavelength behind those reflected from plane X, the X-rays reflected from both the ammonium and chlorine ions will be in phase and will reinforce each other. The resulting amplitude of the diffracted wave will be $(f_{Cl^-} + f_{NH_4^+})$.

Thus

$$I_{110} \propto (f_{Cl^-} + f_{NH_4^+})^2$$

Therefore

$$\frac{I_{110}}{I_{100}} = \frac{(f_{Cl^-} + f_{NH_4^+})^2}{(f_{Cl^-} - f_{NH_4^+})^2} \qquad \text{(i)}$$

The values of f_{Cl^-} and $f_{NH_4^+}$ will not vary greatly between the 110 and 100 reflections, so that equation (i) shows that I_{110} should be very much greater than I_{100}. This is in agreement with the experimental data, so that ammonium chloride has the structure in which a chlorine ion is located at each of the corners of the unit cell, with an ammonium ion at the centre.

The length (a) of the unit cell edge is the distance between the (100) planes. Thus from the Bragg law

$$a = \frac{\lambda}{2 \sin \theta} = \frac{1.537}{2 \times 0.1985} \text{ Å}$$
$$= 3.87 \text{ Å}$$

Ammonium chloride thus has a primitive cubic lattice with $a = 3.87$ Å and one ammonium ion and one chlorine ion per unit cell. If the corner of the unit cell is taken at the centre of a chlorine ion, the ammonium ion lies at the centre of the unit cell.

(*b*) The volume of the unit cell $= (3.87)^3$ Å^3. The relative molecular mass of ammonium chloride $= 53.5$. The unit cell contains one ammonium and one chlorine ion, that is, one molecule of ammonium chloride.

Therefore, the volume occupied by one mole of ammonium chloride

$$= (3.87)^3 \times 10^{-24} \times L \text{ cm}^3.$$

The density of ammonium chloride (1.53 g cm^{-3})

$$= \frac{\text{mass of one mole}}{\text{volume occupied by one mole}}$$

$$= \frac{53.5}{(3.87)^3 \times 10^{-24} \times L} \text{ g cm}^{-3}.$$

Therefore

$$L = \frac{53.5}{(3.87)^3 \times 10^{-24} \times 1.53}$$
$$= 6.03 \times 10^{23}$$

Therefore, Avogadro constant $= 6.03 \times 10^{23}$.

Example 11.3 Calculation of length of cube edge and metallic radius

Tungsten has a body-centred cubic lattice, and each lattice point is occupied by one atom. Calculate the metallic radius of the tungsten atom, given that the density of tungsten is 19.30 g cm^{-3} and its relative atomic mass is 183.9. Avogadro constant is 6.023×10^{23}.

(B.Sc., Birmingham)

In a body-centred cubic structure, with one atom at each lattice point, the unit cell is occupied by two atoms.

Let the unit cell edge length of tungsten be a Å, and hence the volume of the unit cell is $a^3 \times 10^{-24}$ cm³ (since 1 Å = 10^{-8} cm). This volume is occupied by two tungsten atoms.

Therefore, the volume occupied by one mole of tungsten atoms

$$= \frac{a^3 \times 10^{-24} \times 6.023 \times 10^{23}}{2} \text{ cm}^3$$

The mass of one mole of tungsten atoms = 183.9 g.

$$\text{Therefore, the density of tungsten} = \frac{\text{mass of one mole}}{\text{volume of one mole}}$$

$$= \frac{183.9 \times 2 \times 10}{a^3 \times 6.023} \text{ g cm}^{-3}$$

The density of tungsten is given as 19.30 g cm^{-3}

Therefore

$$a^3 = \frac{183.9 \times 2 \times 10}{6.023 \times 19.30} \text{ Å}^3$$

$$= 31.64 \text{ Å}^3$$

and

$$a = 3.163 \text{ Å}.$$

In the body centred cubic arrangement of the tungsten atoms, the atoms at the corners of the unit cell are in contact with the atom at the centre of the cell. Thus the metallic radius of the tungsten atom will be equal to one quarter of the length of a body diagonal of the cell.

$$\text{The length of the body diagonal} = \sqrt{3a^2} \text{ Å} = \sqrt{30.01} \text{ Å}$$

$$= 5.479 \text{ Å}$$

Therefore, the metallic radius of the tungsten atom

$$= 5.479/4 = 1.37 \text{ Å}$$

The metallic radius of the tungsten atom is 1.37 Å.

Additional Examples

1 An X-ray powder photograph was taken of a cubic crystalline substance using radiation of wavelength 1.785 Å. Reflections were obtained at the following Bragg angles: 18.5°, 27.0°, 33.7°, 40.0°, 45.9°, 51.9°, 58.3°, 65.4°, and 74.6°. Calculate the cell size of the material. What is the crystal lattice type? (B.Sc., Wales)

2 Nickel is a face-centred cubic metal with $a = 3.524$ Å. Calculate the Bragg angles and then give the indices of all lines appearing in a diffraction pattern with Cr K_α radiation. ($\lambda = 2.291$ Å) (B.Sc., Wales)

3 A diffraction pattern for copper at room temperature obtained in a powder camera of radius 10.0 cm using Cu K_α radiation ($\lambda = 1.539$ Å), shows lines produced by the reflections of lowest observable order, from the planes (100), (110) and (111), of separations 17.61, 25.8 and 15.15 cm respectively.

Determine (*a*) the structure of copper at room temperature,
(*b*) the Avogadro constant, and
(*c*) the metallic radius of copper.
(Cu = 63.54; density of copper = 8.94 g cm^{-3})

4 Molybdenum is body-centred cubic. Calculate (*i*) the lattice constant (*a*), (*ii*) the density of molybdenum, (*iii*) the metallic radius of molybdenum atoms, given that the 321 reflection in a powder photograph, obtained using Cu K_α radiation ($\lambda = 1.539$ Å), occurs at Bragg angle $\theta = 66.53°$. (Mo = 95.95).

5 Ethanedioic acid monamide (Oxamic acid) $COOH.CO.NH_2$ crystallizes as a hydrate from aqueous solution in rectangular parallelepipeds of density 1.61 g cm^{-3}. X-ray photographs show that the lattice translations parallel to the three edges of the parallelepiped are 6.91, 11.24 and 12.32 Å, and that the unit cell must contain 4 or 8 molecules of oxamic acid. Calculate the formula mass of the unit cell and the number of molecules of water which it contains.

(C = 12; H = 1; O = 16; N = 14)

(R.S.C.)

6 The hydrochloride of pyridine-3,4-dicarboxylic acid ($C_7H_5NO_4$) crystallizes from water as transparent monoclinic parallelepipeds (P. J. F. Griffiths, *Acta Cryst.* **16,** 1074 (1963)) with the following unit cell dimensions:

$$a = 7.4 \text{ Å}; \quad b = 7.6 \text{ Å}; \quad c = 14.6 \text{ Å}; \quad \beta = 99.5°$$

If the density of the crystals is 1.66 g cm^{-3}, and the unit cell must contain 4 or 8 molecules of the acid, determine the number of molecules of HCl associated with each molecule of acid.

(C = 12; H = 1; O = 16; N = 14; Cl = 35.5)

7 A protein forms crystals of the orthorhombic type with unit cell dimensions of $130 \times 74.8 \times 30.9$ Å. If the density of the crystal is 1.315 g cm^{-3} and there are 6 molecules per unit cell, what is the relative molecular mass of the protein?

(University of Connecticut, Storrs, USA)

8 Copper(I) chloride forms a sodium chloride type lattice. Its density is 4.135 g cm^{-3} and the X-ray reflection from the set of (111)-type planes was observed at a Bragg angle of 6° 30′. Calculate the wavelength of the X-rays.

(University of Connecticut, Storrs, USA)

12

Radiochemistry

Example 12.1 Rate of radioactive decay

Calculate the number of alpha-particles emitted per second by 1 g of pure thorium dioxide. (Half-life of ^{232}Th = 1.39 × 10^{10} years.)

(B.Sc., Liverpool)

The decay of a radioactive species follows a first order rate law, since the rate of decay is proportional to the number (n) of nuclei of the given species present. Thus the number of active atoms at time t is related to the number of atoms (n_0) at time $t = 0$ by the equation

$$t = \frac{1}{\lambda}\, 2.303 \log \frac{n_0}{n}$$

where λ is the rate constant, usually referred to as the decay constant. The time, for half-decay ($t_{1/2}$) is given, therefore, by

$$t_{1/2} = \frac{0.693}{\lambda}$$

From the given data, the decay constant for ^{232}Th is given by

$$\lambda = \frac{0.693}{1.39 \times 10^{10}}\ \text{year}^{-1}$$

$$= \frac{0.693}{1.39 \times 10^{10} \times 3\,600 \times 24 \times 365}\ \text{s}^{-1}$$

$$= 1.58 \times 10^{-18}\ \text{s}^{-1}$$

The number of atoms of ^{232}Th in 1 g of the pure oxide (ThO_2)

$$= \frac{1}{264} \times 6.02 \times 10^{23}$$

where 264 is the relative molecular mass of ThO_2

$$= 2.28 \times 10^{21}$$

The rate of decay is given by

$$-\frac{dn}{dt} = \lambda n$$

Therefore

$$-\frac{dn}{dt} = 1.58 \times 10^{-18} \times 2.28 \times 10^{21}\ s^{-1}$$

$$= 3.60 \times 10^{3}\ s^{-1}$$

This is the number of thorium atoms disintegrating per second by alpha-particle emission.

Therefore, the number of alpha-particles emitted by 1 g of pure thorium dioxide is $\underline{3.60 \times 10^{3}\ s^{-1}}$.

Example 12.2 Radiocarbon dating

A large proportional counter is filled in succession with three samples of carbon dioxide and the following counts recorded:

(a) 'Dead' carbon dioxide (from coal): 10 775 counts in 900 min.
(b) Carbon dioxide from contemporary wood: 26 394 counts in 200 min.
(c) Carbon dioxide from sample to be dated: 10 788 counts in 400 min.

What is the 'age' of sample (c)? In each case exactly the same amount of carbon dioxide was introduced into the counter.
(Half-life of ^{14}C = 5570 years) *(B.Sc., Durham)*

Carbon obtained from coal is taken to be inactive because of its great age in comparison with the half-life of ^{14}C. Hence, in making measurements of the radioactivity of carbon from other sources, a sample of 'dead' carbon of the same mass and in the same form as that being investigated is placed in the detector for the determination of the background counting-rate.

From the given data the background counting-rate

$$= \frac{10\,775}{900} = 11.97 \text{ counts per minute (c.p.m.)} \qquad (a)$$

The radiocarbon dating technique is based on two main assumptions. The first is that the radioactive ^{14}C, produced in the atmosphere by the interaction of cosmic radiation with ^{14}N, is in equilibrium distribution between the atmosphere and living organisms, that is, during the life span of the organism, the radiocarbon intake balances the loss of radiocarbon by normal exponential decay. This means that the carbon in contemporary living material has a constant specific activity. On the death of the organism, the intake of radiocarbon ceases abruptly, whereas the radiocarbon already in the organism continues to decay exponentially. Thus if the half-life of radiocarbon is known, the age of carbonaceous material may be calculated once the activity of the material has been determined.

The second assumption is that the intensity of cosmic radiation and the specific activity of carbon in living material have remained substantially unaltered over the last 30 000 years, or thereabouts. If this assumption is valid, then the specific activity of contemporary organic carbon will be the same as that of the carbon in the material under investigation, at the time of the death of the material.

From the given data, the counting-rate of carbon dioxide from contemporary wood

$$= \frac{26\,394}{200} = 131.97 \text{ c.p.m.}$$

On subtracting the background counting-rate, the true counting-rate is found:

$$131.97 - 11.97 = 120 \text{ c.p.m.} \qquad (b)$$

This counting-rate is proportional to the specific activity of the carbon in the contemporary wood from which the carbon dioxide was obtained. The counting-rate for the carbon dioxide from the sample to be dated

$$= \frac{10\,788}{400} = 26.97 \text{ c.p.m.}$$

Correction for background gives a true counting-rate of

$$26.97 - 11.97 = 15 \text{ c.p.m.} \qquad (c)$$

This is proportional to the specific activity of the carbon in the sample to be dated.

The expression for radioactive decay is

$$2.303 \log \frac{n_0}{n} = \lambda t$$

where n_0 is the number of ^{14}C atoms present in the sample to be dated at time $t = 0$, n the number of ^{14}C atoms present at time $t = t$, λ the decay constant of $^{14}C = \dfrac{0.693}{5570}$ year^{-1} and t is equal to the age of the sample.

n_0 and n are proportional to the specific activities of the contemporary and ancient carbon respectively, and hence to the observed counting-rates (*b*) and (*c*), since the same amount of carbon dioxide was introduced into the detector for each observation.

Therefore
$$2.303 \log \frac{120}{15} = \frac{0.693}{5570} t$$

and
$$t = \frac{5570 \times 2.303}{0.693} \log 8 \text{ years}$$
$$= 16\,720 \text{ years}$$

The 'age' of sample (*c*) = <u>16 720 years.</u>

Example 12.3 Radiochemical equilibrium

^{235}U has a half-life of 7.1×10^8 years, and its daughter ^{231}Th has a half-life of 24.6 hours. What is the mass of ^{231}Th in equilibrium with 1 g of ^{235}U, and what is the mean life of the atoms of ^{231}Th?

When the half-life of a parent is long in comparison with that of its daughter, a steady-state is achieved after the lapse of a considerable time, in which the daughter element decays as fast as it is produced. That is, a constant amount of the daughter element is present in equilibrium with the parent. The rate of decay of the parent is given by

$$-\frac{dn_P}{dt} = \lambda_P n_P$$

where λ_P is the decay constant of the parent, and n_P the number of atoms of the parent.

At equilibrium, the rate of decay of the parent, which is also the rate of formation of the daughter, is equal therefore, to the rate of decay of the daughter.

That is
$$-\frac{dn_P}{dt} = -\frac{dn_D}{dt}$$

and hence
$$\lambda_P n_P = \lambda_D n_D \qquad \text{(i)}$$

where λ_D is the decay constant of the daughter and n_D the number of atoms of daughter present.

Equation (i) holds for a decay chain in which several short-lived daughters (*A*, *B*, *C*, etc.) arise from successive decays, commencing with a parent of relatively long half-life. That is,

$$\lambda_P n_P = \lambda_A n_A = \lambda_B n_B = \text{etc.}$$

The half-life of ^{235}U is so long that a completely negligible fraction of it will be transformed during the period of any experiment. Thus $\lambda_P n_P$ may be taken as constant. This type of equilibrium is called *secular equilibrium.*

The half-lives, t_P and t_D, are given by $\frac{0.693}{\lambda_P}$ and $\frac{0.693}{\lambda_D}$ respectively.

Equation (i) may be rewritten, therefore, as

$$\frac{n_P}{t_P} = \frac{n_D}{t_D} \qquad \text{(ii)}$$

1 g of ^{235}U contains $\frac{L}{235}$ atoms, where L is the Avogadro constant.

Let the mass of ^{231}Th in equilibrium with 1 g of ^{235}U be w g.

Therefore, the number of atoms of ^{231}Th in equilibrium $= \frac{Lw}{231}$

Substitution of the relevant data into equation (ii) yields

$$\frac{L}{235 \times 7.1 \times 10^8} = \frac{Lw \times 24 \times 365}{231 \times 24.6}$$

Therefore

$$w = \frac{231 \times 24.6}{235 \times 7.1 \times 10^8 \times 24 \times 365}\text{ g}$$
$$= 3.89 \times 10^{-12}\text{ g}$$

Mass of ^{231}Th in equilibrium with 1 g of $^{235}U = 3.89 \times 10^{-12}$ g.

The decay equation, $t = \frac{1}{\lambda}\ln\frac{n_0}{n}$, may be written as $n = n_0\,e^{-\lambda t}$, so that the rate of decay can be written as

$$-\frac{dn}{dt} = \lambda n = \lambda n_0\,e^{-\lambda t}.$$

The mean life, τ of the radioactive atoms will be the sum of the products of the lifetime t and the number of atoms $(-dn)$ which decay when this lifetime has elapsed, divided by the total number, n_0, of atoms. The sum will be over all values of t from 0 to infinity.

Hence, $$\tau = \int_0^\infty \frac{t(-dn)}{n_0} = \int_0^\infty t\lambda\,e^{-\lambda t}\,dt = \frac{1}{\lambda} = \frac{t_{\frac{1}{2}}}{0.693}$$

The half-life of ^{231}Th is 24.6 hours and hence $\tau = \dfrac{24.6}{0.693}$ hours

$$= 35.5 \text{ hours.}$$

The mean life of the atoms of ^{231}Th is 35.5 hours.

Example 12.4 Radiochemical equilibrium

The fission-product ^{90}Sr (half-life = 28 years) decays to ^{90}Y (half-life = 64.2 hours) according to the following scheme:

$$^{90}Sr \xrightarrow{\beta^-} {}^{90}Y \xrightarrow{\beta^-} {}^{90}Zr \text{ (stable)}$$

If a sample of ^{90}Sr is separated from its ^{90}Y daughter, how long a time would elapse before freshly generated ^{90}Y built up to 99% of its equilibrium activity?

Since the half-life of the parent ^{90}Sr is long in comparison with that of the daughter the situation is the same as that discussed in example 12.3, that is, prior to separation from the daughter product, the ^{90}Sr and ^{90}Y will be in secular equilibrium.

When the ^{90}Sr is separated, fresh ^{90}Y will be generated and the amount of ^{90}Y will increase until its decay rate equals that of the ^{90}Sr.

Let n_1 = the number of ^{90}Sr atoms in the parent sample and n_2 = the number of ^{90}Y atoms after the lapse of a time t.

The rate of formation of ^{90}Y is equal to the rate of decay of ^{90}Sr, that is, $\lambda_1 n_1$, where λ_1 is the decay constant of ^{90}Sr.

The rate at which ^{90}Y atoms decay is given by $\lambda_2 n_2$, where λ_2 is the decay constant of ^{90}Y.

Hence, the rate of accumulation of ^{90}Y atoms is given by the difference between $\lambda_1 n_1$ and $\lambda_2 n_2$, that is

$$\frac{dn_2}{dt} = \lambda_1 n_1 - \lambda_2 n_2 \qquad \text{(i)}$$

Since the parent has a long half-life by comparison with that of the daughter, $\lambda_1 n_1$ may be taken to be constant and equation (1) may be integrated as follows:

$$\int \frac{dn_2}{(\lambda_1 n_1 - \lambda_2 n_2)} = \int dt + A$$

$$-\frac{1}{\lambda_2} \ln(\lambda_1 n_1 - \lambda_2 n_2) = t + A \qquad \text{(ii)}$$

where A is a constant when $t = 0$, $n_2 = 0$ and hence $A = -\dfrac{1}{\lambda_2} \ln(\lambda_1 n_1)$.
Substitution for A in equation (ii) yields

$$t = \frac{1}{\lambda_2}[\ln \lambda_1 n_1 - \ln(\lambda_1 n_1 - \lambda_2 n_2)] \qquad \text{(iii)}$$

At equilibrium $\lambda_1 n_1 = \lambda_2 n_2$ so that the equilibrium value of n_2 is $\lambda_1 n_1/\lambda_2$. Equation (iii) can be used to determine the time for n_2 to reach a fraction F of the equilibrium value, that is for n_2 to reach $F\lambda_1 n_1/\lambda_2$. Substitution of this value for n_2 in equation (iii) yields

$$t = \frac{1}{\lambda_2}[\ln \lambda_1 n_1 - \ln(\lambda_1 n_1 - F\lambda_1 n_1)]$$

$$= \frac{1}{\lambda_2}[\ln \lambda_1 n_1 - \ln \lambda_1 n_1 - \ln(1-F)]$$

The reciprocal of λ_2 equals $t^*_{1/2}/0.693$, in which $t^*_{1/2}$ is the half-life of the radioactive daughter. Hence,

$$t = -t^*_{1/2}\frac{\ln(1-F)}{0.693} \qquad \text{(iv)}$$

Thus, to calculate the time to build up to a particular fraction of the equilibrium activity, the daughter half-life must be known.

The half-life of the ^{90}Y is 64.2 hours so that the time taken for the daughter activity to build up to 99% of the equilibrium activity is given by

$$t = -\frac{64.2 \times 2.303}{0.693}\log\left(1 - \frac{99}{100}\right)\text{ hours} = \frac{64.2 \times 2.303 \times 2}{0.693}\text{ hours}$$

$$= 426.7 \text{ hours}$$

The time taken after separation of ^{90}Sr from its daughter product for build-up to 99% of the equilibrium activity = 427 hours.

Example 12.5 Units of radioactivity

Calculate the mass (in g) of 1 curie (Ci) of (a) Ra C (^{214}Bi); half-life = 19.7 min, (b) ^{40}K; half-life = 1.28×10^9 years, and quote the specific activity (Ci g^{-1}) for each element.

(c) The total potassium content of the sea is estimated to be 380 p.p.m., and natural potassium contains ^{40}K in the proportion of 120 p.p.m. Estimate the activity concentration of sea water in microcuries (μCi) of ^{40}K per dm^3.

The standard unit of radioactivity* is the curie (Ci) which is defined as that quantity of any radioactive material in which 3.7×10^{10} disintegrations occur per second. The millicurie (mCi) and the microcurie (μCi) correspond to quantities of radioactive material in which 3.7×10^7 and 3.7×10^4 disintegrations per second (d.p.s.) occur.

(*a*) From the given data for Ra C, the decay constant is given by

$$\lambda = \frac{0.693}{t_{1/2}} = \frac{0.693}{19.7 \times 60}\ \mathrm{s}^{-1}.$$

and

$$-\frac{dn}{dt} = 3.7 \times 10^{10}\ \mathrm{s}^{-1}.$$

Substitution of these values into the decay equation $-\dfrac{dn}{dt} = \lambda n$, permits the calculation of the number (n) of atoms of Ra C in 1 curie.

Hence
$$n = \frac{3.70 \times 10^{10} \times 19.7 \times 60}{0.693}$$

The mass of n atoms of Ra C

$$= \frac{n}{6.02 \times 10^{23}} \times 214\ \mathrm{g}.$$

Hence, the mass of 1 Ci of Ra C

$$= \frac{3.70 \times 10^{10} \times 19.7 \times 60 \times 214}{6.02 \times 10^{23} \times 0.693}\ \mathrm{g} = 2.24 \times 10^{-8}\ \mathrm{g}.$$

The mass of 1 curie of Ra C = 2.24×10^{-8} g.

The specific activity of a radioactive element is the number of curies per unit mass, that is Ci g^{-1}.

For Ra C the mass of 1 curie is 2.24×10^{-8} g. Therefore, the specific activity

$$= \frac{1}{2.24 \times 10^{-8}}\ \mathrm{Ci\ g^{-1}} = 4.46 \times 10^{7}\ \mathrm{Ci\ g^{-1}}.$$

The specific activity of Ra C = 4.46×10^7 Ci g^{-1}.

(*b*) For ^{40}K

$$\lambda = \frac{0.693}{1.28 \times 10^{9} \times 365 \times 24 \times 3600}\ \mathrm{s}^{-1}$$

* The SI unit of radioactivity is one transformation per second, s^{-1}. It is named the becquerel and given the symbol, Bq. 1 Ci = 3.7×10^{10} Bq = 37 gigabecquerel (GBq).

Proceeding as in (*a*), the number (n) of atoms of ^{40}K in 1 Ci is given by

$$n = \frac{3.70 \times 10^{10} \times 1.28 \times 10^{9} \times 365 \times 24 \times 3600}{0.693}$$

The mass of n atoms of ^{40}K

$$= \frac{n}{6.02 \times 10^{23}} \times 40 \text{ g}.$$

Hence the mass of 1 Ci of ^{40}K

$$= \frac{3.70 \times 10^{10} \times 1.28 \times 10^{9} \times 365 \times 24 \times 3600 \times 40}{6.02 \times 10^{23} \times 0.693} \text{ g}$$

$$= 1.43 \times 10^{5} \text{ g}.$$

The mass of 1 curie of $^{40}K = 1.43 \times 10^{5}$ g.

$$\text{The specific activity} = \frac{1}{1.43 \times 10^{5}} \text{ Ci g}^{-1}$$

$$= 6.99 \times 10^{-6} \text{ Ci g}^{-1}$$

The specific activity of $^{40}K = 6.99 \times 10^{-6}$ Ci g^{-1}.

(*c*) The potassium content of sea water is 380 p.p.m. Taking the mass of 1 dm^3 to be 1000 g, this is the same as saying that the potassium content of sea water is 0.38 g dm^{-3}. The abundance of ^{40}K in natural potassium is 120 p.p.m. = 0.012%. Therefore, the quantity of ^{40}K in sea water

$$= 0.38 \times 0.00012 \text{ g dm}^{-3}$$
$$= 4.56 \times 10^{-5} \text{ g dm}^{-3}$$

Since 1 g of ^{40}K has an activity of 6.99×10^{-6} Ci, then 4.56×10^{-5} g of ^{40}K has an activity of

$$6.99 \times 10^{-6} \times 4.56 \times 10^{-5} \text{ Ci}$$

Therefore, the activity concentration of sea water due to ^{40}K

$$= 6.99 \times 4.56 \times 10^{-11} \text{ Ci dm}^{-3}$$
$$= 6.99 \times 4.56 \times 10^{-5}\ \mu\text{Ci dm}^{-3}$$
$$= 3.19 \times 10^{-4}\ \mu\text{Ci dm}^{-3}.$$

The activity concentration of sea water in microcuries of ^{40}K per dm^{-3} $= 3.2 \times 10^{-4}$.

Summary (*a*) The mass of 1 curie of Ra C = 2.24×10^{-8} g.
The specific activity of Ra C = 4.46×10^{7} Ci g^{-1}.

(*b*) The mass of 1 curie of ^{40}K = 1.43×10^{5} g.
The specific activity of ^{40}K = 6.99×10^{-6} Ci g^{-1}.

(*c*) The activity concentration of sea water = 3.2×10^{-4} microcuries of ^{40}K per dm^3.

Example 12.6 Neutron activation

A thin sample of gold was irradiated in a thermal neutron flux of 10^{12} neutrons $cm^{-2}\,s^{-1}$ for 25.6 hours. In the reaction the nuclide ^{198}Au is produced with a half-life of 64 hours. If the thermal neutron absorption cross-section is 98 barns, what is (i) the specific activity of the sample, (ii) the saturation activity? What is the activity of the sample after 30 min irradiation, if the percentage of saturation activity is 18.8 when the irradiation time is equal to three tenths of the half-life of the element?

The cross-section for any nuclear reaction is the probability of the occurrence of that reaction.

Consider 1 cm^2 of a target material of thickness dx cm and containing n target nuclei per cm^3. Therefore, the number of target nuclei per cm^2 is n dx.

Let N_t be the number of such nuclei which are transformed per second, when the number of incident particles per second per cm^2 is N_i.

The number (σ) of individual transformations per target nucleus per incident particle per second, therefore, is given by

$$\sigma = \frac{N_t}{(n\,\mathrm{d}x)\,.\,N_i}\ \mathrm{cm}^2$$

σ is the cross-section for the particular process. The unit used is the barn (b) = 10^{-24} cm^2.

Consider a thin target, containing n nuclei per cm^2, upon which is incident a flux of particles = ϕ $cm^{-2}\,s^{-1}$.

The number of nuclei transformed by a particular process

$$= n\phi\sigma\ \mathrm{cm}^{-2}\,\mathrm{s}^{-1}$$

where σ is the cross-section (in units of cm^2) for the particular process.

If the transformation product is radioactive it will undergo decay, with its own characteristic half-life.

The rate of increase in the number (N) of product nuclei is therefore given by

$$\frac{dN}{dt} = n\phi\sigma - \lambda N \tag{i}$$

where λ is the decay constant of the radioactive product. Equation (i) may be integrated between the limits $t = 0$ and t for the time of irradiation, with the corresponding values of $N = 0$ and N.

$$\int_0^N \frac{dN}{\dfrac{n\phi\sigma}{\lambda} - N} = \lambda \int_0^t dt$$

Therefore $$-\ln\left(\frac{n\phi\sigma}{\lambda} - N\right) = \lambda t + \text{constant}$$

At time $t = 0$, $N = 0$ *and* $-\ln\left(\dfrac{n\phi\sigma}{\lambda}\right) = \text{constant}$

Therefore $$\frac{n\phi\sigma}{\lambda} - N = \frac{n\phi\sigma}{\lambda} e^{-\lambda t}$$

and $$N = \frac{n\phi\sigma}{\lambda}(1 - e^{-\lambda t}) \tag{ii}$$

where t is the time of irradiation.

In equation (ii) N is the number of radioactive atoms present after time t and therefore λN is the number of disintegrations per unit time. Thus $\dfrac{\lambda N}{3.7 \times 10^{10}}$ is the number of curies produced.

Therefore, the number of curies (c) produced when the number of target nuclei is n, is given by

$$c = \frac{n\phi\sigma}{3.7 \times 10^{10}}(1 - e^{-\lambda t}) \tag{iii}$$

Also n may be expressed in terms of the relative atomic mass (A_r) of the element and the Avogadro constant, e.g. for 1 g of element

$$n = \frac{1}{A_r} \times 6.02 \times 10^{23}$$

Therefore, equation (iii) may be written as

$$c = \frac{6.02 \times 10^{23} \times \phi \times \sigma}{3.7 \times 10^{10} \times A_r}(1 - e^{-\lambda t}) \tag{iv}$$

c is the number of curies produced in 1 g of target material, that is, the specific activity (a). σ in equation (iv) is expressed in units of cm^2, so that if it is expressed in barns (1 b $= 10^{-24}$ cm^2), equation (iv) may be written as

$$a = \frac{0.602\phi\sigma}{3.7\times10^{10}\times A_r}(1-e^{-0.693t/t_{1/2}}) \qquad \text{(v)}$$

where λ (the decay constant of the transformation product) has been replaced by $0.693/t_{1/2}$.

Different isotopes of the same element have different cross-sections for the same type of nuclear reaction, e.g. the isotopic cross-sections for the (n, γ) reaction of silver with thermal neutrons are as shown in the table below:

Isotope	^{107}Ag	^{109}Ag
σ/barns	40	90
% Abundance	51.35	48.65

The cross-section of the normal element (the natural isotopic mixture), for the production of ^{108}Ag is, however, only 51.35% of the isotopic cross-section, because the target (^{107}Ag) has only this percentage abundance. Thus if equation (v) is used to calculate the activity due to ^{108}Ag production by the (n, γ) process in normal silver, σ (= 40 b) would have to be multiplied by 0.5135. Equation (v) is written generally, therefore, as:

$$a = \frac{0.602\phi\sigma\theta}{3.7\times10^{10}\times A_r}(1-e^{-0.693t/t_{1/2}}) \qquad \text{(vi)}$$

where θ is the isotopic abundance of the isotope involved in the reaction.

For mono-isotopic elements, e.g. manganese (^{55}Mn), cobalt (^{59}Co), arsenic (^{75}As), yttrium (^{89}Y) and gold (^{197}Au), the cross-section for the normal element to be used in equation (vi) is the isotopic cross-section, that is $\theta = 1$.

Equation (vi) shows that

(*a*) when $t \gg t_{1/2}$, $e^{-0.693t/t_{1/2}} \rightarrow 0$ so that the specific activity approaches the limiting value (saturation value)

$$a = \frac{0.602\phi\sigma\theta}{3.7\times10^{10}\times A_r}$$

(*b*) when $t = t_{1/2}$, $e^{-0.693t/t_{1/2}} = 0.5$ so that a is equal to half the saturation value.

(*c*) for values of $t/t_{1/2} = 1, 0.5, 0.4, 0.3, 0.2$ and 0.1, the activities are 50, 29.2, 24.1, 18.8, 13.0 and 6.7% respectively, of the saturation value.

These figures show that for values of $t/t_{1/2} \leqslant$ about 0.3, the activity increases almost linearly with time.

The given data may be substituted in equation (vi) to determine the specific activity (a) of gold after 25.6 hours. $\phi = 10^{12}$ neutrons cm^{-2} s^{-1}, $t = 25.6$ hours, $\sigma = 98$ barns, $A_r = 197$, $t_{1/2} = 64$ hours, and since gold is mono-isotopic $\theta = 1$.
Therefore

$$a = \frac{0.602 \times 10^{12} \times 98}{3.7 \times 10^{10} \times 197}(1 - e^{-0.693 \times 25.6/64}) \text{ curies g}^{-1}$$
$$= 8.09\,(1 - e^{-0.277}) \text{ curies g}^{-1}$$
$$= 8.09\,(1 - 0.758) \text{ curies g}^{-1}$$
$$= 1.96 \text{ curies g}^{-1}.$$

(*i*) The specific activity of the gold sample after irradiation for 25.6 hours in a neutron flux of 10^{12} cm^{-2} s^{-1} = 1.96 curies g^{-1}.

(*ii*) The saturation activity = 8.09 curies g^{-1}.

When the irradiation time $= 0.3t_{1/2}$ (= 19.2 hours) the specific activity is 18.8% of the saturation value.

Therefore, the specific activity after 19.2 hours irradiation

$$= 8.09 \times 0.188 = 1.52 \text{ curies g}^{-1}.$$

Since there is an approximately linear relationship between the specific activity and time of irradiation (t) for $t/t_{1/2} \leqslant 0.3$, then the specific activity (a) of the sample after 30 min irradiation will be given by

$$a = \frac{0.5}{19.2} \times 1.52 \text{ curies g}^{-1}$$
$$= 39.6 \text{ mCi g}^{-1}.$$

The specific activity of the sample after 30 minutes irradiation = 40 mCi g^{-1}.

Example 12.7 Isotope dilution analysis

To a protein hydrolysate was added 10.1 mg of labelled alanine of specific activity 128 c.p.m. mg^{-1} measured in a particular counting arrangement. A sample of pure alanine isolated from the mixture was found to have a specific activity of 68.3 c.p.m. mg^{-1}, when measured *in the same counting arrangement. What mass of alanine was present in the hydrolysate?*

The isotope dilution technique is very useful in circumstances where, owing to the chemical similarity of the compounds involved, a quantitative method for the separation of the components of a mixture is not known or is very difficult to perform.

Suppose it is desired to determine the mass (w) of a given compound (A) in a mixture of other substances. w_a g of labelled A of specific activity a_a is added to the mixture and thoroughly mixed in. A chemically pure sample of A is then separated from the mixture and its specific activity (a) is determined.

The total activity in the system remains constant so that

$$w_a a_a = (w_a + w)a$$

or

$$w = w_a \left(\frac{a_a}{a} - 1\right) \qquad \text{(i)}$$

when $a_a \gg a$ equation (i) becomes

$$w = w_a a_a / a$$

From the given data

$w_a = 10.1$ mg, $\quad a_a = 128$ c.p.m. mg^{-1}, $\quad a = 68.3$ c.p.m. mg^{-1}

and

$$w = 10.2 \left(\frac{128 - 68.3}{68.3}\right) \text{ mg}$$

$$= 8.83 \text{ mg.}$$

The mass of alanine in the hydrolysate = 8.83 mg.

Example 12.8 Nuclear binding energy

The isotopic mass of calcium-40 ($^{40}_{20}Ca$) is 39.9625 u. Calculate the nuclear binding energy in MeV per nucleon for this nuclide, given that the masses of the hydrogen atom and the neutron are 1.0078 u and 1.0087 u respectively.

In 1960 a scale of relative atomic mass based on ^{12}C replaced the old scale which was based on ^{16}O. The new unit of atomic mass is one-twelfth of the mass of a neutral unexcited ^{12}C atom, and the symbol u is used for this unit. The justification for the use of this unit in preference to the kg is the convenient magnitudes of atomic masses which are obtained. Furthermore, atomic masses can be measured relative to the atomic mass of ^{12}C with very high accuracy.

The mass defect of a nucleus is the change in mass (Δm) when the separate nucleons combine to produce the particular nucleus. From the principle of equivalence of mass and energy, an amount of energy, $\Delta E = \Delta mc^2$, is released in the process.

This amount of energy represents the binding energy of the particles in the nucleus, and is a measure of the stability of the nucleus. It is the energy which would be required to separate the nucleus into its component nucleons. For a nuclide, ${}^A_Z X$, the mass defect is

$$Zm_P + (A-Z)m_n - m_x$$

in which, m_P = proton mass; m_n = neutron mass; m_x = mass of nucleus of X.

In performing the calculation the mass (m_H) of the neutral atom of hydrogen (${}^1_1H$) can be used instead of the proton mass and the mass of the neutral atom X, (M_x) instead of the nuclear mass (m_x) since the electron rest masses will cancel out.

Therefore, $\Delta m = Zm_H + (A-Z)m_n - M_x$ u.

Since 1 u = 931.5 MeV, the energy equivalent of the mass defect, that is, binding energy (ΔE), expressed in MeV, is given by:

$$\Delta E = \Delta m \times 931.5 = 931.5(Zm_H + (A-Z)m_n - M_x) \text{ MeV} \qquad \text{(i)}$$

The binding energy of the orbital electrons to the nucleus will be very small in comparison with the magnitudes of the other quantities involved so that it may be neglected. (The binding energy of the electron in the hydrogen atom is about 14 eV which is negligible when compared with the rest mass of an electron which is equivalent to 0.511 MeV.)

If the binding energies of nuclei are divided by their mass numbers, the binding energy per nucleon ($\Delta E/A$) is obtained.

By equation (i) the mass defect, ΔE, for ^{40}Ca is given by

$$\begin{aligned}\Delta E &= 931.5[1.0078 \times 20 + 1.0087 \times 20 - 39.9625] \text{ MeV} \\ &= 931.5 \times [40.330 - 39.9625] \text{ MeV} \\ &= 931.5 \times 0.3675 \text{ Mev} = \underline{342.3 \text{ MeV.}}\end{aligned}$$

$$\text{The binding energy per nucleon} = \frac{342.3}{40} = 8.56 \text{ MeV.}$$

The binding energy of ${}^{40}_{20}Ca$ = 8.6 MeV per nucleon.

Example 12.9 Thermonuclear fusion

A reaction which could be used in a thermonuclear fusion reactor is

$$^{2}_{1}H+^{2}_{1}H \rightarrow ^{3}_{2}He+^{1}_{0}n$$

Estimate the energy (in joules) which would be released by the thermonuclear fusion of 1 g of deuterium gas, given that the masses of the neutron, the deuterium atom and the helium-3 atom are 1.0087, 2.0141 and 3.0160 u respectively.

$$(1\ eV = 1.602\times 10^{-19}\ J;\ 1\ u = 9.315\times 10^{8}\ eV).$$

The energy released in the given reaction arises from the conversion of matter into energy in the fusion process. The sum of the masses of the two deuterium atoms exceeds the sum of the masses of the helium-3 atom and the neutron. This decrease in mass appears as the reaction energy.

The decrease in mass when the two deuterium atoms fuse

$$= (2\times 2.0141)-(3.0160+1.0087) = 0.0035\ \text{u} = 0.0035\times 9.315\times 10^{8}\ \text{eV}$$
$$= \underline{3.26\ \text{MeV}}$$

Thus, the energy released on fusion of two deuterium atoms

$$= 3.26\ \text{MeV} = 3.26\times 10^{6}\times 1.602\times 10^{-19}\ \text{J}$$
$$= 5.222\times 10^{-13}\ \text{J},$$

and the energy released per deuterium atom $= 2.611\times 10^{-13}$ J. 2.0141 g of deuterium will contain 6.02×10^{23} atoms, so that the fusion of 1 g of deuterium gas will produce the energy

$$= \frac{6.02\times 10^{23}}{2.0141}\times 2.611\times 10^{-13}\ \text{J} = 7.805\times 10^{10}\ \text{J}$$

The energy produced in the thermonuclear fusion of 1 g of deuterium gas $= 7.81\times 10^{10}$ J.

Additional Examples

1 Describe the principle of the experiments you would use to determine whether a given sample of radioactive material contained one or more active substances.

If the half-life of a radioactive substance is 1000 years, how many moles must be used in a tracer experiment if 100 counts per minute are to be registered by a Geiger counter having a geometrical factor of 50%?

(B.Sc., Liverpool)

2 One gram of radon produces 1.16×10^{18} α-particles in a minute. Calculate the fraction of radon decomposed in this time. (A_r radon = 222)

(B.Sc., B.Met., Sheffield)

3 A certain radioactive element emits beta-particles. When the beta activity of a freshly prepared sample of the element is measured as a function of time, the following data are obtained:

Time/min	*Activity/(Arbitrary units)*
0	860
20	535
50	265
70	165
100	81
130	40
150	25

Determine, using a graphical method, the disintegration constant and half-life of the element. What will be the average life-time of an atom?

(Intermediate B.Sc., Queen's University, Belfast)

4 A radioactive source is observed to undergo 100 disintegrations per second. If the source is composed of a nuclide with a half-life of 10 hours, how long will it take the activity to decay to 5 counts per second? Assume that the source decays to a stable nuclide.

(First M.B., Queen's University, Belfast)

5 1 gram of a radioactive element of relative atomic mass 226 was prepared in the year 1908. Calculate the number of radioactive atoms remaining in 1968, given that the half-life is 1622 years.

(B.Pharm., London)

6 ^{230}Th ($t_{1/2} = 8.0 \times 10^4$ years) is an α-emitter and the immediate precursor of Ra in the ^{238}U decay series ($4n+2$). From 93.4 g of broggerite, a very old uranium mineral, all of the ^{230}Th was separated with lanthanum as carrier. In this preparation, the amount of Ra was found to increase by 2.31×10^{-11} g per day. One gram of the broggerite contained 2.20×10^{-7} of Ra. The amounts of Ra were estimated from the amount of Rn formed. Calculate the half-life of Ra ($\ln 2 = 0.693$). (R.S.C.)

7 State the law of radioactive decay and obtain an expression for the fraction of a radioactive sample remaining after a given time.

The half-life of uranium (238) is 4.51×10^9 years. Calculate the age of a mineral in which the atomic ratio lead (206) to uranium (238) is 0.231 : 1. Assume that all the lead has arisen from the decay of the uranium and that all half-lives in the decay chain are small in comparison with that given.

(B.Sc., Wales)

8 A late Bronze-Age hoard was found to contain a lump of beeswax. The age of the hoard, determined from other identifiable objects present, was known to be very nearly 2700 years.

Carbon dioxide produced from the beeswax was counted in a large proportional counter at a fixed pressure, and gave a count of 44 550 in 300 minutes. The experiment was repeated with 'dead' carbon dioxide from coal, and then with carbon dioxide from contemporary wood, the gas being at the same fixed pressure as before. The following counts were obtained:

CO_2 from coal:	11 400 counts in 950 minutes
CO_2 from contemporary wood:	33 000 counts in 200 minutes.

Use the data to ascertain whether or not the sample is an original part of the hoard. (Half-life of ^{14}C = 5570 years)

9 The fission product strontium-90 has a half-life of 27.5 years and decays by β-emission to yttrium-90 of half-life 64.2 hours.

Calculate the mass of yttrium-90 in equilibrium with 1 g of strontium-90.

10 A reference solution of ^{144}Ce (half-life = 285 days) has a radioactive concentration of 20 μCi cm^{-3} at 16.00 hours on the day it is prepared. What will be the radioactive concentration at 16.00 hours 150 days later?

The decay scheme for ^{144}Ce is:

$$^{144}Ce \xrightarrow{\beta^-} {}^{144}Pr \xrightarrow{\beta^-} {}^{144}Nd \text{ (stable)}$$

If the ^{144}Ce present in a sample was separated from its praseodymium daughter, what would be the time lapse for freshly generated ^{144}Pr (half-life = 1050 s) to build up to 99.9% of its equilibrium activity?

11 Calculate the mass (in g) of 1 curie of (*i*) Ra B (^{214}Pb; $t_{1/2} = 26.8$ minutes), (*ii*) U_1 (^{238}U; $t_{1/2} = 4.5 \times 10^9$ years). Quote the specific activity for each element.

12 The isotopic abundances of ^{63}Cu and ^{65}Cu are 69.1% and 30.9% respectively. A piece of copper foil 0.02 cm thick and 1 cm^2 in area is irradiated in a thermal neutron flux of 10^{12} cm^{-2} s^{-1} for 768 min. If the cross-sections for ^{63}Cu and ^{65}Cu are 4.5 and 2.0 barns respectively, calculate (*i*) the activity of the foil on being removed from the reactor, (*ii*) the activity of the foil after 2 hours, given that the half-lives of ^{64}Cu and ^{66}Cu are 12.8 hours, and 5 minutes respectively. (Cu = 63.5; density of copper = 8.95 g cm^{-3}).

13 Describe the essential features of neutron activation analysis stressing both the advantages and the limitations of this technique.

Molybdenum foil, 0.5 g (containing the natural abundance of 9.6% of the isotope $^{100}_{42}Mo$) was irradiated in a nuclear reactor at a flux of 2×10^{12} neutron cm^{-2} s^{-1}. Given that the cross-section of the reaction ^{100}Mo (n, γ) ^{101}Mo is 3 barns, calculate the rate of production of ^{101}Mo in atoms per second (1 barn = 10^{-24} cm^2). The isotope ^{101}Mo and its daughter both decay by β-emission; write balanced equations for these decays. (R.S.C.)

14 Deuteron irradiation of a Ni target led in a particular experiment to the formation of radioactive ^{61}Cu in the specimen at the rate of 5×10^8 atoms per second. If the half-life of this isotope is 3.4 hours, show that the corresponding activity of the specimen attained a level of 13.5 mCi and calculate the amount of ^{61}Cu then present. (B.Sc., Wales)

15 In a study of slag formation in an open hearth furnace, ^{140}La (β, γ emitter, half-life = 40.2 hours) as La_2O_3 was added to the furnace charge, 0.6 g of oxide being used. The distribution coefficient for La_2O_3 between slag and molten iron is so large that tracer loss to the melt is negligible.

A sample of the slag removed later, had an activity of 450 c.p.m. g^{-1}. A reference sample of La_2O_3 which was irradiated with the sample of La_2O_3 used in the furnace, had an activity of 30 000 c.p.s. mg^{-1}. Find the mass of the slag.

16 The atomic mass of iron-57 ($^{57}_{26}Fe$) is 56.9354 u, and that of uranium-235 ($^{235}_{92}U$) is 235.0439 u. Calculate the nuclear binding energy in MeV per nucleon for these nuclides, given that the masses of the hydrogen atom and the neutron are 1.0078 u and 1.0087 u respectively. Comment on the difference between the values for the two nuclides. (1 u = 9.315×10^8 eV).

17 Which of the following fusion reactions gives the greatest yield of energy?

$$^{2}_{1}H + ^{3}_{1}H \longrightarrow ^{4}_{2}He + ^{1}_{0}n$$
$$^{6}_{3}Li + ^{1}_{0}n \longrightarrow ^{3}_{1}H + ^{4}_{2}He$$
$$^{2}_{1}H + ^{2}_{1}H \longrightarrow ^{3}_{1}H + ^{1}_{1}H$$

Nuclide	$^{2}_{1}H$	$^{3}_{1}H$	$^{1}_{0}n$	$^{6}_{3}Li$	$^{4}_{2}He$	$^{1}_{1}H$
Atomic mass/u	2.0141	3.0160	1.0087	6.0151	4.0026	1.0078

(1 eV = 1.602×10^{-19} J; 1 u = 9.315×10^8 eV.)

13

Statistical Treatment of Data

Example 13.1 Extreme results, standard deviation, coefficient of variation and confidence limits

A series of experiments for determining the conductance of sodium chloride at infinite dilution at 25°C gave the following data:

$$126.2 \quad 124.8 \quad 126.9 \quad 120.0 \quad 128.0 \quad 125.2 \text{ ohm}^{-1}\text{ cm}^2\text{ mol}^{-1}$$

(*a*) *Determine whether or not the extreme result should be rejected.*
(*b*) *Calculate the arithmetic mean, standard deviation and coefficient of variation for the results not rejected.*
(*c*) *Calculate the confidence limits for the results of* (*b*) *for* (*i*) $P = 0.05$ *and* (*ii*) $P = 0.01$.

(*a*) The problem of what to do with one result which seems far away from the average arises frequently in scientific work. If there is some definite proof of error in the extreme result, then that result should definitely be rejected before calculating the mean. However, if no definite error can be assigned to the extreme result, additional determinations under the same conditions should be made. It is only when there is no time or when the conditions cannot be repeated that a statistical test should be used to determine whether or not the extreme result should be rejected. One such test is the Q-test and its use is illustrated here.

Q is the quotient of the difference between the extreme result and its nearest neighbour divided by the range. If the calculated Q exceeds the following values, the result may be discarded with 90% confidence.

Q Test Confidence Quotients (90% Confidence Level)

Number of measurements	3	4	5	6	7	8	9	10
Q	0.94	0.76	0.64	0.56	0.51	0.47	0.44	0.41

Inspection reveals that the extreme result is 120.0. The decision on whether or not this result should be rejected depends on the value of the quotient (Q):

$$\frac{\text{nearest neighbour} - \text{extreme result (or vice versa)}}{\text{range}}$$

In the present case

$$Q = \frac{124.8 - 120.0}{128.0 - 120.0} = \frac{4.8}{8.0} = 0.60$$

From the Q-test confidence quotient table for the 90% confidence level (above) the rejection quotient for 6 determinations is 0.56. The value of 0.60 for Q is greater than this and the result, 120.0, should be rejected.

(*b*) The arithmetic mean ($\bar{x}$) of the remaining five conductances may be calculated, *either* by summing the individual values (x) and dividing by the number of observations, N (now 5):

$$\bar{x} = \frac{\Sigma x}{N} = \frac{631.1}{5} = 126.22 \text{ ohm}^{-1} \text{ cm}^2 \text{ mol}^{-1};$$

or by taking a *working mean*, say 125, and applying to it an adjustment—obtained by taking the mean of the deviations from the working mean:

Conductance/ohm^{-1} cm^2 mol^{-1}	126.2	124.8	126.9	128.0	125.2
Deviations from working mean	+1.2	−0.2	+1.9	+3.0	+0.2

$$\text{Mean of deviations from working mean} = \frac{+6.1}{5} = +1.22.$$

Thus, the arithmetic mean is 1.22 more positive than the working mean and is 126.22 ohm^{-1} cm^2 mol^{-1}.

The two methods are, strictly speaking, identical, for in the first method the working mean is zero. A working mean obtained by inspection, as in the second method, is useful where there is a large number of values which may, or may not, have had to be grouped.

The standard deviation (s) is the square root of the variance (s^2)

which is a mean value of the sum of squares of deviations of the observations from the mean:

Conductance/ohm^{-1} cm^2 mol^{-1}	126.2	124.8	126.9	128.0	125.2
Deviations from the mean ($\times 10^2$)	−2	−142	+68	+178	−102
Deviation^2 ($\times 10^4$)	4	20 164	4624	31 684	10 404

Sum of ($10^4 \times$ deviation^2) = 66 880

$$\text{Variance } (\times 10^4) = \frac{66\,880}{\text{degrees of freedom}} = \frac{66\,880}{N-1} = \frac{66\,880}{4} = 16\,720$$

Hence

$$s = \sqrt{16\,270 \times 10^{-4}}$$
$$= \underline{1.29 \text{ ohm}^{-1} \text{ cm}^2 \text{ mol}^{-1}}$$

The coefficient of variation is the standard deviation expressed as a percentage of the arithmetic mean and in this case is

$$\frac{1.29}{126.22} \times 100 = \underline{1.02\%}$$

(*c*) Confidence limits concern chance variations. In (*c*) (i) they determine the limits outside which the odds are 19 to 1 against (that is, $P = 0.05$) a single result falling. In (ii) the odds are 99 to 1 against (that is, $P = 0.01$).

In the calculation of confidence limits, the standard deviation is multiplied by a factor obtained from the table of probability points of the *t*-distribution (p. 275) appropriate to the number of degrees of freedom and probability (P) level.

The confidence limits of the present example are given by

$$126.22 \pm 1.29 \times t.$$

(i) The value for t may be found in the $P = 0.05$ column of the *t*-table corresponding to 4 degrees of freedom and is 2.78.
Hence, the $P = 0.05$ confidence limits are

$$126.22 \pm 1.29 \times 2.78 \text{ ohm}^{-1} \text{ cm}^2 \text{ mol}^{-1}$$
$$= \underline{126.22 \pm 3.59 \text{ ohm}^{-1} \text{ cm}^2 \text{ mol}^{-1}}.$$

(ii) For $P = 0.01$, the appropriate value of t corresponding to 4 degrees of freedom is 4.60.
Hence, the $P = 0.01$ confidence limits are

$$126.22 \pm 1.29 \times 4.60 \text{ ohm}^{-1} \text{ cm}^2 \text{mol}^{-1}$$

$$= \underline{126.22 \pm 5.93 \text{ ohm}^{-1} \text{ cm}^2 \text{mol}^{-1}}.$$

Probability Points of the t-Distribution

Degrees of Freedom	*P*		
	0.1	*0.05*	*0.01*
1	6.31	12.7	63.7
2	2.92	4.30	9.92
3	2.35	3.18	5.84
4	2.13	2.78	4.60
5	2.01	2.57	4.03
6	1.94	2.45	3.71
7	1.89	2.36	3.50
8	1.86	2.31	3.36
9	1.83	2.26	3.25
10	1.81	2.23	3.17
12	1.78	2.18	3.05
18	1.73	2.10	2.88
27	1.70	2.05	2.77

Summary

(*a*) The result 120.0 should be rejected.

(*b*) The mean value $= 126.2 \text{ ohm}^{-1} \text{ cm}^2 \text{mol}^{-1}$.
Standard deviation $= 1.29 \text{ ohm}^{-1} \text{ cm}^2 \text{mol}^{-1}$.
Coefficient of variation $= 1.02\%$.

(*c*) Confidence limits (i) $= 126.6 \pm 3.6 \text{ ohm}^{-1} \text{ cm}^2 \text{mol}^{-1}$.
(ii) $= 126.2 \pm 5.9 \text{ ohm}^{-1} \text{ cm}^2 \text{mol}^{-1}$.

Note An alternative method of obtaining the standard deviation (s), in (*b*) is to square the figures themselves, and sum (Σx^2), that is, the deviations from *zero* are squared instead of the deviations from the mean. A 'correction term' obtained, by squaring the sum of the figures $(\Sigma x)^2$, divided by the number (N), is then subtracted to obtain the sum of squares of deviations from the mean ($\Sigma(x-\bar{x})^2$):

$$\Sigma(x-\bar{x})^2 = \Sigma x^2 - \frac{(\Sigma x)^2}{N}$$

s is then equal to $\sqrt{\dfrac{\Sigma(x-\bar{x})^2}{N-1}}$ as in (b) above.

Example 13.2 Difference between two means

The following data were accumulated during a comparison of the Berkeley and Hartley and the Frazer and Myrick methods of determining the osmotic pressure (in atm) of a sucrose solution (370g per 1000g water) at 30°C.

Method	*No. of replicates*	*Mean* ($\bar{x}$)	$\Sigma(x_i-\bar{x})^2$
Berkeley and Hartley	*8*	*29.68*	*0.73*
Frazer and Myrick	*6*	*28.89*	*0.69*

Determine whether the two means differ significantly (at P = 0.05).

Tests of significance provide a very useful aid to the interpretation of experimental data. In the present instance, the objective is to determine whether the Berkeley and Hartley and the Frazer and Myrick methods give results that are comparable, that is, whether or not there is a significant difference in the results produced. If there is a significant difference then the reasons can be determined and corrections made in any stage that is found to be faulty.

The procedure leading to the appropriate statistical tests are summarized in the table on p. 277.

Key

1. The variance is obtained by taking the quotient $\Sigma(x_i-\bar{x})^2$/degrees of freedom, the degrees of freedom being 7 and 5, respectively.
2. This is the square root of (1).
3. The fundamental property of the standard error of a mean is that it is inversely proportional to the square root of the number of observations contributing to the mean. Thus, the standard error of the Berkeley and Hartley mean is the standard error, 0.3229,

Calculation of the significance of the difference between two means

	Berkeley and Hartley		*Frazer and Myrick*
Mean	29.68		29.89
Difference between the means		0.21	
Variance (1)	0.104		0.138
Standard error (or deviation) (2)	0.3229		0.3715
Standard error of mean (3)	0.1141		0.1517
Variance of mean (4)	0.0130		0.0230
Variance (5) (of a single observation)	0.1042		0.1379
*Sum of squares (6)**	0.7300		0.6897
Pooled sum of squares		1.4197	
Pooled variance (7)		0.1180	
Variance of difference between means (8)		0.03443	
Standard error of difference between means (9)		0.1856	
t and p (degrees of freedom = 12) (10)		$t = 1.16$ $P = >0.05$	

divided by the square root of 8, giving 0.1141. The Frazer and Meyrick mean has a standard error of $0.3715/\sqrt{6} = 0.1517$.

4. The variance of the mean is obtained by squaring its standard error.
5. The variance (of a single observation) is obtained by multiplying (4) by the number of observations.
6. The 'sum of squares' is obtained by multiplying by the degrees of freedom, that is, 7 and 5, respectively.
7. The sums of squares (of deviations from the mean) are added together to give the pooled sum which is then divided by the *total* degrees of freedom ($7+5 = 12$) to obtain the pooled variance.
8. If two means having the same variance, V, are derived from n_1 and n_2 observations, respectively, the variance of their difference (or sum) is $V\left(\frac{1}{n_1}+\frac{1}{n_2}\right)$. In the present case, 0.1180 is multiplied by $1/8+1/6 = 7/24$ to obtain the variance of the difference, 0.21.
9. The square root of (8) gives the standard error of the difference.

* In this case the details of the original observations, that is, the sums of squares of deviations from the mean are available and it would, therefore, have been possible to commence the calculations at this point. The preceding steps would be necessary where the means and their variances had been given. In addition, the steps for the calculation of the standard error of the mean are given; means being themselves only an estimate of the true population mean.

10. The difference, 0.21, is then divided by its standard error to obtain the value of t, that is, $t = 0.21/0.1856 = 1.16$. This value, 1.16, is then compared with the entries in the t table (given in previous example, p. 275) for the total degrees of freedom ($7 + 5 = 12$).

Conclusion

The t value is seen to be *not* as much as that for $P = 0.05$ for 12 degrees of freedom, that is, $P = >0.05$. *The difference between the means is not significant*, t would have to be greater than 2.18 for significance. The value is, in fact, less than that for $P = 0.10$. The two methods for determining osmotic pressure are comparable.

Example 13.3 Analysis of variance

Three students determined the conductance of 0.05 mol dm^{-3} silver nitrate at 25°, each student carrying out four determinations on three separate conductivity bridges. All the results were in the region of 115.00 ohm^{-1} cm^2 mol^{-1} and for the purpose of compiling the following table of results, 115.00 has been subtracted from each result. What conclusions may be drawn from the figures?

	Conductivity Bridge A		*Conductivity Bridge B*		*Conductivity Bridge C*	
Student 1	*0.28*	*0.52*	*−0.66*	*−0.60*	*−0.84*	*0.18*
	−0.24	*0.80*	*0.02*	*1.20*	*0.32*	*−0.40*
Student 2	*−0.58*	*0.28*	*0.34*	*−0.12*	*−0.82*	*−0.20*
	0.58	*−0.10*	*−0.04*	*1.20*	*−0.40*	*−0.52*
Student 3	*0.36*	*1.16*	*0.72*	*−0.24*	*−0.54*	*−0.07*
	0.68	*0.50*	*0.62*	*0.56*	*−0.32*	*0.60*

Analysis of variance is a powerful test in statistics and may profitably be employed in analysing almost any type of experimental results involving quantitative measurements, particularly when several independent sources of variation are present. The arithmetical steps are as follows:

1. Calculate totals for each group, each student and each conductivity bridge as in Table 1.
2. Calculate the total crude sum of squares, that is, square all thirty-six items of the Table in the question and add. This gives 11.9789.

Table 1 Totals of Groups of Four Replicates

	Conductivity Bridge A	*Conductivity Bridge B*	*Conductivity Bridge C*	*Total*
Student 1	1.36	−0.04	−0.74	0.58
Student 2	0.18	1.38	−1.94	−0.38
Student 3	2.70	1.66	−0.33	4.03
Total	4.24	3.00	−3.01	4.23

3. Calculate the crude sum of squares between the groups of four replicates.
   Square each of the nine sub-group totals, add them together, and divide by the number in each group, that is, 4. This gives $(1.36^2+(-0.04)^2+\ldots+(-0.33)^2)/4 = 4.5634$.
4. Calculate the crude sum of squares between students. Square the sum for each student, add them together, and divide by the number of observations for each student. This gives $(0.58^2+(-0.38)^2+4.03^2)/12 = 1.3935$.
5. Calculate the crude sum of squares between conductivity bridges.
   Square the sum for each conductivity bridge, add, and divide by the number of observations for each conductivity bridge. This gives
   $$(4.24^2+3.00^2+(-3.01)^2)/12 = 3.0031.$$
6. Calculate the correction factor due to the mean. This is the grand total squared divided by the total number of observations. This gives
   $$\text{Correction factor} = (4.23)^2/36 = 0.4970$$

From the above the following may be calculated:

7. Total sum of squares = Item 2 − Item 6:
   $$= 11.9789-0.4970 = 11.4819$$
8. Sum of squares between sub-groups of four
   $$= \text{Item } 3-\text{Item } 6$$
   $$= 4.5634-0.4970 = 4.0664$$
9. Sum of squares between students
   $$= \text{Item } 4-\text{Item } 6$$
   $$= 1.3935-0.4970 = 0.8965.$$

10. Sum of squares between conductivity bridges

$$= \text{Item 5} - \text{Item 6}$$
$$= 3.0031 - 0.4970 = 2.5061.$$

11. Construct the Analysis of Variance Table:

Table 2 Analysis of Variance Table

Source of Variation	*Sum of Squares*	*Degrees of Freedom (n)*	*Variance*
Between Students	0.8965	2	0.4482
Between Conductivity Bridges	2.5061	2	1.2530
Interaction of Students and Conductivity Bridges	0.6638	4	0.1659
Total between sub-groups	4.0664	8	
Within groups of four (Error or residual)	7.4155	27	0.2746
Total	11.4819	35	

Interpretation

The interaction variance (0.1659) does not differ greatly from the error variance (0.2746) so that the variances between students and between conductivity bridges may be assessed against the error variance. Had the interaction variance been significantly larger than the error variance, it would have meant that another source of error was present in addition to that within groups of four.

The ratios of the variances with respect to error and interaction are compared as follows:

Between students/Error = 0.4482/0.2746 = 1.63: $n_1 = 2$, $n_2 = 27$
(5% value of F (Table 3) = 3.35)

This is not significant.
Between conductivity bridges/Error = 1.2530/0.2746 = 4.56:
$n_1 = 2$, $n_2 = 27$
(5% value of F (Table 3) = 3.35)

This is significant.

In applying the *t*-test to the differences between the means for the conductivity bridges, the error variance of 0.2746 based on 27 degrees of freedom is used. (Had the interaction variance been significant, the interaction based on 4 degrees of freedom would have had to be used as the error variance.)

Table 3 Selected Probability Levels of F-Distribution

Per cent Point	n_2	n_1 corresponding to the greater variance: 1	2	3	5	7	9
5	1	161	199	216	230	237	241
1		4052	4999	5403	5764	5928	6022
5	2	18.5	19.0	19.2	19.3	19.4	19.4
1		98.5	99.0	99.2	99.3	99.4	99.4
5	3	10.1	9.55	9.28	9.01	8.89	8.81
1		34.1	30.8	29.5	28.2	27.7	27.3
5	5	6.61	5.79	5.41	5.05	4.88	4.77
1		16.3	13.3	12.1	11.0	10.5	10.2
5	7	5.59	4.74	4.35	3.97	3.79	3.68
1		12.2	9.55	8.45	7.46	6.99	6.72
5	10	4.96	4.10	3.71	3.33	3.14	3.02
1		10.0	7.56	6.55	5.64	5.20	4.94
5	18	4.41	3.55	3.16	2.77	2.58	2.46
1		8.29	6.01	5.09	4.25	3.84	3.60
5	27	4.21	3.35	2.96	2.57	2.37	2.25
1		7.68	5.49	4.60	3.78	3.39	3.15

The means for the conductivity bridges are:

$$A = 0.353 \qquad B = 0.250 \qquad C = -0.251$$

The variance of a mean of twelve observations is 0.2746/12, and the variance of the difference between two means is twice this. The standard deviation is then =

$$\sqrt{(0.2746 \times 2/12)} = \sqrt{0.04577} = 0.214.$$

The 5% value of t for 27 degrees of freedom is 2.05 (page 275). A difference of $2.05 \times 0.214 = 0.439$ is therefore required for significance. It follows that A and B do not differ significantly, but both are significantly larger than C.

Additional Examples

(A table of probability points of the *t*-distribution is given on page 275, and of the *F*-distribution on page 281.)

1 Calculate the confidence limits for the freezing point of a solution of iodine (9.20 g) in benzene (1000 g) for the following probabilities, given that the mean reading for the freezing point is 5.283°C and the standard deviation is 0.093°.

(*a*) $P = 0.05$ for 8 readings and 5 readings.
(*b*) $P = 0.01$ for 3 readings and 6 readings.
(*c*) $P = 0.01$ for 7 readings and 9 readings.

2 A class of nine undergraduate students obtained $\Delta G^{\ominus}$ values for the reaction

$$2\,Ag^{+}(aq) + Sn^{2+}(aq) = 2\,Ag(s) + Sn^{4+}(aq)$$

by studying the electrode systems $Ag(s)/Ag^{+}$, $Pt/Sn^{2+}/Sn^{4+}$ and normal calomel. The values obtained by each student were −132.9, −140.5, −174.0, −124.9, −137.1, −102.5, −127.9, −106.4 and −124.5 kJ, respectively.

(*a*) Determine whether the extreme result should be rejected.
(*b*) Calculate the mean, standard deviation, and coefficient of variation of the results not rejected.
(*c*) Calculate the confidence limits for the results of (*b*) for $P = 0.05$.

3 The following data were accumulated during the comparison of two samples, *A* and *B*, of a given compound.

Sample	*No. of replicates*	*Mean* ($\bar{x}$)	$\Sigma(x-\bar{x})^2$
A	4	99.2	0.18
B	3	96.8	0.32

Are the two sample means significantly different (at $P = 0.05$)?
(B. Pharm., London)

4 Solutions of 0.05 mol dm^{-3} potassium hydrogen phthalate, prepared from two samples of the salt, gave the following results when measured on the same pH meter:

(i) 3.96, 3.98, 3.98, 4.00, 3.97.
(ii) 4.04, 3.99, 4.02, 4.04, 4.05.

Do the means of these two sets of results differ significantly?
(B. Pharm., London)

5 Measurement of a given absorbing layer on two spectrophotometers gave the following sets of absorbances:

(i) 0.503, 0.506, 0.504, 0.505,
and (ii) 0.511, 0.508, 0.508, 0.509.

Can the two instruments be said to differ at the 0.05 probability level?
(B. Pharm., London)

6 A membrane electrode selective to calcium ions has been made by incorporating an ion exchanger in a pvc matrix (pvc electrode) and its effectiveness for determining calcium in tap water has been compared with an EDTA titration method and with a commercial liquid ion exchange membrane electrode. What conclusion may be drawn from the following results obtained?

Sample Number	*Calcium content/mg dm^{-3}*		
	By EDTA method	*By commercial electrode*	*By pvc electrode*
1	36.4	35.8	36.1
2	31.1	30.9	31.0
3	32.1	32.0	31.9
4	37.2	37.5	37.7
5	34.6	34.3	34.1
6	26.9	27.1	27.0
7	29.1	28.6	28.5
8	30.6	30.5	30.3
9	39.7	29.4	30.0
10	28.5	29.0	28.9

7 In formulating standards and an assay for the pharmacopoeial monograph on a given product, 6 laboratories assayed a common sample by means of 3 different processes, carrying out 2 replicates on each. The following data then emerged in the subsequent statistical analysis:

Source of variation	*Sum of squares*
Between laboratories	20.0
Between assays	0.4
Laboratories × assays	1.5
Residual	0.9

What conclusion may be drawn from these figures? How would you continue the analysis in the light of the initial objective? (B. Pharm., London)

Answers to Additional Examples

Chapter 1 FIRST LAW OF THERMODYNAMICS (page 14)

1 $\Delta H_{298} = -88$ kJ.

2 $\Delta H_{1000} = -80.4$ kJ.

3 $\Delta H^{\ominus} = -798$ kJ mol^{-1}.

4 $\Delta H_{333} = -176.0$ kJ.

5 $\Delta H = -397$ kJ mol^{-1}.

6 $\Delta H_{2773} = -269.4$ kJ.

7 $\Delta H_{398} = -49.1$ kJ; $\Delta U_{398} = -45.8$ kJ.

8 $\Delta H_f = -5373$ kJ mol^{-1}; difference is the resonance energy of benzene.

9 (*a*) 352 kJ; (*b*) 134 kJ.

10 $\Delta H_{\text{sublimation}} = +612$ kJ mol^{-1}.

11 569.5 kJ.

12 Energy of C—H bond = 416 kJ.
,, ,, C—C ,, = 343 ,,
,, ,, C═C ,, = 611 ,,
,, ,, C—Cl ,, = 346 ,,

13 ΔH_f of phenyl methyl radical = 158 kJ mol^{-1}. Energy of C—C bond in 1,2-diphenylethane = 199 kJ.

14 $\Delta H = -368$ kJ.

15 $\Delta H_{f(MCl)} = -388$ kJ mol^{-1}; $\Delta H_{f(MCl_2)} = +285$ kJ mol^{-1}. MCl will be formed preferentially.

16 (b) $Li \rightarrow Li^+ = +532$ kJ mol^{-1};
$Na \rightarrow Na^+ = +508$ kJ mol^{-1};
$K \rightarrow K^+ = +435$ kJ mol^{-1}.

17 Work done = 233 kJ. Internal energy change is nil, because the temperature is held constant.

18 1802 J.

19 1196 J.

20 4383 K.

21 876 K.

Chapter 2 SECOND AND THIRD LAWS OF THERMODYNAMICS (page 40)

1 (*a*) 0.248; (*b*) 0.398.

2 (*a*) 1037 J; (*b*) 903 J.

3 5.76 J K^{-1}.

4 3.67×10^4 J kg^{-1}.

5 $1.304\,J\,K^{-1}\,g^{-1}$.
6 $0.046\,J\,K^{-1}$.
7 $K_p = 10^{-10}$.
8 $132.1\,J\,K^{-1}\,mol^{-1}$.
9 $43.38\,J\,K^{-1}\,mol^{-1}$.
10 $-1.81\,J\,K^{-1}\,mol^{-1}$.
11 $173.6\,J\,K^{-1}$.
12 $15.0\,J\,K^{-1}\,mol^{-1}$.
13 $T = 350.1\,K$; pressure $= 1.53\,atm$; $\Delta S = 5.7\,J$.
14 $\Delta G^{\ominus} = -18.8$ kJ; $\Delta H^{\ominus} = -11.2$ kJ; $\Delta S^{\ominus} = 18.9\,JK^{-1}$.
15 $309\,kJ\,mol^{-1}$.
16 $2C + 2H_2 \rightarrow C_2H_4$; $\Delta H^{\ominus} = +33\,kJ$; $\Delta G^{\ominus} = +49.03\,kJ$.
Reaction is NOT thermodynamically feasible.
$2C + 3H_2 \rightarrow C_2H_6$; $\Delta H^{\ominus} = -87\,kJ$; $\Delta G^{\ominus} = -35.22\,kJ$.
Reaction IS thermodynamically feasible.
$C_2H_4 + H_2O \rightarrow C_2H_5OH$; $\Delta H^{\ominus} = -27\,kJ$; $\Delta G^{\ominus} = +10.49\,kJ$.
Reaction is NOT thermodynamically feasible.
$C_2H_4 + H_2 \rightarrow C_2H_6$; $\Delta H^{\ominus} = -120\,kJ$; $\Delta G^{\ominus} = -84.25\,kJ$.
Reaction IS thermodynamically feasible.
$C_2H_6 + H_2O \rightarrow C_2H_5OH + H_2$; $\Delta H^{\ominus} = +93\,kJ$; $\Delta G^{\ominus} = +94.73\,kJ$.
Reaction is NOT thermodynamically feasible.
17 (*a*) 75.54 kJ; (*b*) −23.99 kJ.
18 $-29\,kJ\,mol^{-1}$.
19 $\Delta G^{\ominus} = +78.6\,kJ\,mol^{-1}$. Reaction is NOT thermodynamically feasible.
20 $3.55 \times 10^{-2}\,atm^{-1}$.
21 4.17×10^{-5}.
22 $56.8\,kJ\,mol^{-1}$.
23 1.47×10^{-14}.
24 $\Delta S^{\ominus}_{10°C} = -85.4\,J\,K^{-1}\,mol^{-1}$;
$\Delta S^{\ominus}_{35°C} = -98.2\,J\,K^{-1}\,mol^{-1}$.
25 0.253 atm.
26 (*a*) $\Delta H^{\ominus}_{f2000} = -252\,kJ$; $\Delta S^{\ominus}_{f2000} = -55.2\,J\,K^{-1}$;
(*b*) 1%.
27 (*a*) $\Delta G^{\ominus}{}_{298} = -239\,kJ$; (*b*) $\Delta G^{\ominus}{}_{308} = -237\,kJ$.
28 $K_{p100°C} = 4.3 \times 10^9\,atm^{-3}$; $\Delta G_{\text{hydrogenation }100°C} = -68.8\,kJ$;
$\log K_{p90°C} = 10.39$.
29 $\Delta H = -94.3\,kJ$; $\Delta G_{727°C} = -5.16\,kJ$; $\Delta S_{727°C} = -89.1\,J\,K^{-1}$;
ΔC_p is constant over the temperature range.
30 $\Delta H_{1173} = 570\,kJ$; $\Delta S_{1173} = 182\,J\,K^{-1}$.
31 $\Delta H = -17.46\,kJ$; $\Delta S = 89.3\,J\,K^{-1}$.
32 1.462×10^{-10}.
33 $154.4\,J\,K^{-1}$.
34 (*a*) $37.23\,kJ\,mol^{-1}$; (*b*) $29.44\,kJ\,mol^{-1}$.

35 31.58 kJ mol^{-1}.

36 A pressure of 120 atm will increase the m.p. of sodium by only 0.899 K to 98.5°C. Liquid sodium can be used at 100°C and 120 atm without fear of solidification.

37 Equilibrium pressure (p_{CO_2}) = 9.86×10^{-3} atm ≃ 0.01 atm. Hence the air circulating through the oven should contain at least 1% by volume of CO_2 to repress dissociation.

38 (*a*) ΔH = 48.4 kJ mol^{-1}; (*b*) 489.4 K; (*c*) 7.66 mm.

Chapter 3 THE GASEOUS STATE (page 56)

1 1.30×10^3 m s^{-1} for helium; 4.13×10^2 m s^{-1} for argon.

2 (*a*) 179 atm; (*b*) 174 atm.

3 2.64×10^{-4} m^3.

4 1.47×10^{-10} m.

5 (*a*) 0.0446 mol; (*b*) 1.32×10^{-10} m.

6 5.06×10^{-8} m.

7 (*b*) 28.04.

8 82.5 atm.

9 378 atm.

10 Fugacity at 50 atm = 49.6 atm.
,, ,, 200 ,, = 200.2 ,,
,, ,, 500 ,, = 589 ,,
,, ,, 1000 ,, = 1848 ,,

Chapter 4 LIQUIDS, VAPOURS AND SOLUTIONS (page 82)

1 Ramsay and Shields constant = 2.08×10^{-5} J m deg^{-1}.

2 1.20×10^{-3} N s m^{-2}.

3 8.52×10^{-1} N s m^{-2}.

4 Molar refraction = 21.6 cm^3. Molar polarization = 52.85 cm^3.

5 (*a*) 587 J; (*b*) 6.14 kJ; (*c*) 5.55 kJ; (*d*) 6.14 kJ; (*e*) 17.4 J K^{-1}; (*f*) ≈0.

6 (*a*) 3.19 kJ; (*b*) 33.3 kJ; (*c*) 33.3 kJ; (*d*) 30.1 kJ; (*e*) ≈0; (*f*) = 86.7 kJ K^{-1}.

7 Work = −86.0 kJ; q = −11.30 kJ; ΔH = −11.30 kJ; ΔU = −10.44 kJ.

8 (*a*) 144 mmHg; (*b*) 45.9%.

9 125.

10 0.249 mole fraction of 1,4-dibromobenzene in ethanol.
0.527 ,, ,, ,, 1,4-dichlorobenzene,, ,,

11 M_r = 64.1; ebullioscopic constant = 0.513.

12 127.5.

13 0.568.

14 x_s = 0.188.

15 Molality 0.001 0.002 0.005 0.01 0.02 0.05 0.10 0.20 0.30 0.50 0.70 1.0
γ 0.978 0.963 0.939 0.914 0.884 0.860 0.819 0.791 0.784 0.789 0.794 0.753

16 (*a*) Activity of mercury = 0.478; activity coefficient of mercury = 0.742;
(*b*) -1.84 kJ mol^{-1}.

17 (*a*) 0.738; (*b*) 0.882; (*c*) $\Delta G = -3.87$ kJ mol^{-1}.

18 3.69 D.

19 $P_M = 70.0$ cm^3 at 70°C; 65.4 cm^3 at 90°C and 61.2 cm^3 at 114°C. The substance has a dipole moment of 2.09D.

20 $\mu = 1.05$ D; $\alpha = 3.01 \times 10^{-30}$ m^3.

21 $\mu_{1,3\text{-dinitrobenzene}} = 3.05$; $\mu_{1,2\text{-dichlorobenzene}} = 2.92$; $\mu_{\text{chloro-3-nitrobenzene}} = 3.07$.

22 101° 46′.

Chapter 5 SURFACE CHEMISTRY AND MACROMOLECULAR SYSTEMS (page 103)

1 To test applicability of the Freundlich isotherm, plot log (mass adsorbed) against log (pressure). The requirements of the isotherm are met satisfactorily at low pressures, but at higher pressures ($p = 1.70$ and 3.40 N m^{-2}) the experimental results lie away from the straight line.

To test the applicability of the Langmuir isotherm, plot p/(mass adsorbed) against p. The excellent straight line obtained confirms Langmuir's adsorption equation.

The Langmuir constants have the values:

$$k_1 = 1.61\ \text{m}^2\text{N}^{-1};\quad k_2 = 4.57 \times 10^{-1}\ \text{g m}^{-2}.$$

2 448 m^2 g^{-1}.

3 11 m^2 g^{-1}.

4 11 m^2 g^{-1}.

5 -11.6 kJ.

6 For $m = 0.11$, $\Gamma = 3.39 \times 10^{-6}$ mol m^{-2}; area $= 4.90 \times 10^{-19}$ m^2 mol^{-1}.
For $m = 0.28$, $\Gamma = 8.63 \times 10^{-6}$ mol m^{-2}; area $= 1.93 \times 10^{-19}$ m^2 mol^{-1}.

7 0.0209 m.

8 Radius $= 5.32 \times 10^{-9}$ m; $M_r = 5.00 \times 10^5$.

9 71 030.

10 50 000.

11 (*a*) Using $[\eta] = \lim_{C \to O} \dfrac{\eta_{sp}}{c}$ where $\eta_{sp} = \eta_r - 1$, $[\eta] = 1.400$.

Using $[\eta] = \lim_{C \to O} \dfrac{\ln \eta_r}{c}$, $[\eta] = 1.322$.

(*b*) Using $[\eta] = 1.400$, $M_r = 25.8 \times 10^6$.
Using $[\eta] = 1.322$, $M_r = 23.5 \times 10^6$.

12 $M_r = 49\,060$; freezing point $= -0.00189°C$.
13 (*a*) pH = 5.0 inside the membrane and 9.0 outside the membrane; (*b*) 0.236V.

Chapter 6 TRANSPORT NUMBERS, CONDUCTANCE AND IONIC EQUILIBRIA (page 126)

1 (*i*) 0.163 g; (*ii*) gain of 0.0864 g.
2 $t_{Na^+} = 0.390$; $t_{Cl^-} = 0.610$.
3 426.2 $ohm^{-1}\,cm^2\,mol^{-1}$.
4 5.05×10^{-4} $cm\,V^{-1}\,s^{-1}$.
5 1.81×10^{-5}.
6 After 50 cm³ titrant, pH $= 1.841 \times 10^{-3}$ $ohm^{-1}\,cm^{-1}$; pH = 2.48;
,, 100 ,, ,, ,, $= 6.323 \times 10^{-4}$,, ,, ; pH = 7.00;
,, 150 ,, ,, ,, $= 1.003 \times 10^{-3}$,, ,, ; pH = 11.3.
7 6.59×10^{-5} mol dm^{-3}.
8 8.54×10^{-11}.
9 (*i*) 61%; (*ii*) 9.11×10^{-6} mol dm^{-3}.
10 (*a*) 2.19; (*b*) 3.38; (*c*) 8.04.
11 7.4.
12 1.40 mol dm^{-3} sodium formate and 1.00 mol dm^{-3} formic acid.
13 8.45.
14 7.45×10^{-5}.
15 (*c*) 4.71.
16 K_h (phenylamine hydrochloride) $= 2.35 \times 10^{-5}$;
K_b (phenylamine) $= 4.25 \times 10^{-10}$.
17 1/21.
18 0.12 mol dm^{-3}.
19 (*a*) $A = 0.5$; (*b*) $K_s = 3.04 \times 10^{-8}$; (*c*) $\gamma\pm = 0.985$.
20 $\alpha = 0.741$; $K = 1.74 \times 10^{-4}$.
21 $\alpha = 0.988$; $K = 5.33 \times 10^{-3}$.

Chapter 7 ELECTROCHEMICAL CELLS (page 146)

1 -1.17×10^{-3} V K^{-1}.
2 $\Delta G^\ominus = -4390$ J; $\dfrac{dE}{dT} = +3.40 \times 10^{-4}\,V\,K^{-1}$.
3 $\Delta G^\ominus = -86.5$ kJ; $\Delta H^\ominus = 152$ kJ; $\Delta S^\ominus = 239$ J K^{-1};
$\log P^{\frac{1}{2}}_{O_2} = -\dfrac{13\,850}{T} + 3.40$; 2350 K.
4 0.0591V.

5 2.

6 4.27.

7 0.374.

8 78.5.

9 1.28×10^7.

10 0.30V.

11 1.25V.

12 (*a*) and (*c*) $2Ag^+(aq) + Sn^{2+}(aq) = 2Ag(s) + Sn^{4+}(aq)$; $\Delta G = -125\,kJ$;
(*b*) and (*d*) $\frac{1}{2}Hg_2Cl_2(s) + \frac{1}{2}H_2(1\,atm) = Cl^-(aq) + H^+(aq) + Hg(l)$;
$\Delta G = -27.0\,kJ$;
(*c*)and(*d*)$Sn^{4+}(aq) + H_2(1\,atm) = Sn^{2+}(aq) + 2H+(aq)$; $\Delta G = -29.0\,kJ$;

13 $1.37 \times 10^{-5}\,mol\,dm^{-3}$.

14 St. potential of silver chloride electrode = 0.2225V.
Activity coefficient of HCl in 0.05391 m solution = 0.829.
,, ,, ,, ,, ,, 0.1238 m ,, = 0.788.

15 Mean activity coefficient of 0.0005*M* zinc sulphate = 0.744; Debye-Hückel value= 0.811.

16 $a_{Zn^{2+}}/a_{Cu^{2+}} = 1.55 \times 10^{37}$.

17 $1.54 \times 10^{-5}\,cm^2\,s^{-1}$.

18 $1.25 \times 10^{-2}\,cm$.

19 $4.8 \times 10^{-2}\,cm$ at $2.5 \times 10^{-4}\,mol\,cm^{-3}$;
$5.4 \times 10^{-2}\,cm$ at $6.3 \times 10^{-5}\,mol\,cm^{-3}$.

20 $D_{M^+}/D_{N^+} = 0.956$.

21 2 electrons.

Chapter 8 PHASE EQUILIBRIA (page 166)

1 247 K.

2 $58.3\,kJ\,mol^{-1}$.

3 $1.65\,kJ\,mol^{-1}$.

4 87%.

5 From the vapour pressure data, the latent heat of evaporation of ethanoic acid is 38.6 kJ mol^{-1}, compared with 24.4 kJ mol^{-1} (407 J g^{-1}) given in the question. This suggests that the dimerized ethanoic acid undergoes dissociation in the vapour phase. The figure of 38.6 kJ mol^{-1} for the latent heat of evaporation suggests a relative molecular mass of 95 for ethanoic acid.

6 5.55 kJ.

7 (*a*) 0.048 g; (*b*) 0.0083 g.

8 5.

9 M_r in water = 124; M_r in benzene = 248.

10 *K* for the equilibrium $KI + I_2 = KI_3$ has the values 716.4, 710.9 and 721.9; hence there is an association of KI and I_2 to form KI_3.

11 35.1%; 57.6%.

12 1.48 parts by mass of bromobenzene to 1 part by mass of water.

13 (*i*) 240°C; (*ii*) 11.3 mass % tin; (*iii*) 46.1 mass %; (*iv*) 41.9 mass %; (*v*) 71.3 mass %.

14 (*i*) 230°C; (*ii*) 37.5 mass %; (*iii*) 50 mass %; (*iv*) 8.93 g cm^{-3}.

15 $FeSO_4.7H_2O$; $FeSO_4.(NH_4)_2SO_4.6H_2O$.

16 Compounds formed are $K_2CO_3.3/2H_2O$; $K_2CO_3.Na_2CO_3$; and $Na_2CO_3.H_2O$.
Solid phase deposited is $K_2CO_3.Na_2CO_3$.

17

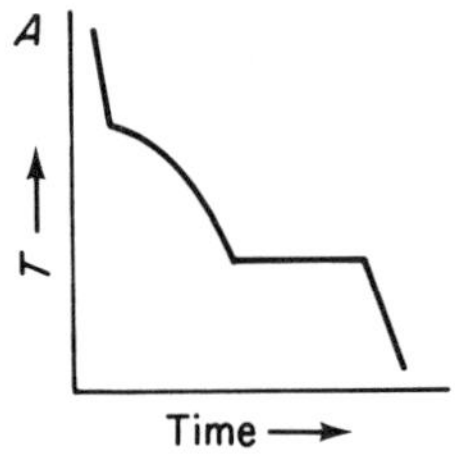

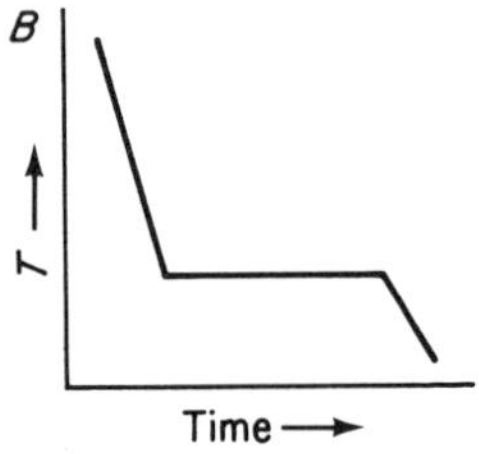

C: Liquid (3); *D*: Solid solution of compound $CoO.ZrO_2$ in excess ZrO_2 + Liquid (2); *E*: Solid solution + Compound $Co.ZrO_2$ (2); *F*: Compound $CoO.ZrO_2$ + Liquid (2); *G*: CoO + Liquid (2); *H*: Solid solution of compound $CoO.ZrO_2$ in excess ZrO_2 (3); *I*: Solid compound $CoO.ZrO_2$ + Solid CoO (2).
Note Since pressure will be fixed, the variances (given in parentheses) will in reality be reduced by 1 in each case.
J: is the *congruent melting point* of the compound ($CoO.ZrO_2$) formed between ZrO_2 and CoO, since solid and liquid of the same composition can coexist.
K: is the *freezing point* of pure CoO.

Chapter 9 REACTION KINETICS (page 200)

1 2.4×10^{-5} s^{-1}.

2 4.71×10^{-4} s^{-1}.

3 Reaction is first order; $k_1 = 1.14 \times 10^{-3}$ s^{-1}; $t_{1/2} = 609$ s.

4 0.36 h^{-1}.

5 (*a*) 108.4 min; (*b*) 21.6%.

6 3.27×10^{-4} s^{-1}.

7 $k_1 = 5.91 \times 10^{-5}$ s^{-1}. Time taken to invert 50% of a kilogram of sucrose $= 1.17 \times 10^4$ s.

8 3.29×10^{-3} dm^3 mol^{-1} s^{-1}.

9 (*a*) (*i*) 2.7×10^{-5} mol dm^{-3} s^{-1};
(*ii*) 2.7×10^{-5} mol dm^{-3} s^{-1};
(*b*) 6.5×10^{-6} mol dm^{-3}.

10 4.96×10^{-1} dm^3 mol^{-1} min^{-1} $= 8.27 \times 10^{-3}$ dm^3 mol^{-1} s^{-1}.

11 Reaction is second order; $k_2 = 1.96\,dm^3\,mol^{-1}\,s^{-1}$; $t_{1/2}$ at 40°C = 188 s.

12 Reaction is first order; $k_1 = 6.49 \times 10^{-5}\,s^{-1}$; $t_{1/2} = 1.07 \times 10^4\,s$.

13 $\frac{1}{3}$ mol.

14 $K = 2.33$; k_1 (forward reaction) $= 2.35 \times 10^{-3}\,s^{-1}$; k_1 (reverse reaction) $= 1.01 \times 10^{-3}\,s^{-1}$.

15 1.5.

16 1.5; 244 kJ mol^{-1}.

17 51.0 kJ mol^{-1}.

18 Activation energy = 270 kJ mol^{-1}.

19 k_1 at 504°C $= 4.38 \times 10^{-4}\,s^{-1}$; k_1 at 552°C $= 4.88 \times 10^{-3}\,s^{-1}$; activation energy = 267 kJ mol^{-1}.

20 Reaction is first order, k_1 being $1.63 \times 10^{-3}\,s^{-1}$ at 500°C, $3.23 \times 10^{-3}\,s^{-1}$ 520°C and $6.15 \times 10^{-3}\,s^{-1}$ at 540°C. The Arrhenius energy of activation, $E = 173$ kJ mol^{-1}. The enthalpy of activation, $\Delta H^{\ominus\ddagger} = 166$ kJ mol^{-1} for 500°C. Frequency factor $= 7.4 \times 10^8\,s^{-1}$. Entropy of activation, $\Delta S^{\ominus\ddagger} = -83\,J\,K^{-1}\,mol^{-1}$.

21 $\Delta H^{\ominus\ddagger} = 50.9$ kJ mol^{-1} for 60°C; $\Delta S^{\ominus\ddagger} = -144\,J\,K^{-1}\,mol^{-1}$; $\Delta H^{\ominus\ddagger}$ would not be affected by a change in concentration units; $\Delta S^{\ominus\ddagger}$ becomes $-87\,J\,K^{-1}\,mol^{-1}$ if concentration units are in mol cm^{-3}.

22 Reaction is second order. (*a*) $1.35 \times 10^{-1}\,dm^3\,mol^{-1}\,s^{-1}$; (*b*) $\frac{2}{5}$; (*c*) 243 kJ mol^{-1}.

23 The reaction is zero order at pressures greater than 58 mmHg. At lower pressures, the reaction tends towards first order.

24 Reaction is second order. (When $a = 0.0214\,mol\,dm^{-3}$, $k_2 = 1.59 \times 10^{-2}\,dm^3\,mol^{-1}\,min^{-1} = 2.65 \times 10^{-4}\,dm^3\,mol^{-1}\,s^{-1}$. When $a = 0.03990\,mol\,dm^{-3}$, $k_2 = 1.98 \times 10^{-2}\,dm^3\,mol^{-1}\,min^{-1} = 3.30 \times 10^{-4}\,dm^3\,mol^{-1}\,s^{-1}$.)

25 Predicted Brönsted-Bjerrum slope = 2.04. Actual (observed) Brönsted-Bjerrum slope = 2.05. $k = 1.59 \times 10^{-1}\,dm^3\,mol^{-1}\,min^{-1} = 2.65 \times 10^{-3}\,dm^3\,mol^{-1}\,s^{-1}$.

26 Michaelis constant, $K_m = 4.6 \times 10^{-3}\,mol\,dm^{-3}$; Limiting rate $= 2.3 \times 10^{-7}\,mol\,dm^{-3}\,s^{-1}$.

27 $k_{H^+} = 2.46 \times 10^{-1}\,dm^3\,mol^{-1}\,h^{-1} = 6.83 \times 10^{-5}\,dm^3\,mol^{-1}\,s^{-1}$.

Chapter 10 SPECTRA (page 240)

1 Energy $= 2.09 \times 10^{-18}$ J. Wavelength = 95 nm.

2 1258 kJ mol^{-1}.

3 54.4eV(87.0×10^{-19}J).

4 4.

5 (*a*) The ratio of the Rydberg constants for hydrogen and doubly ionized beryllium may be written as

$$\frac{R_H}{R_{Be}} = \frac{(m + M_{Be})\,M_H}{(m + M_H)\,M_{Be}}$$

where m is the mass of the electron and M the mass of the appropriate nuclei.

Even after allowing for the beryllium nucleus being 9 times greater in mass than hydrogen, the Rydberg constant in the present context with three significant figures will not be affected since at this level of significance $1.10 \times 10^{-7}\,m^{-1}$ is its limiting value for all cases.
(*b*) This corresponds to $n_2 = 5$, and $\lambda = 4.33 \times 10^{-7}\,m$ (433 nm).

6 (*a*) $6.02 \times 10^{-18}\,J$; (*b*) $4.96 \times 10^{-17}\,J$.

7 (*a*) $9.83 \times 10^{-18}\,J$ for $n = 1$; $3.93 \times 10^{-17}\,J$ for $n = 2$;
(*b*) $1.81 \times 10^{-11}\,J$.

8 μ for the 110 GHz molecule is twice that of the 220 GHz molecule.

9 2.5 cm.

10 C—S bond length = 1.54 Å. Force constant = $8.51 \times 10^{2}\,N\,m^{-1}$.

11 1.41 Å.

12 $\lambda_{rot} = 2.93 \times 10^{-3}\,m$; λ of fundamental vibration band = $4.62\,\mu m$. (To calculate true origin of fundamental band, a knowledge of the anharmonicity constant is required.)

13 $431.8\,kJ\,mol^{-1}$.

14 $\nu_e = 8.97 \times 10^{13}\,s^{-1}$; $\alpha = 1.747 \times 10^{-2}$; force constant = $5.16 \times 10^{2}\,N\,m^{-1}$; dissociation energy = $493\,kJ\,mol^{-1}$.

15 Using the relation: $f = 4\pi^2\bar{\nu}_0^2 c^2 \mu$ (*a*) $1.5 \times 10^{5}\,m^{-1}$;
(*b*) $4.24 \times 10^{5}\,m^{-1}$.

16 $0.964 \times 10^{-3}\,mol\,dm^{-3}$.

17 11 800.

18 34 050 units g^{-1}.

19 ν for $^{2}H = 1.31 \times 10^{7}\,Hz$; ν for $^{19}F = 8.01 \times 10^{7}\,Hz$; ν for $^{29}Si = 1.69 \times 10^{7}\,Hz$.

20 $1.724 \times 10^{7}\,Hz$.

21 1T for the proton; 8.06 T for ^{10}B.

22 $\lambda = 58.6\,nm$; binding energies 12.2eV and 11.4eV.

23 (*a*) $129.1\,J\,K^{-1}\,mol^{-1}$; (*b*) $157.2\,J\,K^{-1}\,mol^{-1}$.

24 $260.3\,J\,K^{-1}$ mol.

25 6.47×10^{33}.

26 $U—U_0 = 20.9\,kJ\,mol^{-1}$; $H—H_0 = 29.2\,kJ\,mol^{-1}$.

27 $191.6\,J\,K^{-1}\,mol^{-1}$.

28 0.175.

29 1193.

30 $154\,kJ\,mol^{-1}$.

Chapter 11 THE CRYSTALLINE STATE (page 251)

1 Cell edge length = 3.93 Å. Lattice type = body-centred cubic.

2 Bragg angles observable = 34.27°, 40.56°, 66.86°. Indices 111, 200, 220.

3 (*a*) Face centred cubic (cell edge length 3.62 Å);
(*b*) 6.03×10^{23}; 1.28 Å.

4 (*i*) 3.139 Å; (*ii*) 10.31 g cm^{-3}; (*iii*) 1.36 Å.
5 Formula mass = 232; 3 molecules of water.
6 4 formula masses per cell; 1 molecule of HCl.
7 3.96×10^4.
8 70.8 pm.

Chapter 12 RADIOCHEMISTRY (page 268)

1 2.52×10^{-13} mol.
2 4.28×10^{-4}.
3 $\lambda = 2.36 \times 10^{-2}\,min^{-1}$; $t_{1/2} = 29.4$ min; $\tau = 42.4$ min.
4 43.2 hours.
5 2.60×10^{21}.
6 1689 years.
7 1.354×10^9 years.
8 918 years. The beeswax is NOT an original part of the hoard.
9 2.67×10^{-4} g.
10 13.9 μCi cm^{-3}; 10 470 s.
11 (*i*) 3.1×10^{-8} g, $a = 3.23 \times 10^7\,Ci\,g^{-1}$;
(*ii*) 3.2×10^6 g, $a = 3.13 \times 10^{-7}\,Ci\,g^{-1}$.
12 (*i*); 0.100 Ci; (*ii*) 0.064 Ci.
13 1.73×10^9.
14 9.0×10^{-10} g.
15 2.4×10^6 g.
16 8.8 MeV for $^{57}_{26}Fe$; 7.6 MeV for $^{235}_{92}U$.
17 Energies for the respective reactions are 17.5, 4.84 and 4.10 MeV.

Chapter 13 STATISTICAL TREATMENT OF DATA (page 282)

1 (*a*) 5.283±0.220°C and 5.283±0.259°C;
(*b*) 5.283±0.923°C and 5.283±0.375°C;
(*c*) 5.283±0.345°C and 5.283±0.313°C.
2 (*a*) −174.0 kJ should be rejected;
(*b*) Mean = −124.5 kJ; Standard deviation = 13.6 kJ; coefficient of variation = 10.9%;
(*c*) −124.5±32.1 kJ.
3 The *t* value is 9.93 and is significantly greater than 2.57 for $P = 0.05$ for 5 degrees of freedom. The value is in fact greater than 4.03 for $P = 0.01$; hence, the difference between the two sample means is, therefore, *highly* significant.
4 $t = 3.55$; it is significantly greater than $t = 2.31$ for 8 degrees of freedom. It is also greater than 3.36 at $P = 0.01$; hence the difference between the means can be said to be *highly* significant.

5 $t = 4.07$; compared with 3.71 for $P = 0.01$ for 6 degrees of freedom, the difference can be said to be *highly* significant.

6 The analysis of variance table is

Source of variation	*Degrees of freedom*	*Variance*
Between samples	9	34.92
Between methods	2	0.03
Remainder	18	0.05

The between samples variance is highly significant since it is many times greater than the remainder variance, the ratio being considerably greater than the 0.1% point for $F(n_1 = 9, n_2 = 18)$. This is not unexpected because of different origin of samples.

The really important result of the analysis is that the between methods variance is less than the remainder variance, indicating that the three methods for assessing the calcium content of tap water at this level of concentration are comparable and that the pvc electrode is satisfactory.

7 The interaction (laboratories × assays) variance at 0.15 (10 degrees of freedom) is significantly larger than the residual at 0.05 (18 degrees of freedom) so that the significance of the first two variances (between laboratories and between assays) are assessed against the interaction and NOT against the residual:

Between laboratories/Interaction = 4.0/0.15 = 25.56
$(n_1 = 5, n_2 = 10)$ 5% value of $F = 3.33$. **This is significant**
Between assays/Interaction = 0.2/0.15 = 1.33 $(n_1 = 2, n_2 = 10)$
5% value of $F = 4.10$. **This is NOT significant**

In applying the t-test to the difference between the means for the laboratories, it is found that a difference of $2.23 \times 0.224 = 0.49$ is required for significance. If the means of laboratories differs by more than this, the analysis ought to be extended.

Index

(The pages quoted are those on which the questions to the Worked Examples appear)

LOGARITHMS

	0	1	2	3	4	5	6	7	8	9	1	2	3	4	5	6	7	8	9
10	0000	0043	0086	0128	0170	0212	0253	0294	0334	0374	4	8	12	17	21	25	29	33	37
11	0414	0453	0492	0531	0569	0607	0645	0682	0719	0755	4	8	11	15	19	23	26	30	34
12	0792	0828	0864	0899	0934	0969	1004	1038	1072	1106	3	7	10	14	17	21	24	28	31
13	1139	1173	1206	1239	1271	1303	1335	1367	1399	1430	3	6	10	13	16	19	23	26	29
14	1461	1492	1523	1553	1584	1614	1644	1673	1703	1732	3	6	9	12	15	18	21	24	27
15	1761	1790	1818	1847	1875	1903	1931	1959	1987	2014	3	6	8	11	14	17	20	22	25
16	2041	2068	2095	2122	2148	2175	2201	2227	2253	2279	3	5	8	11	13	16	18	21	24
17	2304	2330	2355	2380	2405	2430	2455	2480	2504	2529	2	5	7	10	12	15	17	20	22
18	2553	2577	2601	2625	2648	2672	2695	2718	2742	2765	2	5	7	9	12	14	16	19	21
19	2788	2810	2833	2856	2878	2900	2923	2945	2967	2989	2	4	7	9	11	13	16	18	20
20	3010	3032	3054	3075	3096	3118	3139	3160	3181	3201	2	4	6	8	11	13	15	17	19
21	3222	3243	3263	3284	3304	3324	3345	3365	3385	3404	2	4	6	8	10	12	14	16	18
22	3424	3444	3464	3483	3502	3522	3541	3560	3579	3598	2	4	6	8	10	12	14	15	17
23	3617	3636	3655	3674	3692	3711	3729	3747	3766	3784	2	4	6	7	9	11	13	15	17
24	3802	3820	3838	3856	3874	3892	3909	3927	3945	3962	2	4	5	7	9	11	12	14	16
25	3979	3997	4014	4031	4048	4065	4082	4099	4116	4133	2	3	5	7	9	10	12	14	15
26	4150	4166	4183	4200	4216	4232	4249	4265	4281	4298	2	3	5	7	8	10	11	13	15
27	4314	4330	4346	4362	4378	4393	4409	4425	4440	4456	2	3	5	6	8	9	11	13	14
28	4472	4487	4502	4518	4533	4548	4564	4579	4594	4609	2	3	5	6	8	9	11	12	14
29	4624	4639	4654	4669	4683	4698	4713	4728	4742	4757	1	3	4	6	7	9	10	12	13
30	4771	4786	4800	4814	4829	4843	4857	4871	4886	4900	1	3	4	6	7	9	10	11	13
31	4914	4928	4942	4955	4969	4983	4997	5011	5024	5038	1	3	4	6	7	8	10	11	12
32	5051	5065	5079	5092	5105	5119	5132	5145	5159	5172	1	3	4	5	7	8	9	11	12
33	5185	5198	5211	5224	5237	5250	5263	5276	5289	5302	1	3	4	5	6	8	9	10	12
34	5315	5328	5340	5353	5366	5378	5391	5403	5416	5428	1	3	4	5	6	8	9	10	11
35	5441	5453	5465	5478	5490	5502	5514	5527	5539	5551	1	2	4	5	6	7	9	10	11
36	5563	5575	5587	5599	5611	5623	5635	5647	5658	5670	1	2	4	5	6	7	8	10	11
37	5682	5694	5705	5717	5729	5740	5752	5763	5775	5786	1	2	3	5	6	7	8	9	10
38	5798	5809	5821	5832	5843	5855	5866	5877	5888	5899	1	2	3	5	6	7	8	9	10
39	5911	5922	5933	5944	5955	5966	5977	5988	5999	6010	1	2	3	4	5	7	8	9	10
40	6021	6031	6042	6053	6064	6075	6085	6096	6107	6117	1	2	3	4	5	6	8	9	10
41	6128	6138	6149	6160	6170	6180	6191	6201	6212	6222	1	2	3	4	5	6	7	8	9
42	6232	6243	6253	6263	6274	6284	6294	6304	6314	6325	1	2	3	4	5	6	7	8	9
43	6335	6345	6355	6365	6375	6385	6395	6405	6415	6425	1	2	3	4	5	6	7	8	9
44	6435	6444	6454	6464	6474	6484	6493	6503	6513	6522	1	2	3	4	5	6	7	8	9
45	6532	6542	6551	6561	6571	6580	6590	6599	6609	6618	1	2	3	4	5	6	7	8	9
46	6628	6637	6646	6656	6665	6675	6684	6693	6702	6712	1	2	3	4	5	6	7	7	8
47	6721	6730	6739	6749	6758	6767	6776	6785	6794	6803	1	2	3	4	5	5	6	7	8
48	6812	6821	6830	6839	6848	6857	6866	6875	6884	6893	1	2	3	4	4	5	6	7	8
49	6902	6911	6920	6928	6937	6946	6955	6964	6972	6981	1	2	3	4	4	5	6	7	8
50	6990	6998	7007	7016	7024	7033	7042	7050	7059	7067	1	2	3	3	4	5	6	7	8
51	7076	7084	7093	7101	7110	7118	7126	7135	7143	7152	1	2	3	3	4	5	6	7	8
52	7160	7168	7177	7185	7193	7202	7210	7218	7226	7235	1	2	2	3	4	5	6	7	7
53	7243	7251	7259	7267	7275	7284	7292	7300	7308	7316	1	2	2	3	4	5	6	6	7
54	7324	7332	7340	7348	7356	7364	7372	7380	7388	7396	1	2	2	3	4	5	6	6	7

LOGARITHMS

	0	1	2	3	4	5	6	7	8	9	1	2	3	4	5	6	7	8	9
55	7404	7412	7419	7427	7435	7443	7451	7459	7466	7474	1	2	2	3	4	5	5	6	7
56	7482	7490	7497	7505	7513	7520	7528	7536	7543	7551	1	2	2	3	4	5	5	6	7
57	7559	7566	7574	7582	7589	7597	7604	7612	7619	7627	1	2	2	3	4	5	5	6	7
58	7634	7642	7649	7657	7664	7672	7679	7686	7694	7701	1	1	2	3	4	4	5	6	7
59	7709	7716	7723	7731	7738	7745	7752	7760	7767	7774	1	1	2	3	4	4	5	6	7
60	7782	7789	7796	7803	7810	7818	7825	7832	7839	7846	1	1	2	3	4	4	5	6	6
61	7853	7860	7868	7875	7882	7889	7896	7903	7910	7917	1	1	2	3	4	4	5	6	6
62	7924	7931	7938	7945	7952	7959	7966	7973	7980	7987	1	1	2	3	3	4	5	6	6
63	7993	8000	8007	8014	8021	8028	8035	8041	8048	8055	1	1	2	3	3	4	5	5	6
64	8062	8069	8075	8082	8089	8096	8102	8109	8116	8122	1	1	2	3	3	4	5	5	6
65	8129	8136	8142	8149	8156	8162	8169	8176	8182	8189	1	1	2	3	3	4	5	5	6
66	8195	8202	8209	8215	8222	8228	8235	8241	8248	8254	1	1	2	3	3	4	5	5	6
67	8261	8267	8274	8280	8287	8293	8299	8306	8312	8319	1	1	2	3	3	4	5	5	6
68	8325	8331	8338	8344	8351	8357	8363	8370	8376	8382	1	1	2	3	3	4	4	5	6
69	8388	8395	8401	8407	8414	8420	8426	8432	8439	8445	1	1	2	2	3	4	4	5	6
70	8451	8457	8463	8470	8476	8482	8488	8494	8500	8506	1	1	2	2	3	4	4	5	6
71	8513	8519	8525	8531	8537	8543	8549	8555	8561	8567	1	1	2	2	3	4	4	5	5
72	8573	8579	8585	8591	8597	8603	8609	8615	8621	8627	1	1	2	2	3	4	4	5	5
73	8633	8639	8645	8651	8657	8663	8669	8675	8681	8686	1	1	2	2	3	4	4	5	5
74	8692	8698	8704	8710	8716	8722	8727	8733	8739	8745	1	1	2	2	3	4	4	5	5
75	8751	8756	8762	8768	8774	8779	8785	8791	8797	8802	1	1	2	2	3	3	4	5	5
76	8808	8814	8820	8825	8831	8837	8842	8848	8854	8859	1	1	2	2	3	3	4	5	5
77	8865	8871	8876	8882	8887	8893	8899	8904	8910	8915	1	1	2	2	3	3	4	4	5
78	8921	8927	8932	8938	8943	8949	8954	8960	8965	8971	1	1	2	2	3	3	4	4	5
79	8976	8982	8987	8993	8998	9004	9009	9015	9020	9025	1	1	2	2	3	3	4	4	5
80	9031	9036	9042	9047	9053	9058	9063	9069	9074	9079	1	1	2	2	3	3	4	4	5
81	9085	9090	9096	9101	9106	9112	9117	9122	9128	9133	1	1	2	2	3	3	4	4	5
82	9138	9143	9149	9154	9159	9165	9170	9175	9180	9186	1	1	2	2	3	3	4	4	5
83	9191	9196	9201	9206	9212	9217	9222	9227	9232	9238	1	1	2	2	3	3	4	4	5
84	9243	9248	9253	9258	9263	9269	9274	9279	9284	9289	1	1	2	2	3	3	4	4	5
85	9294	9299	9304	9309	9315	9320	9325	9330	9335	9340	1	1	2	2	3	3	4	4	5
86	9345	9350	9355	9360	9365	9370	9375	9380	9385	9390	1	1	2	2	3	3	4	4	5
87	9395	9400	9405	9410	9415	9420	9425	9430	9435	9440	0	1	1	2	2	3	3	4	4
88	9445	9450	9455	9460	9465	9469	9474	9479	9484	9489	0	1	1	2	2	3	3	4	4
89	9494	9499	9504	9509	9513	9518	9523	9528	9533	9538	0	1	1	2	2	3	3	4	4
90	9542	9547	9552	9557	9562	9566	9571	9576	9581	9586	0	1	1	2	2	3	3	4	4
91	9590	9595	9600	9605	9609	9614	9619	9624	9628	9633	0	1	1	2	2	3	3	4	4
92	9638	9643	9647	9652	9657	9661	9666	9671	9675	9680	0	1	1	2	2	3	3	4	4
93	9685	9689	9694	9699	9703	9708	9713	9717	9722	9727	0	1	1	2	2	3	3	4	4
94	9731	9736	9741	9745	9750	9754	9759	9763	9768	9773	0	1	1	2	2	3	3	4	4
95	9777	9782	9786	9791	9795	9800	9805	9809	9814	9818	0	1	1	2	2	3	3	4	4
96	9823	9827	9832	9836	9841	9845	9850	9854	9859	9863	0	1	1	2	2	3	3	4	4
97	9868	9872	9877	9881	9886	9890	9894	9899	9903	9908	0	1	1	2	2	3	3	4	4
98	9912	9917	9921	9926	9930	9934	9939	9943	9948	9952	0	1	1	2	2	3	3	4	4
99	9956	9961	9965	9969	9974	9978	9983	9987	9991	9996	0	1	1	2	2	3	3	3	4

ANTILOGARITHMS

	0	1	2	3	4	5	6	7	8	9	1	2	3	4	5	6	7	8	9
·00	1000	1002	1005	1007	1009	1012	1014	1016	1019	1021	0	0	1	1	1	1	2	2	2
·01	1023	1026	1028	1030	1033	1035	1038	1040	1042	1045	0	0	1	1	1	1	2	2	2
·02	1047	1050	1052	1054	1057	1059	1062	1064	1067	1069	0	0	1	1	1	1	2	2	2
·03	1072	1074	1076	1079	1081	1084	1086	1089	1091	1094	0	0	1	1	1	1	2	2	2
·04	1096	1099	1102	1104	1107	1109	1112	1114	1117	1119	0	1	1	1	1	2	2	2	2
·05	1122	1125	1127	1130	1132	1135	1138	1140	1143	1146	0	1	1	1	1	2	2	2	2
·06	1148	1151	1153	1156	1159	1161	1164	1167	1169	1172	0	1	1	1	1	2	2	2	2
·07	1175	1178	1180	1183	1186	1189	1191	1194	1197	1199	0	1	1	1	1	2	2	2	2
·08	1202	1205	1208	1211	1213	1216	1219	1222	1225	1227	0	1	1	1	1	2	2	2	3
·09	1230	1233	1236	1239	1242	1245	1247	1250	1253	1256	0	1	1	1	1	2	2	2	3
·10	1259	1262	1265	1268	1271	1274	1276	1279	1282	1285	0	1	1	1	1	2	2	2	3
·11	1288	1291	1294	1297	1300	1303	1306	1309	1312	1315	0	1	1	1	2	2	2	2	3
·12	1318	1321	1324	1327	1330	1334	1337	1340	1343	1346	0	1	1	1	2	2	2	2	3
·13	1349	1352	1355	1358	1361	1365	1368	1371	1374	1377	0	1	1	1	2	2	2	3	3
·14	1380	1384	1387	1390	1393	1396	1400	1403	1406	1409	0	1	1	1	2	2	2	3	3
·15	1413	1416	1419	1422	1426	1429	1432	1435	1439	1442	0	1	1	1	2	2	2	3	3
·16	1445	1449	1452	1455	1459	1462	1466	1469	1472	1476	0	1	1	1	2	2	2	3	3
·17	1479	1483	1486	1489	1493	1496	1500	1503	1507	1510	0	1	1	1	2	2	2	3	3
·18	1514	1517	1521	1524	1528	1531	1535	1538	1542	1545	0	1	1	1	2	2	2	3	3
·19	1549	1552	1556	1560	1563	1567	1570	1574	1578	1581	0	1	1	1	2	2	3	3	3
·20	1585	1589	1592	1596	1600	1603	1607	1611	1614	1618	0	1	1	1	2	2	3	3	3
·21	1622	1626	1629	1633	1637	1641	1644	1648	1652	1656	0	1	1	2	2	2	3	3	3
·22	1660	1663	1667	1671	1675	1679	1683	1687	1690	1694	0	1	1	2	2	2	3	3	3
·23	1698	1702	1706	1710	1714	1718	1722	1726	1730	1734	0	1	1	2	2	2	3	3	4
·24	1738	1742	1746	1750	1754	1758	1762	1766	1770	1774	0	1	1	2	2	2	3	3	4
·25	1778	1782	1786	1791	1795	1799	1803	1807	1811	1816	0	1	1	2	2	2	3	3	4
·26	1820	1824	1828	1832	1837	1841	1845	1849	1854	1858	0	1	1	2	2	3	3	3	4
·27	1862	1866	1871	1875	1879	1884	1888	1892	1897	1901	0	1	1	2	2	3	3	3	4
·28	1905	1910	1914	1919	1923	1928	1932	1936	1941	1945	0	1	1	2	2	3	3	4	4
·29	1950	1954	1959	1963	1968	1972	1977	1982	1986	1991	0	1	1	2	2	3	3	4	4
·30	1995	2000	2004	2009	2014	2018	2023	2028	2032	2037	0	1	1	2	2	3	3	4	4
·31	2042	2046	2051	2056	2061	2065	2070	2075	2080	2084	0	1	1	2	2	3	3	4	4
·32	2089	2094	2099	2104	2109	2113	2118	2123	2128	2133	0	1	1	2	2	3	3	4	4
·33	2138	2143	2148	2153	2158	2163	2168	2173	2178	2183	0	1	1	2	2	3	3	4	4
·34	2188	2193	2198	2203	2208	2213	2218	2223	2228	2234	1	1	2	2	3	3	4	4	5
·35	2239	2244	2249	2254	2259	2265	2270	2275	2280	2286	1	1	2	2	3	3	4	4	5
·36	2291	2296	2301	2307	2312	2317	2323	2328	2333	2339	1	1	2	2	3	3	4	4	5
·37	2344	2350	2355	2360	2366	2371	2377	2382	2388	2393	1	1	2	2	3	3	4	4	5
·38	2399	2404	2410	2415	2421	2427	2432	2438	2443	2449	1	1	2	2	3	3	4	4	5
·39	2455	2460	2466	2472	2477	2483	2489	2495	2500	2506	1	1	2	2	3	3	4	5	5
·40	2512	2518	2523	2529	2535	2541	2547	2553	2559	2564	1	1	2	2	3	4	4	5	5
·41	2570	2576	2582	2588	2594	2600	2606	2612	2618	2624	1	1	2	2	3	4	4	5	5
·42	2630	2636	2642	2649	2655	2661	2667	2673	2679	2685	1	1	2	2	3	4	4	5	6
·43	2692	2698	2704	2710	2716	2723	2729	2735	2742	2748	1	1	2	3	3	4	4	5	6
·44	2754	2761	2767	2773	2780	2786	2793	2799	2805	2812	1	1	2	3	3	4	4	5	6
·45	2818	2825	2831	2838	2844	2851	2858	2864	2871	2877	1	1	2	3	3	4	5	5	6
·46	2884	2891	2897	2904	2911	2917	2924	2931	2938	2944	1	1	2	3	3	4	5	5	6
·47	2951	2958	2965	2972	2979	2985	2992	2999	3006	3013	1	1	2	3	3	4	5	5	6
·48	3020	3027	3034	3041	3048	3055	3062	3069	3076	3083	1	1	2	3	4	4	5	6	6
·49	3090	3097	3105	3112	3119	3126	3133	3141	3148	3155	1	1	2	3	4	4	5	6	6

ANTILOGARITHMS

	0	1	2	3	4	5	6	7	8	9	1	2	3	4	5	6	7	8	9
·50	3162	3170	3177	3184	3192	3199	3206	3214	3221	3228	1	1	2	3	4	4	5	6	7
·51	3236	3243	3251	3258	3266	3273	3281	3289	3296	3304	1	2	2	3	4	5	5	6	7
·52	3311	3319	3327	3334	3342	3350	3357	3365	3373	3381	1	2	2	3	4	5	5	6	7
·53	3388	3396	3404	3412	3420	3428	3436	3443	3451	3459	1	2	2	3	4	5	6	6	7
·54	3467	3475	3483	3491	3499	3508	3516	3524	3532	3540	1	2	2	3	4	5	6	6	7
·55	3548	3556	3565	3573	3581	3589	3597	3606	3614	3622	1	2	2	3	4	5	6	7	7
·56	3631	3639	3648	3656	3664	3673	3681	3690	3698	3707	1	2	3	3	4	5	6	7	8
·57	3715	3724	3733	3741	3750	3758	3767	3776	3784	3793	1	2	3	3	4	5	6	7	8
·58	3802	3811	3819	3828	3837	3846	3855	3864	3873	3882	1	2	3	4	4	5	6	7	8
·59	3890	3899	3908	3917	3926	3936	3945	3954	3963	3972	1	2	3	4	5	5	6	7	8
·60	3981	3990	3999	4009	4018	4027	4036	4046	4055	4064	1	2	3	4	5	6	6	7	8
·61	4074	4083	4093	4102	4111	4121	4130	4140	4150	4159	1	2	3	4	5	6	7	8	9
·62	4169	4178	4188	4198	4207	4217	4227	4236	4246	4256	1	2	3	4	5	6	7	8	9
·63	4266	4276	4285	4295	4305	4315	4325	4335	4345	4355	1	2	3	4	5	6	7	8	9
·64	4365	4375	4385	4395	4406	4416	4426	4436	4446	4457	1	2	3	4	5	6	7	8	9
·65	4467	4477	4487	4498	4508	4519	4529	4539	4550	4560	1	2	3	4	5	6	7	8	9
·66	4571	4581	4592	4603	4613	4624	4634	4645	4656	4667	1	2	3	4	5	6	7	9	10
·67	4677	4688	4699	4710	4721	4732	4742	4753	4764	4775	1	2	3	4	5	7	8	9	10
·68	4786	4797	4808	4819	4831	4842	4853	4864	4875	4887	1	2	3	4	6	7	8	9	10
·69	4898	4909	4920	4932	4943	4955	4966	4977	4989	5000	1	2	3	5	6	7	8	9	10
·70	5012	5023	5035	5047	5058	5070	5082	5093	5105	5117	1	2	4	5	6	7	8	9	11
·71	5129	5140	5152	5164	5176	5188	5200	5212	5224	5236	1	2	4	5	6	7	8	10	11
·72	5248	5260	5272	5284	5297	5309	5321	5333	5346	5358	1	2	4	5	6	7	9	10	11
·73	5370	5383	5395	5408	5420	5433	5445	5458	5470	5483	1	3	4	5	6	8	9	10	11
·74	5495	5508	5521	5534	5546	5559	5572	5585	5598	5610	1	3	4	5	6	8	9	10	12
·75	5623	5636	5649	5662	5675	5689	5702	5715	5728	5741	1	3	4	5	7	8	9	10	12
·76	5754	5768	5781	5794	5808	5821	5834	5848	5861	5875	1	3	4	5	7	8	9	11	12
·77	5888	5902	5916	5929	5943	5957	5970	5984	5998	6012	1	3	4	5	7	8	10	11	12
·78	6026	6039	6053	6067	6081	6095	6109	6124	6138	6152	1	3	4	6	7	8	10	11	13
·79	6166	6180	6194	6209	6223	6237	6252	6266	6281	6295	1	3	4	6	7	9	10	11	13
·80	6310	6324	6339	6353	6368	6383	6397	6412	6427	6442	1	3	4	6	7	9	10	12	13
·81	6457	6471	6486	6501	6516	6531	6546	6561	6577	6592	2	3	5	6	8	9	11	12	14
·82	6607	6622	6637	6653	6668	6683	6699	6714	6730	6745	2	3	5	6	8	9	11	12	14
·83	6761	6776	6792	6808	6823	6839	6855	6871	6887	6902	2	3	5	6	8	9	11	13	14
·84	6918	6934	6950	6966	6982	6998	7015	7031	7047	7063	2	3	5	6	8	10	11	13	15
·85	7079	7096	7112	7129	7145	7161	7178	7194	7211	7228	2	3	5	7	8	10	12	13	15
·86	7244	7261	7278	7295	7311	7328	7345	7362	7379	7396	2	3	5	7	8	10	12	13	15
·87	7413	7430	7447	7464	7482	7499	7516	7534	7551	7568	2	3	5	7	9	10	12	14	16
·88	7586	7603	7621	7638	7656	7674	7691	7709	7727	7745	2	4	5	7	9	11	12	14	16
·89	7762	7780	7798	7816	7834	7852	7870	7889	7907	7925	2	4	5	7	9	11	13	14	16
·90	7943	7962	7980	7998	8017	8035	8054	8072	8091	8110	2	4	6	7	9	11	13	15	17
·91	8128	8147	8166	8185	8204	8222	8241	8260	8279	8299	2	4	6	8	9	11	13	15	17
·92	8318	8337	8356	8375	8395	8414	8433	8453	8472	8492	2	4	6	8	10	12	14	15	17
·93	8511	8531	8551	8570	8590	8610	8630	8650	8670	8690	2	4	6	8	10	12	14	16	18
·94	8710	8730	8750	8770	8790	8810	8831	8851	8872	8892	2	4	6	8	10	12	14	16	18
·95	8913	8933	8954	8974	8995	9016	9036	9057	9078	9099	2	4	6	8	10	12	15	17	19
·96	9120	9141	9162	9183	9204	9226	9247	9268	9290	9311	2	4	6	8	11	13	15	17	19
·97	9333	9354	9376	9397	9419	9441	9462	9484	9506	9528	2	4	7	9	11	13	15	17	20
·98	9550	9572	9594	9616	9638	9661	9683	9705	9727	9750	2	4	7	9	11	13	16	18	20
·99	9772	9795	9817	9840	9863	9886	9908	9931	9954	9977	2	5	7	9	11	14	16	18	20